BRAZIL

BRAZIL

PRESTON E. JAMES
Author of "Latin America"

THE ODYSSEY PRESS
NEW YORK

PRINTED IN THE UNITED STATES
FIRST EDITION

The text of this book is a reprint of the section on Brazil in the same author's "Latin America," with the data brought up to date and with the addition of new material, particularly to the chapter "Brazil as a Political Unit."

CONTENTS

CHAPTER		PAGE
I	The Land	1
II	The People	27
III	The Northeast	45
IV	The Southeast	71
V	São Paulo	120
VI	The South	171
VII	The North	206
VIII	Brazil as a Political Unit	232
	Index	257

LIST OF MAPS

MAP		PAGE
1	South America: Surface Configuration	4
2	Northeastern Brazil: Surface Configuration	6
3	Southeastern Brazil: Surface Configuration	7
4	São Paulo: Surface Configuration	8
5	Southern Brazil: Surface Configuration	9
6	South America: January Temperatures	12
7	South America: July Temperatures	13
8	South America: Average Annual Rainfall in Inches	15
9	January: Warm Air Masses, Etc.	16
10	July: Warm Air Masses, Etc.	17
11	Climatic Regions of South America	20
12	South America: Natural Vegetation	21
13	Calamity Map	22
14	States and Capitals of Brazil	23
15	South America: Population	30
16	South America: Present-Day Racial Composition of the Population	31
17	South America: Spanish Primary Settlement Centers, Etc.	32
18	South America: Selected Indian Cultures	33
19	Northeastern Brazil: Natural Vegetation	50

MAP		PAGE
20	Northeastern Brazil: Land Use	55
21	Northeastern Brazil: Population	56
22	Southern Bahia and Northern Espírito Santo	63
23	Southeastern Brazil: Population	72
24	Southeastern Brazil	75
25	Southeastern Brazil: Natural Vegetation	80
26	Southeastern Brazil: Land Use	90
27	Railroads and Their Territories	92
28	São Paulo, Brazil: Natural Vegetation	128
29	(Map showing woods, truck crops, pasture, brush, and coffee)	139
30	Coffee Production 1835–1836	140
31	São Paulo, Brazil: Land Use	142
32	São Paulo, Brazil: Population	143
33	The Chaco and Paraguay: Surface Configuration	147
34	The Chaco and Paraguay: Land Use	163
35	The Chaco and Paraguay: Natural Vegetation	166
36	Southern Brazil	173
37	Southern Brazil: Population	175
38	Southern Brazil: Natural Vegetation	176
39	Southern Brazil: Land Use	177
40	The Amazon Region	211
41	The Amazon and Guiana Coast: Surface Configuration	212
42	The Amazon and Guiana Coast: Natural Vegetation	213
43	The Amazon and Guiana Coast: Land Use	214
44	The Amazon and Guiana Coast: Population	215

BRAZIL

ESTADOS UNIDOS DO BRASIL

Total area, 3,286,170 square miles
Total population, 45,002,176
Capital city, Rio de Janeiro; population, 1,896, 998
Trade per capita:
    Imports: $6.71
    Exports: $6.72
Unit of currency, cruzeiro ($.06, gold content value)
Major commercial products in order of value:

coffee	oilseeds
cotton	carnauba wax
cacao	tobacco
hides and skins	maté
meats	rubber
fruits	

Railroad mileage, 20,945 (1937)

(The above statistics except when noted are for the year 1938.)

Chapter I

THE LAND

NEARLY HALF of the continent of South America belongs to the United States of Brazil. With 3,286,170 square miles of area, Brazil is surpassed in continuous territory only by the Soviet Union, China, and the Dominion of Canada. Brazil's area is greater than that of the forty-eight states of the United States of America, and about the same size as Europe without the Scandinavian Peninsula and Finland. Yet this vast area is occupied by only 45,000,000 people [1]—about one third of the population of the United States of America and about the same as the population of Italy. Brazilians make up more than half of the people of South America, to be sure, but their numbers are not enough to occupy effectively more than a small part of their national territory.

Brazil seems to offer great possibilities for pioneer settlement and for population increase. The Brazilians estimate that under present conditions and methods of agriculture and stock raising about 80 per cent of their land is potentially productive; the geographer Friedrich Freise, in a recent study, raises this estimate to 90 per cent, excluding, as unproductive, slopes which are very steep, areas which are too swampy or too dry, soils which are too sterile, and places which have been rendered

[1] Preliminary returns from the census of 1940 indicate that this estimate is much too high. Apparently the population of Brazil numbers only a little over 40,000,000.

unproductive through destructive methods of use. Brazil possesses, moreover, an important supply of mineral resources, including the world's largest and purest deposit of iron ore.

Why, then, after four hundred years of settlement, is so large a part of Brazil still outside the areas of concentrated population (Map 15, Page 30)? Why, in short, are there so few people in Brazil? Is Brazil on the threshold of a great pioneer movement, similar to the westward movement of the North American frontier during the period between 1870 and 1914? These questions do not have simple answers, because problems of habitability involve also the objectives, attitudes, and technical abilities of the people, and world economic conditions. Moreover, no answer can be given for the whole of Brazil without reference to the diversity of its parts. The theory is frequently advanced that Brazil's difficulties are primarily due to the fact that most of the country lies within the tropics. This, however, is oversimplification, for within the tropics there are many varieties of climate, and some of the most densely populated parts of the earth—Java and India, for example—are in lands with rainy tropical climates. To formulate more clearly some of the problems and conditions of Brazilian settlement we shall first consider this vast territory and its people in some of the broader aspects; later we shall proceed to a detailed discussion of the various parts of the country.

The Brazilian land, as a matter of fact, does contain a number of superlative advantages for an Occidental commercial people. No other large political division of the earth has anything like the proportion of potentially productive area that Brazil possesses. Within this territory of continental size, moreover, there are many kinds of minerals and many species of plants which have brought in the past, or could be expected to bring in the future, large financial returns by sale in foreign markets. But a study of Brazil uncovers example after example of the poor geographical arrangement of these superlative qualities. The absence of coal which can be made into coke at low cost is a serious handicap in a land so rich in iron ore. The lack of any large natural focus of the routes of travel, as guided by the pattern of valleys and lowlands, scatters and isolates the clusters of people. And those relatively small parts of the Brazilian territory which mountainous slopes or uncertain rainfall render unproductive are situated on the very borders of the areas of dense settlement, that is, where the limiting effect on expansion is most keenly felt.

Surface Features

Only a very little of Brazil's vast territory can be described as a plain (Map 1, Page 4). Along the western border of the country, in the south, Brazil does include a portion, but a very small portion, of the lowlands of the upper Paraguay. The largest area of plain, however, is in the upper Amazon Basin, where level lands stretch eastward into Brazil from the base of the Andes in Bolivia, Peru, Ecuador, and Colombia. The Amazon lowland, unlike most river lowlands, becomes narrower downstream: in the eastern part of the Basin only a ribbon of floodplain carries the river through the highlands. The Atlantic coast, especially in those areas which are densely populated, is bordered by only small, discontinuous bits of lowlands; there is no real coastal plain like that of eastern North America.

The greater part of the Brazilian territory is made up of highlands. The Brazilian Highlands, south of the Amazon, and the Guiana Highlands north of it, are both constructed of a basement of geologically ancient crystalline rocks, covered, in part, by stratified sandstones and limestones, and by sheets of diabase. Where the crystallines are exposed at the surface, the rapid decomposition of such rocks as granite and gneiss has resulted in a deep mantle of fine-grained soil, and in the formation of gently rounded hills. The stratified sandstones and the diabase, on the other hand, are so much more resistant to the proc-

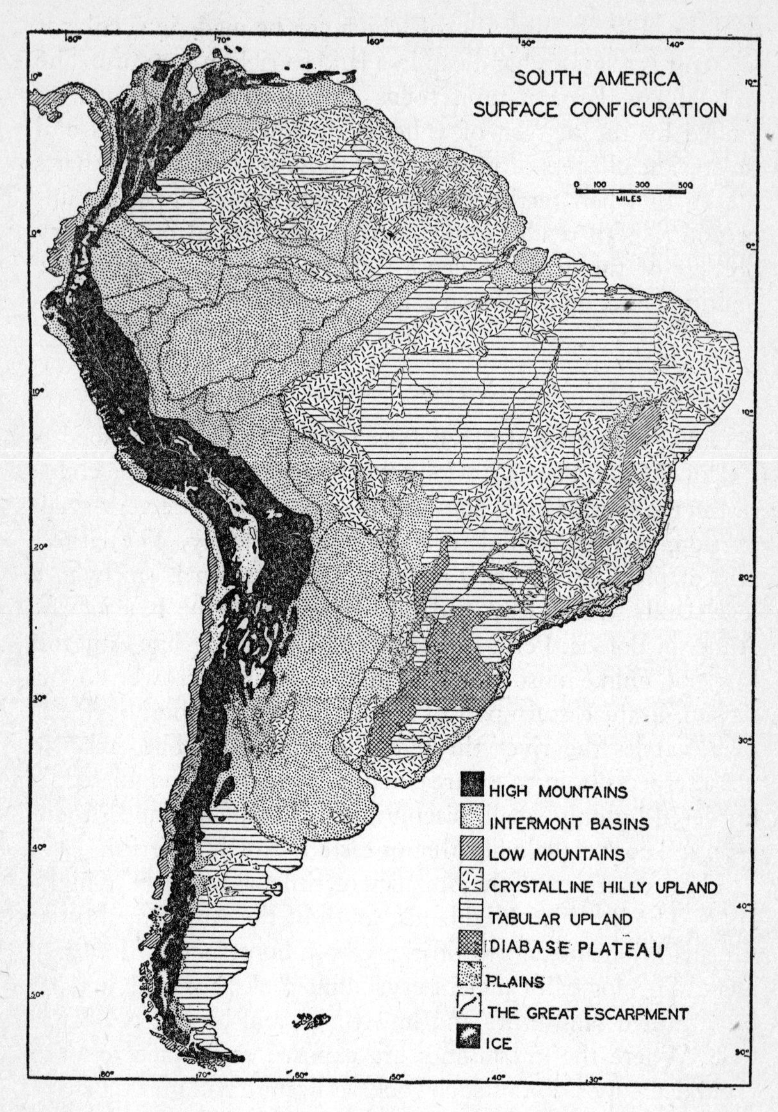
SOUTH AMERICA
SURFACE CONFIGURATION
0 100 300 500
MILES
HIGH MOUNTAINS
INTERMONT BASINS
LOW MOUNTAINS
CRYSTALLINE HILLY UPLAND
TABULAR UPLAND
DIABASE PLATEAU
PLAINS
THE GREAT ESCARPMENT
ICE

MAP I

esses of denudation in the rainy tropics than the granites that they stand distinctly above the general level of the crystallines, and the margins of the sandstone or diabase cover are marked by steep cliffs. The elevation of these two highlands varies from only a few hundred feet to a little over three thousand feet above the sea.

In only a few places do mountain ranges rise above the general highland surface. These occur especially in Southeastern Brazil, where there are several such ranges, composed also of crystalline rocks, but of types which are more resistant to erosion than the granites and gneisses. These stand above the crystalline hilly uplands with rounded outlines, strongly reminiscent of the outlines of the Great Smoky Mountains of the Southern Appalachians in North America. The highest elevation in Brazil, the Pico da Bandeira, a little northeast of Rio de Janeiro, is only 9,462 feet above sea level. In the Guiana Highlands, Mount Roraima, which is really not a mountain but a plateau held up by an unusually resistant portion of the sandstone cover, is almost as high as the Pico da Bandeira, reaching 8,635 feet above the sea.

The Brazilian Highlands, for the most part, drop off sharply toward the Atlantic. In the northeastern part of the country, north of the city of Salvador in Bahia (Map 2, Page 6), there is a gradual rise from coast to interior; but from Salvador southward to Porto Alegre in Rio Grande do Sul, the coast is backed by a steep, wall-like slope—the Great Escarpment—which, from the ocean, so much resembles a range of mountains that one part of it is called the Serra do Mar. Back of Rio de Janeiro and Santos, the Great Escarpment rises to an elevation of 2,600 feet, and in certain places in this part of Brazil it is surmounted by ranges which reach elevations between seven and eight thousand feet above sea level. Between latitudes 18° S. and 30° S. the Great Escarpment is crossed by only two deeply cut river valleys—those of the Rio Doce and the Rio Paraíba; otherwise it remains scarcely notched along its crest. In only two places

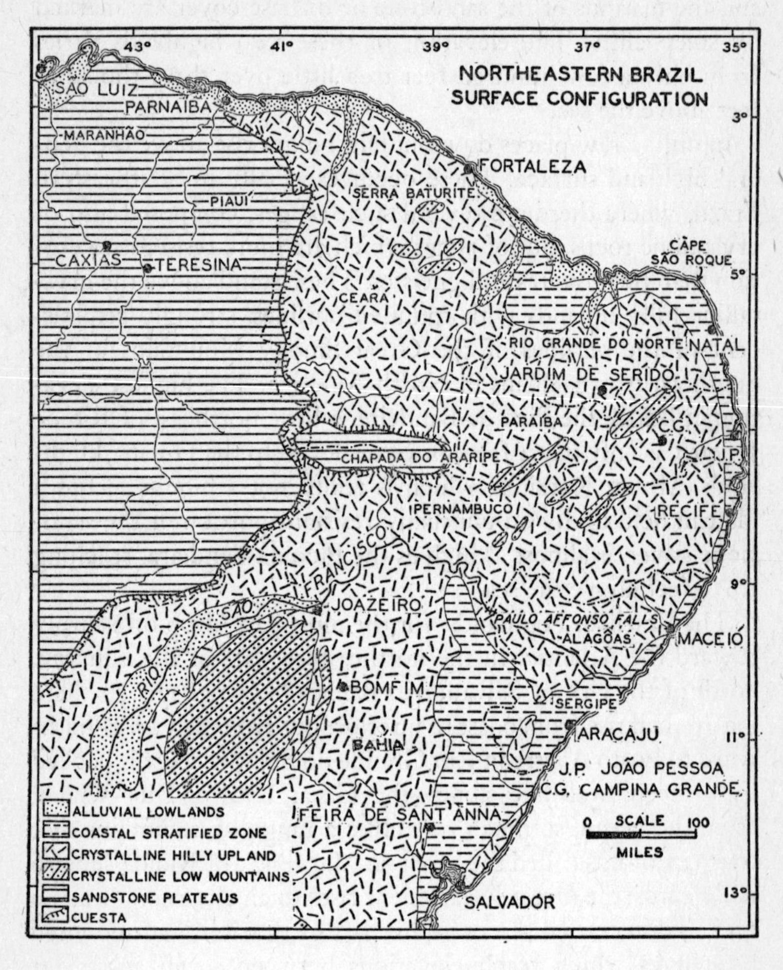

NORTHEASTERN BRAZIL
SURFACE CONFIGURATION
43°
41°
39°
37°
35°
3°
5°
9°
11°
13°
SÃO LUIZ
PARNAIBA
MARANHÃO
PIAUI
CAXIAS
TERESINA
FORTALEZA
SERRA BATURITE
CEARA
CAPE
SÃO ROQUE
RIO GRANDE DO NORTE
NATAL
JARDIM DE SERIDO
PARAIBA
C.G.
J.P.
CHAPADA DO ARARIPE
PERNAMBUCO
RECIFE
FRANCISCO
SÃO
RIO
JOAZEIRO
PAULO AFFONSO FALLS
ALAGOAS
MACEIO
BOMFIM
SERGIPE
ARACAJU
BAHIA
J.P. JOÃO PESSOA
C.G. CAMPINA GRANDE
FEIRA DE SANT ANNA
SALVADOR
0 SCALE 100
MILES
ALLUVIAL LOWLANDS
COASTAL STRATIFIED ZONE
CRYSTALLINE HILLY UPLAND
CRYSTALLINE LOW MOUNTAINS
SANDSTONE PLATEAUS
CUESTA

MAP 2

—between Santos and São Paulo, and between Paranaguá and Curitiba—is this escarpment concentrated in one sea-facing

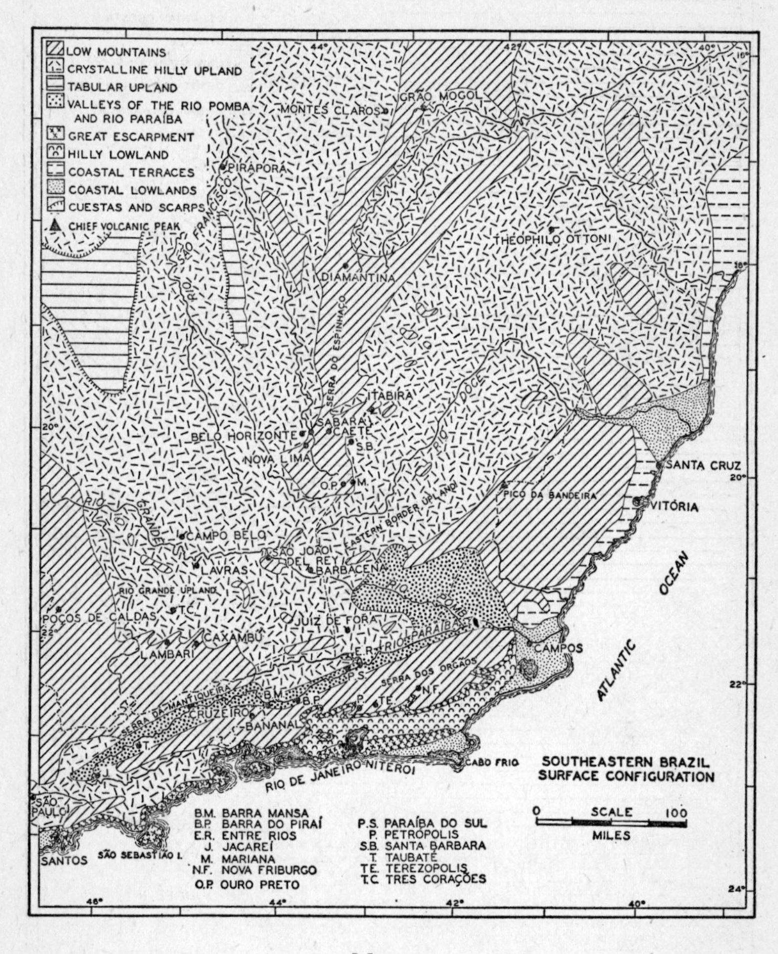

MAP 3

slope. Along most of its course it is broken into a series of steps, forming parallel escarpments with deep valleys between (Maps 3, 4, and 5, Pages 7, 8, and 9).

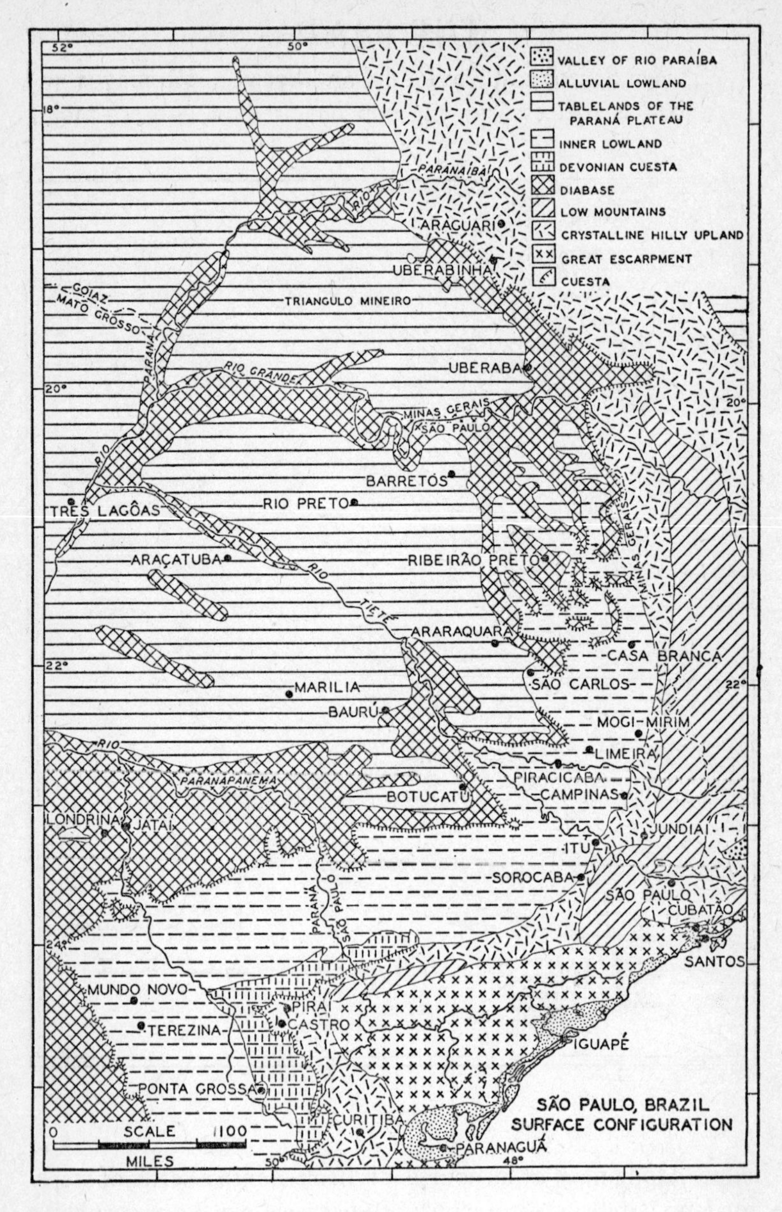
VALLEY OF RIO PARAÍBA
ALLUVIAL LOWLAND
TABLELANDS OF THE PARANÁ PLATEAU
INNER LOWLAND
DEVONIAN CUESTA
DIABASE
LOW MOUNTAINS
CRYSTALLINE HILLY UPLAND
GREAT ESCARPMENT
CUESTA
SÃO PAULO, BRAZIL
SURFACE CONFIGURATION
SCALE
MILES
0
100
52°
50°
48°
18°
20°
22°
24°
RIO PARANAÍBA
ARAGUARI
UBERABINHA
GOIAZ
MATO GROSSO
TRIANGULO MINEIRO
PARANÁ
RIO GRANDE
UBERABA
MINAS GERAIS
SÃO PAULO
RIO
BARRETOS
TRES LAGÔAS
RIO PRETO
ARAÇATUBA
RIBEIRÃO PRETO
RIO TIETÊ
ARARAQUARA
CASA BRANCA
MARILIA
SÃO CARLOS
BAURÚ
MOGI-MIRIM
LIMEIRA
RIO PARANAPANEMA
PIRACICABA
BOTUCATÚ
CAMPINAS
LONDRINA
JATAÍ
JUNDIAÍ
ITÚ
SOROCABA
SÃO PAULO
CUBATÃO
SANTOS
MUNDO NOVO
PIRAÍ
CASTRO
TEREZINA
IGUAPÉ
PONTA GROSSA
CURITIBA
PARANAGUÁ

MAP 4

The rivers which drain the Brazilian Highlands all descend over the steep margins in falls and rapids. Most of these rivers

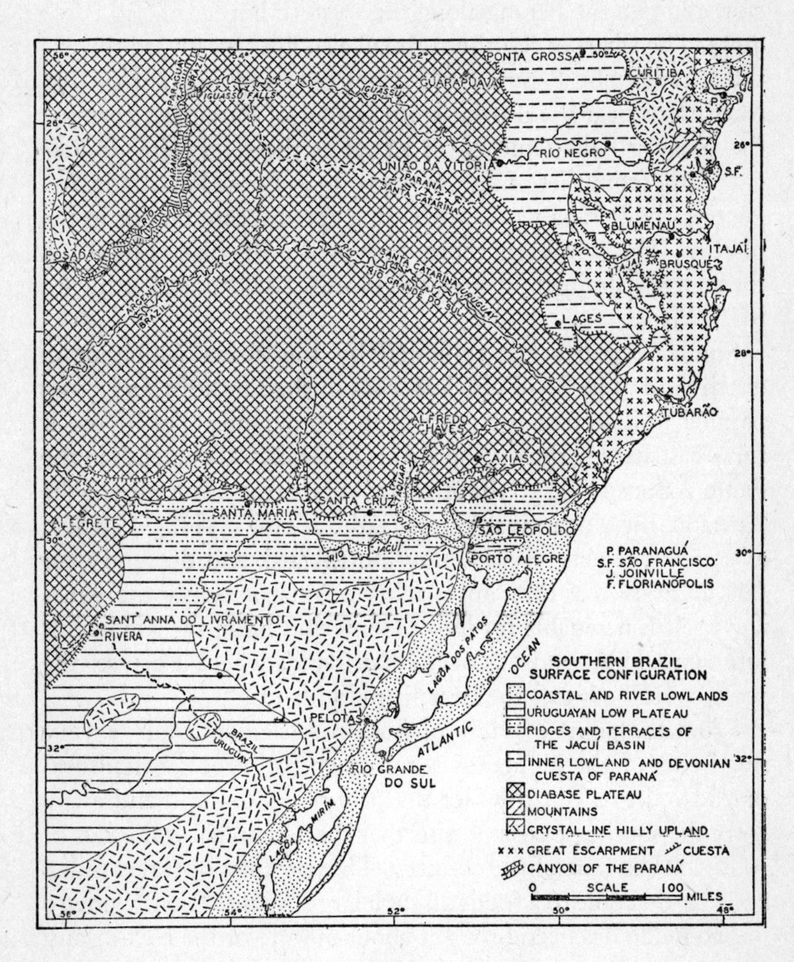

MAP 5

have their sources in the central and southeastern part of the highlands—some on the very crest of the Great Escarpment. For instance, the Paraná system to the west of the highlands is fed by several tributaries in São Paulo State which rise within sight of the Atlantic Ocean, flow northwestward into the interior, and join the Paraná along the western border of São Paulo State. The rivers of Southern Brazil also flow westward toward the Paraná. The Paraná itself drops over the resistant diabase formations near the northeastern border of Paraguay, forming the Guayra Falls (known in Brazil as the *Cachoeira de Sete Quedas*); from these falls downstream as far as Posadas in Argentina the Paraná passes through a narrow canyon cut in the plateau. The whole southern part of the Brazilian Highland, therefore, is drained through this circuitous channel southward to the Plata.

Similar features are exhibited by the rivers which drain northward. The São Francisco rises in the southeast and flows parallel to the coast for more than a thousand miles before it turns eastward in the northern part of Bahia and descends in the Paulo Affonso Falls to the Atlantic. The great tributaries of the Amazon, the Tocantins-Araguaia, the Xingú, and the Tapajóz, all rise in the central area, flow northward, and descend over falls and rapids as they approach the Amazon. Only the Amazon itself is navigable far into the interior. Even the Madeira is interrupted by hundreds of miles of rapids where it crosses the westernmost edge of the Brazilian Highlands.

From the point of view of human settlement, only a very small part of the highlands is too steep for either agricultural or pastoral use. But the fact that the rivers drain inland away from the southeast coast means that there is no natural focus of routes on this part of the country. That the lines of travel today actually do come to a focus on such large cities as Rio de Janeiro or São Paulo has been brought about in spite of the lack of any large natural convergence of routes on these places.

The Climates

In that large portion of the continent of South America which belongs to Brazil there are many varieties of climate. In no part of Brazil are to be found those conditions of temperature and humidity which Huntington and others have shown to have a favorable effect on human energy.[2] Brazilian climates contain few extremes, either of temperature or of moisture; yet they are by no means so monotonously uniform, or so unbearably hot and damp, that the human spirit is deadened. If the Brazilian people in certain regions appear to be lacking in energy, this cannot be interpreted as the inevitable result of the climate until such other elements as diet and disease have been evaluated.

A considerable amount of misinformation exists regarding the temperatures of tropical countries like Brazil. The world's highest temperatures are not found near the equator, but in the deserts more than 30° of latitude from it. Average annual temperatures increase as one approaches the heat equator—which, in South America, passes along the Caribbean and Guiana coasts through such places as Maracaibo and Georgetown. The ranges of temperature between coldest and warmest months, however, decrease as one comes closer to the heat equator. In the equatorial regions temperatures are moderately high throughout the year, but they never are so high in those regions as they are in summer in the lower middle latitudes. In South America the places where the highest extreme temperatures have been recorded are found along the Caribbean Coast, and, during the southern summer, in the Argentine Chaco (Map 6, Page 12). At Santarém, on the Amazon and only a few degrees from the equator, the highest temperature ever recorded is 96.3°, and the lowest 65.3°. At this same place the average annual temperature is 78.1°. In the dry region in Northeast Brazil, the highest temperature recorded by any station is 106.7°; but as one proceeds southward along the coast where the rainfall and cloudiness are greater than in the Northeast, the maximum temperatures are much lower. At Rio de Janeiro the average temperature of the warmest month is 79.0°—about the same as the average of the warmest month at Raleigh, North Carolina. The

[2] Ellsworth Huntington, *Civilization and Climate*, New York, 1924.

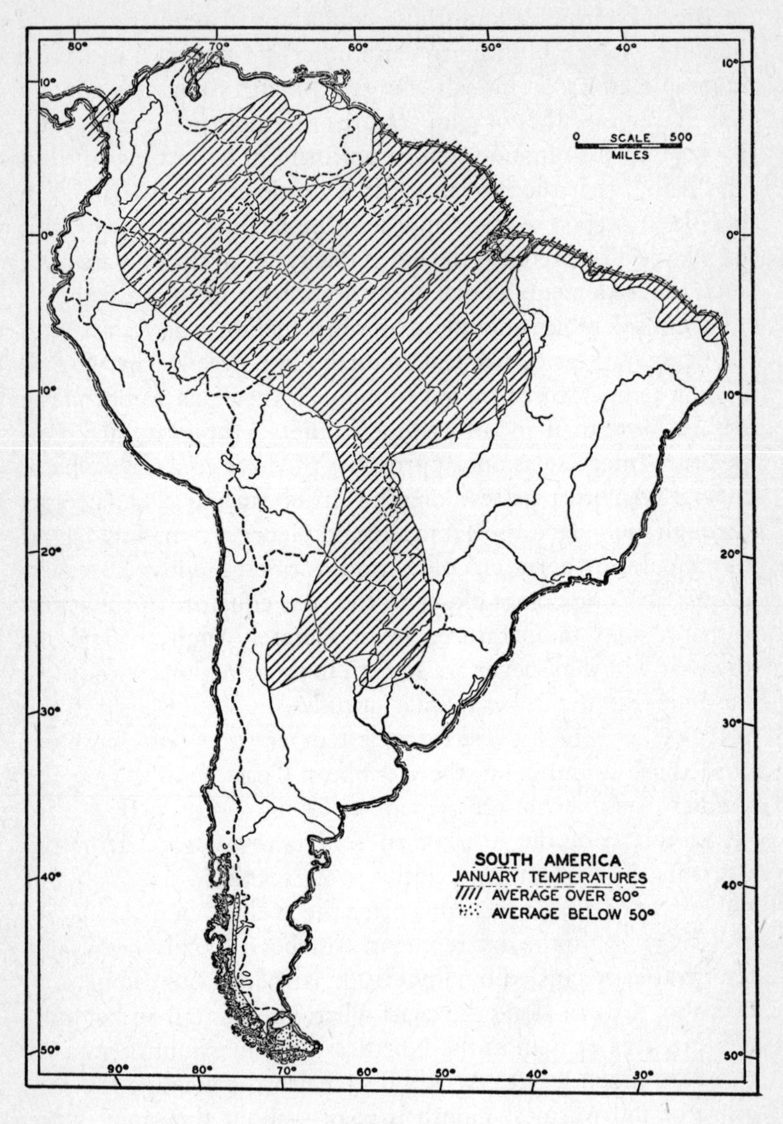
SOUTH AMERICA
JANUARY TEMPERATURES
AVERAGE OVER 80°
AVERAGE BELOW 50°
0 SCALE 500
MILES
80°
70°
60°
50°
40°
30°
90°
10°
0°
20°

MAP 6

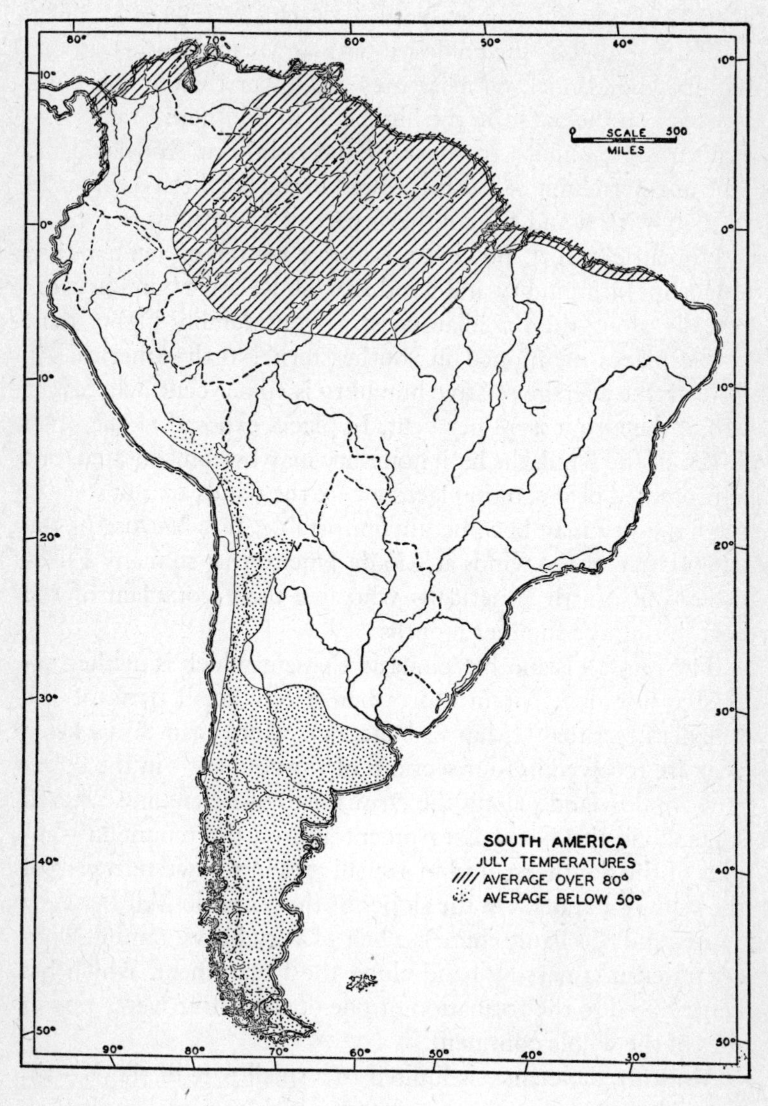
SCALE
0
500
MILES
SOUTH AMERICA
JULY TEMPERATURES
AVERAGE OVER 80°
AVERAGE BELOW 50°
80°
70°
60°
50°
40°
10°
0°
10°
20°
30°
40°
50°
90°
30°

MAP 7

average of the coldest month at Rio de Janeiro is 68.7°—which is similar to that of the coldest month at Miami, Florida. In the highlands of Brazil, temperatures are lower than at the same latitudes on the coast; in the highlands of Southern Brazil temperatures are similar to those of the Southern Appalachians. The northern limit of frosts is found in the northern part of the state of Paraná and the southern part of São Paulo.

Human comfort, however, is not a matter of temperature alone, but of humidity and wind as well. Relative humidity, especially along the Brazilian coast, is considerably higher than at the places mentioned in southeastern North America. At Raleigh the average relative humidity is 60 per cent, whereas at Rio de Janeiro it is 78 per cent. In places exposed to the open sweep of the wind, the high humidity may be compensated, but in protected places, or in places where the winds are not steady, the humidity may become uncomfortable. It is because of the irregularity of the winds at Rio de Janeiro that so many Europeans and North Americans who live there complain of the heat during the summer months.

The rainfall is another climatic element which is neither excessive nor deficient in more than a few small parts of the Brazilian territory (Map 8, Page 15). More than 80 inches a year are received in four sections of the country—in the upper Amazon lowlands, along the coast north of Belém, in scattered spots along the Great Escarpment and on the mountain summits of the Southeast, and in a small area in the western part of the state of Paraná. On the slopes of the Serra do Mar between Santos and São Paulo there is a belt of very heavy rainfall, concentrated in a narrow band along the Escarpment, which has contributed to the formation of one of the better water-power sites of the whole continent.

Moisture deficiency is limited to a small part of the Northeast. There are spots in this region which receive less than 10 inches a year; but most of the area receives between 20 and 25 inches. The problem of the Northeast is one of rainfall irregu-

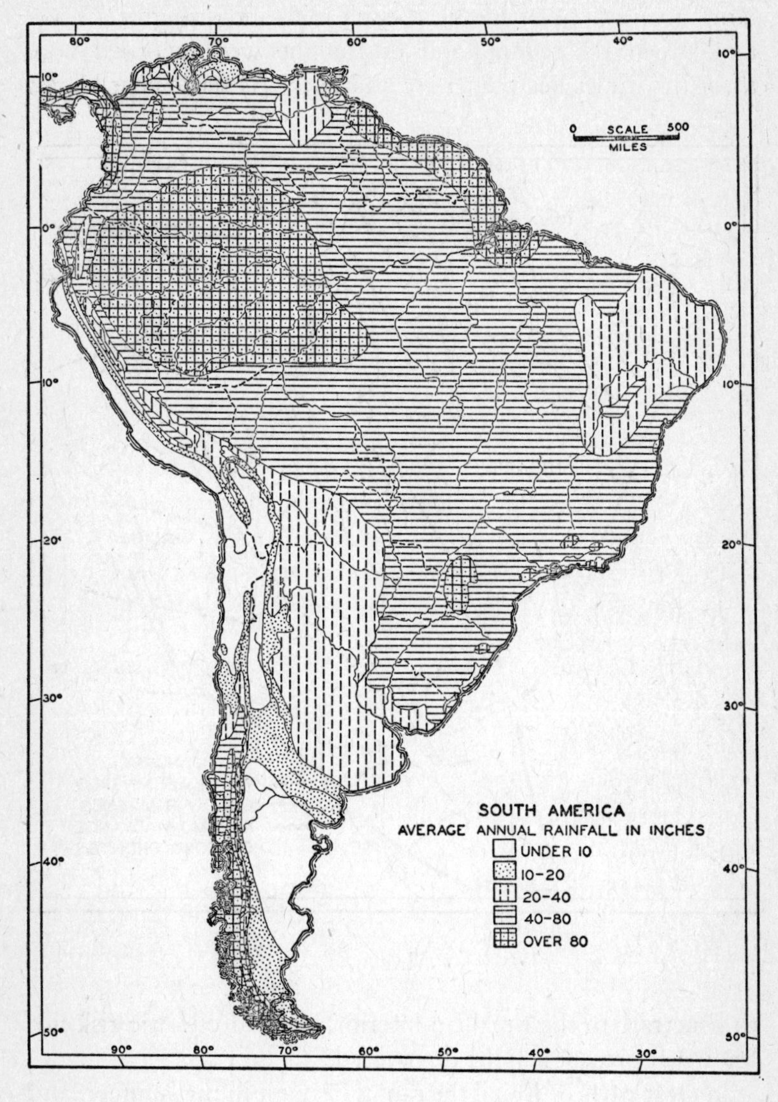

SOUTH AMERICA
AVERAGE ANNUAL RAINFALL IN INCHES
UNDER 10
10-20
20-40
40-80
OVER 80
0 SCALE 500
MILES

MAP 8

larity—variations between excessive rains and droughts. In certain parts of this region floods or droughts were recorded more than fifty times between 1835 and 1935. As settlement begins

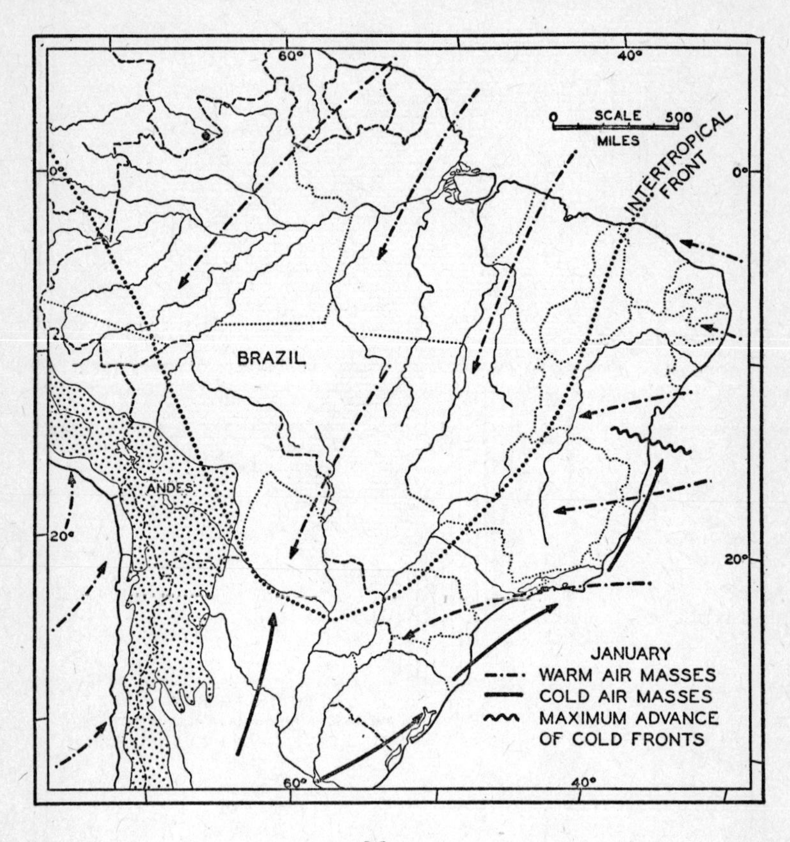

MAP 9

to penetrate to the Brazilian interior, areas of climatic risk not known at present may be discovered.

In most parts of Brazil the rain is heaviest in the summer, and a winter dry season is a regular occurrence. The southern states, however, from the southern part of São Paulo State southward, have no real dry season, but only a season of somewhat less rain in winter. In the Amazon Basin the rains come mostly from January to June; the other half of the year is less rainy.

Brazilian weather is produced by the interaction of moving

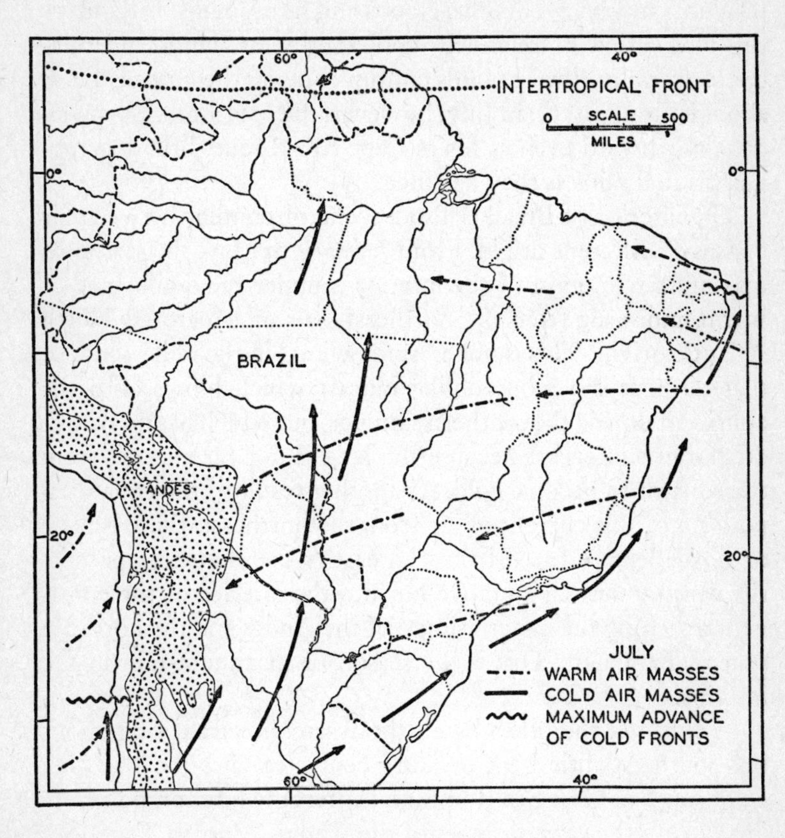

Map 10

air masses of different origins (Maps 9 and 10, Pages 16 and 17). Along the east coast from Cape São Roque southward two kinds of air are involved: first, the warm air masses which originate as part of the whirl of air around the South Atlantic high-pressure center and move along the coast from northeast to southwest, bringing predominantly clear skies or high stratus clouds; and second, the cold air masses of polar origin which, having crossed Argentina from the southwest, continue northeastward along the Brazilian coast. The impact of the two kinds of air masses produces towering cumulus clouds and heavy rains. In January this alternation of relatively cool southwest winds and relatively warm northeast winds continues along the coast as far as about latitude 20° S.; in July, however, the cool air masses penetrate northward even as far as Cape São Roque, bringing regular frontal rains as they advance.

The interior of Brazil is also a scene of conflict between air masses of different origin. From January to May, the season of maximum rain, most of the interior is under the dominance of warm, moist air from the northeast—air of equatorial North Atlantic origin. This is not a "trade wind" in the older sense of that term; it is a monsoonlike indraft which blows onto the continent during the southern summer, but which has no winter offshore counterpart because the land is not far enough from the equator to become cold. As another result of the equatorial position of this current of air from the northeast, there is little or no deflective force from the earth's rotation; this permits the warm, moist air to move far into the interior of the continent, reaching the eastern slopes of the Andes and the northern part of Paraguay. This is the season of maximum rain in the interior.

In July, on the other hand, the warm air circulating about the South Atlantic high-pressure center reaches the Brazilian coast south of Cape São Roque and enters the interior, penetrating even to the eastern slopes of the Andes (Map 10, Page 17). This air is relatively dry, and while air masses of tropical Atlantic origin are present in any locality the weather is clear. The cold air masses of polar origin are more vigorous at this period of the year also, and not only penetrate farther toward the equator along the coast, but also move northward through the Paraguay Valley, bringing cool, showery weather even as far as the Amazon. In the equatorial parts of Brazil the cool spells, or *friagems*, of the southern winter season are anything but comfortable.

The dry region of the Northeast is on the margin between the more or less regular rains along the coast south of Cape São Roque and the more or less regular rains west of São Luiz de Maranhão. The eastern edge of the monsoonlike indraft from the equatorial North Atlantic extends farther and farther eastward as the rainy season—January to May—progresses. Each year it moves east of São Luiz; some years it moves eastward all the way to Cape São Roque, and the result is heavy rains and floods; in other years it fails to move much beyond São Luiz, and the result is drought. No way to predict these irregularities has yet been discovered.

Natural Vegetation

The various conditions of climate together with those of the underlying surfaces and soils are expressed in the cover of natural vegetation (Map 12, Page 21). The heavy rainfall of the Amazon Basin and of the coast south of Salvador is reflected in the tropical rain forest, or selva. The Amazon Region contains the world's largest area of such forest. The selva is composed of evergreen, broadleaf trees, some of great size mixed with others of lesser size. In places where the selva has been carefully studied, as many as three thousand different species of trees per square mile have been identified. The branches are interlaced overhead in such a dense canopy of foliage that not much light can reach the forest floor, and as a result these forests contain little underbrush except along the banks of rivers, or in places where, for some reason or other, the foliage has been thinned. The soils under such forests, where they are not covered at frequent intervals by newly deposited material, are generally very poor in plant foods and in humus, for the heavy rains percolating through the upper layers of the soil dissolve the soluble minerals, and the vigorous bacterial action under conditions of

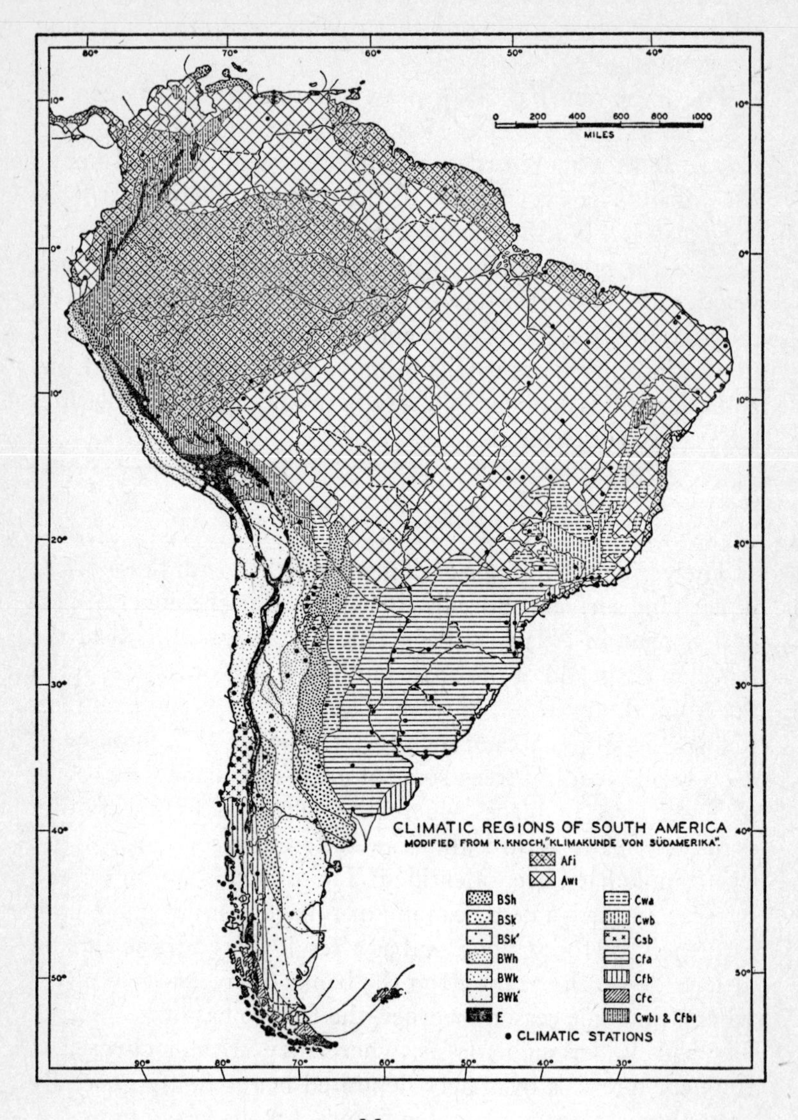
CLIMATIC REGIONS OF SOUTH AMERICA
MODIFIED FROM K. KNOCH, "KLIMAKUNDE VON SÜDAMERIKA".
MILES
0
200
400
600
800
1000
AFi
Awi
BSh
BSk
BSk'
BWh
BWk
BWk'
E
Cwa
Cwb
Csb
Cfa
Cfb
Cfc
Cwbi & Cfbi
CLIMATIC STATIONS

MAP 11

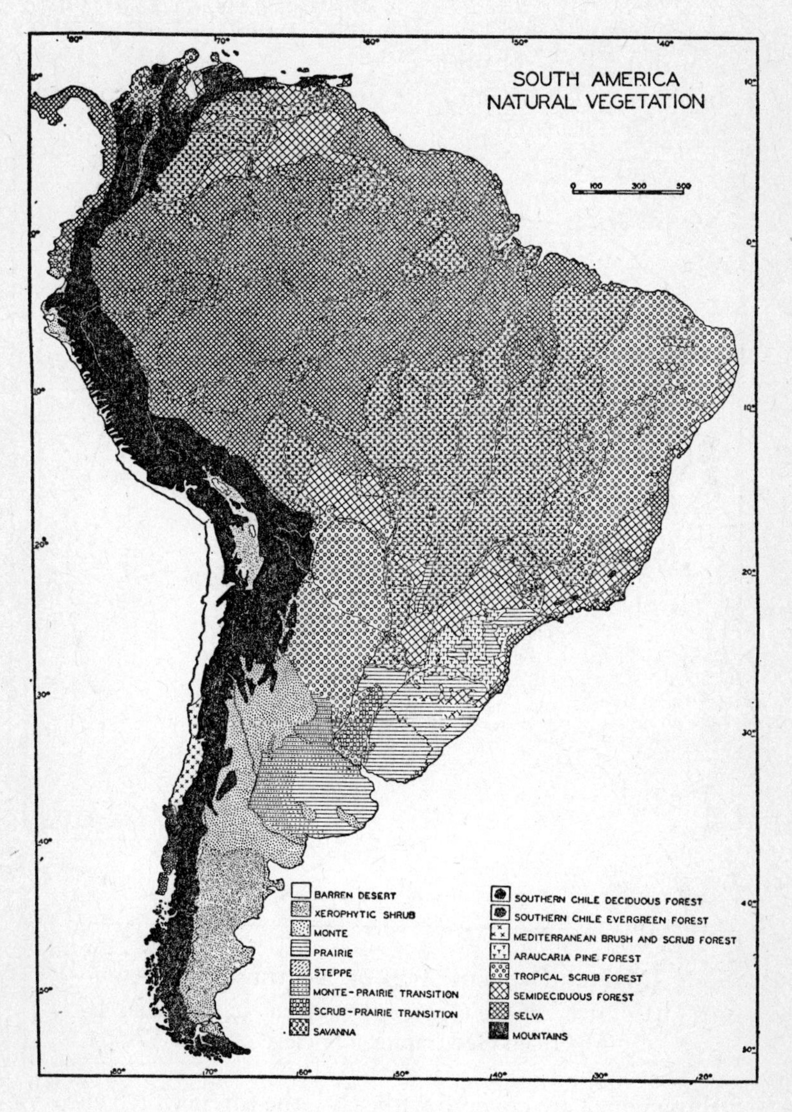
SOUTH AMERICA
NATURAL VEGETATION
0 100 300 500
BARREN DESERT
XEROPHYTIC SHRUB
MONTE
PRAIRIE
STEPPE
MONTE-PRAIRIE TRANSITION
SCRUB-PRAIRIE TRANSITION
SAVANNA
SOUTHERN CHILE DECIDUOUS FOREST
SOUTHERN CHILE EVERGREEN FOREST
MEDITERRANEAN BRUSH AND SCRUB FOREST
ARAUCARIA PINE FOREST
TROPICAL SCRUB FOREST
SEMIDECIDUOUS FOREST
SELVA
MOUNTAINS

MAP 12

high temperature and humidity quickly destroys any organic matter that falls to the ground.

In places which are not quite so rainy and not quite so warm

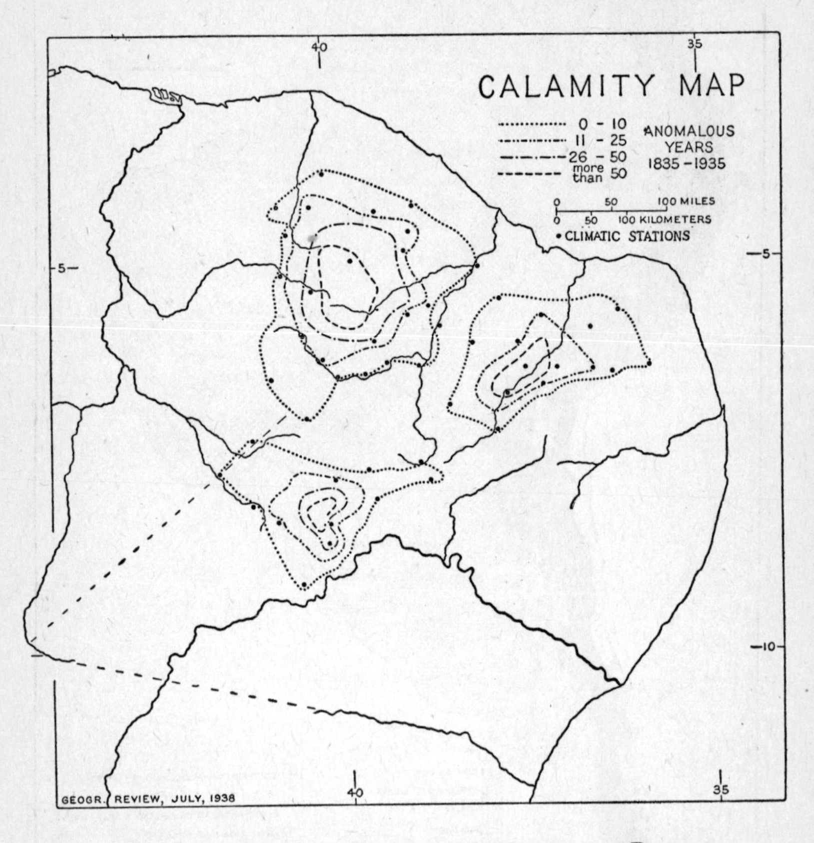

MAP 13. DROUGHT AREA OF NORTHEASTERN BRAZIL
(Courtesy of the *Geographical Review*, published by the American Geographical Society of New York.)

as those which are covered with selva, the forest which appears is described as semideciduous. It is composed of smaller trees, some of which lose their leaves during the dry season. Because light can more easily penetrate to the ground, the semideciduous forests have more underbrush and may actually be more difficult to traverse than the selva. Forests of this kind occupy the coast of the Northeast, south of Cape São Roque; south of

Map 14

Salvador the semideciduous forest covers the eastern margin of the highlands as far as southern São Paulo State, and extends even farther southward along the valley of the Paraná.

The greater part of the interior of Brazil, however, is covered with a mixture of dry savanna and scrub forest. The distinction between these is not in every place clear, for the savanna is covered with scattered scrub trees, and the scrub forest includes not only a grass-covered floor, but also many savanna-like openings. To identify the boundary along which trees become so numerous that the formation merits classification as a forest rather than as a savanna is difficult. The scrub forest is found usually in the drier places, as in the interior of the Northeast; most of western Brazil, south of the Amazon forests, is savanna. In all these areas of scrub forest and savanna the stream courses are followed by ribbons of evergreen or semideciduous galeria forests.

In the southern part of São Paulo State two types of vegetation appear which belong to the middle latitudes rather than to the tropics. These are the Araucaria forests and the prairies. The Araucaria forest is composed of a mixture of pine and broadleaf species; it is sharply set off from the tropical semideciduous forest by the northern limit of frosts. At about the same latitude, also, the savannas with their scattered scrub trees give way to pure tall-grass prairies, with dense forests in the deeper river valleys—a vegetation type characteristic of Uruguay.

These various categories of natural vegetation offer a clue to the relative potential value of the various parts of Brazil for different kinds of agricultural and pastoral uses. The tall-grass prairies, for instance, are better grazing lands for cattle than the tropical savannas, even for animals bred to withstand the insects which abound in the savannas. The best agricultural land for rice is offered by the floodplain of the Amazon, although the utilization of this resource would require the presence of an Oriental rather than an Occidental people. Outside of the alluvial areas, however, the regions of tropical rain forest are relatively poor lands, having little sustained fertility in their impoverished soils. From an agricultural point of view the savannas and scrub forests are also relatively poor. For shallow-rooted crops the semideciduous forest regions having soils which are richer in soluble minerals and in humus than those under the selva constitute Brazil's best agricultural areas; in these areas, both in general and in detail, the chief centers of sugar and coffee production have been established. The tropical crops which are limited by the recurrence of frosts are excluded from the regions of the Araucaria forest.

The map of the natural vegetation (Map 12, Page 21), therefore, suggests that a very large part of the Brazilian interior is relatively low-grade country from an agricultural or pastoral point of view. Whatever effort in terms of money or labor is put into the work of making it productive would yield much higher returns if applied to the still unoccupied portions covered, or formerly covered, with the semideciduous forests. These interior lands are not unproductive, for they could furnish a living for subsistence cultivators or stock raisers, and there are certain areas where conditions are suited to certain kinds of crops—for example, the valley of the São Francisco where the soils are excellent for cotton. Nevertheless, it seems apparent that Brazil is much more narrowly limited in its supply of first-class agricultural land than is generally thought.

Mineral Resources

When the French geologist Gorceix in a poetic moment exclaimed that Brazil's state of Minas Gerais had a "breast of iron and a heart of gold," he neglected to point out that there was in that state a deficiency of fuels which could be used to produce the high temperatures necessary for smelting. The gold and diamonds of this region did form the basis of the prosperity of Brazil during the eighteenth century—in fact, during that period Brazil produced 44 per cent of all the gold of the world. But the iron and manganese, and the many other industrial metals apparently available in this part of Brazil, have yet to be developed on a large scale. Manganese has been mined; iron smelting with the aid of charcoal has been carried on for many years, and an excellent quality of steel is produced. But the problem of maintaining the supply of charcoal becomes more acute every year as, little by little, the forests are stripped away. Brazil's coal, located in Santa Catarina and Rio Grande do Sul, contains such a high proportion of ash and sulphur that it must be processed before it can be used as a fuel. Nevertheless, the deposits of iron and manganese, and perhaps other metals, such as copper, lead, zinc, nickel, and chromium, will probably before long be exploited on a larger scale. The chief zone of minerals is the prominent range of mountains running roughly north and south through central Minas Gerais (Maps 1 and 14, Pages 4 and 23).

Chapter II

THE PEOPLE

NONE OF THE many advantages and disadvantages inherent in the physical make-up of Brazil have real significance for us in terms of human settlement until we know about the people and their way of living. Perhaps nowhere on the earth is there a greater mixture of different kinds of people than in Brazil. The primary ingredients are Portuguese, Indian, and Negro, but during the past century the population has been much altered by the arrival of millions of immigrants from Europe and Asia. All these elements have mixed freely, for one of the important traits brought by the Portuguese was the absence of any taboo against race mixture, except among the aristocracy. Each ingredient, therefore, has given certain easily observable physical characteristics to the new race of Brazilians, and has contributed numerous culture traits to the Brazilian civilization.

Early Racial Ingredients

The Indians who inhabited Brazil in 1500 were chiefly of Tupi-Guarani stock—a linguistic group to which the Indians of Paraguay also belong (Map 18, Page 33). In almost every respect these Indians of eastern South America were a contrast to the Quechuas of the Andes. The Tupi-Guarani tribes were hunters, fishers, collectors, and shifting cultivators. They lived in small, scattered groups with no form of intertribal political organization. Their basic food crop was manioc rather than maize. It is estimated that the Indian population of 1500 in all of Brazil was only about 800,000.

As a source of labor, the Tupi-Guarani proved quite inadequate. In the first place, great numbers of them died of European diseases in the early years of the conquest. Those who survived were handicapped by the traditional Indian attitude toward work. Agriculture was left to the women; the men devoted themselves to hunting, fishing, and fighting. The men could not adjust themselves to the agricultural work demanded by the Europeans. Free intermarriage, however, between the Portuguese men and the Indian women introduced many of the physical and psychological traits of the Indians into the resulting population.

Negroes, also, made an important contribution to the composition and character of the Brazilian people. Beginning in 1538, Negro slaves from Africa were brought across the ocean, especially to the Brazilian Northeast, where there was a demand for field hands in the new sugar industry. The Negro was not only a good worker, but he also possessed a knowledge of technological processes which has often been overlooked. The Negroes of the Sudan, it should be remembered, were the inventors of the process of iron smelting. This technological ability they brought with them to Brazil, along with their rhythmic music and their superstitions. The Negro foremen on the plantations, or later in the gold mines, knew more about the technological processes than did many of the Portuguese owners. From the seventeenth to the nineteenth century, agricultural and mining enterprise in Brazil owed a large debt to the Negro laborers and technicians.

From the Portuguese, however, came the main characteristics of the Brazilians. Even before their departure from Europe, the Portuguese were already made up of a most remarkable variety of racial and cultural elements, inherited from the various peoples who had successively conquered the Iberian Peninsula. Like the Spaniards, they included ingredients of Celtic, Nordic, and Mediterranean origin; and especially in the south of Portugal, around Lisbon, there was a large mixture of Moorish blood and of Moorish and Semitic culture traits. Moreover, the Portuguese from Lisbon were familiar with the use of Negro labor, for slaves had been brought to this part of Portugal in considerable numbers during the period of Moorish rule. Like the Spaniards, too, the Portuguese had the traditions of feudalism and of large private estates—traditions which profoundly influenced the relations of people to the land throughout Latin America.

The Portuguese had long been accustomed to commerce and to adventuring in distant places when they came to America in search of quick wealth. Like most of the Europeans who came to the New World—including the English—the foremost objective was to loot the rich resources of a virgin land. The Portuguese were much less interested than the Spaniards in implanting their institutions in America; they had little of the fanatical zeal for the spread of Christianity that their Spanish brothers possessed. They were attracted less by the prospects of earning a living by persistent toil than by the opportunities for speculative profit. As one Brazilian writer puts it, the ideal was "to collect the fruit without planting the tree." Whereas some of the peoples of America have been led by force of circumstances to be content with less spectacular returns from more intensive forms of economy, the Brazilians, with their huge land area, their superlative resources, and their small numbers, are still seeking new ways for the speculative exploitation of the treasures stored up in nature. This is the Brazilian variation of the theme of El Dorado.

Course of Settlement

History and geography have both contributed to the settlement of Brazil and to the development of the present patterns

SOUTH AMERICA
POPULATION
1,000 RURAL PEOPLE
URBAN UNITS
UNDER 10,000
10,000 - 50,000
50,000 - 100,000
100,000 - 1,000,000
OVER 1,000,000
SCALE OF MILES
0 100 200 300 400 500
RELATIVE RELIABILITY
1
2
3
4

MAP 15

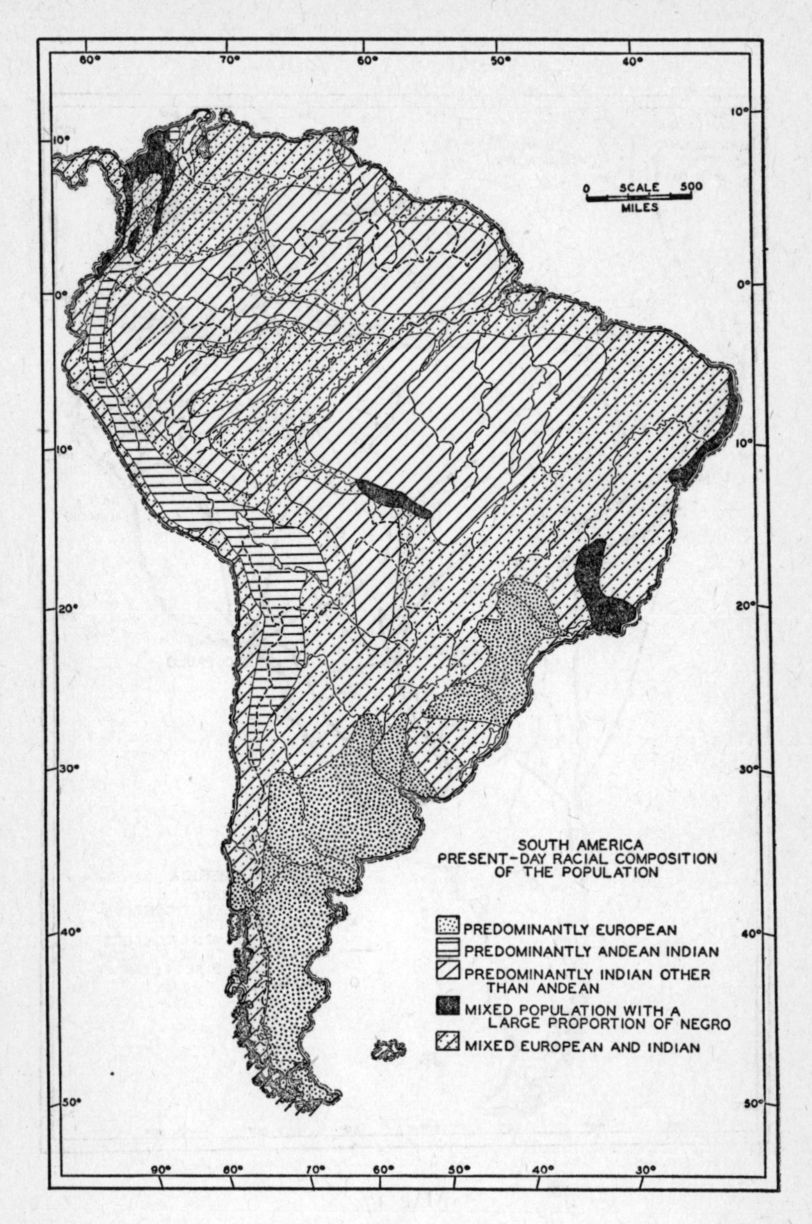
SOUTH AMERICA
PRESENT-DAY RACIAL COMPOSITION
OF THE POPULATION
PREDOMINANTLY EUROPEAN
PREDOMINANTLY ANDEAN INDIAN
PREDOMINANTLY INDIAN OTHER THAN ANDEAN
MIXED POPULATION WITH A LARGE PROPORTION OF NEGRO
MIXED EUROPEAN AND INDIAN
0 SCALE 500
MILES
80° 70° 60° 50° 40°
10° 0° 10° 20° 30° 40° 50°
90° 80° 70° 60° 50° 40° 30°

MAP 16

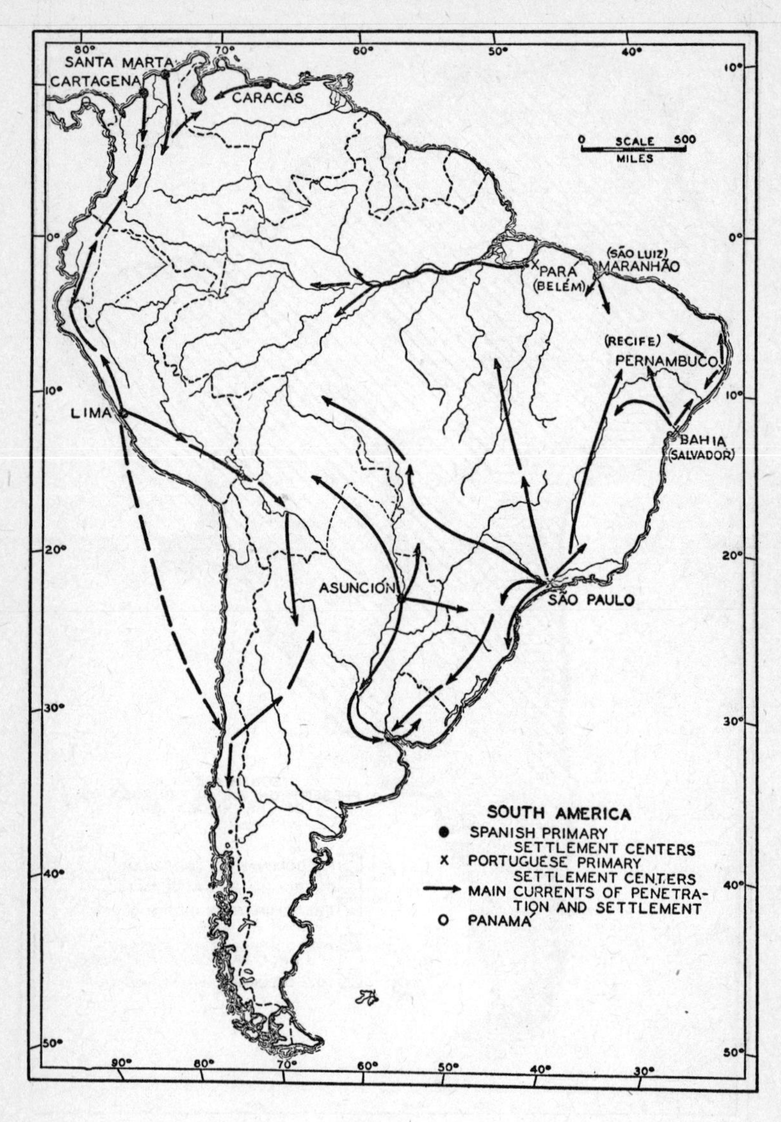
SANTA MARTA
CARTAGENA
CARACAS
LIMA
ASUNCIÓN
SÃO PAULO
BAHIA
(SALVADOR)
PERNAMBUCO
(RECIFE)
(SÃO LUIZ)
MARANHÃO
PARÁ
(BELÉM)
0 SCALE 500
MILES
SOUTH AMERICA
SPANISH PRIMARY SETTLEMENT CENTERS
PORTUGUESE PRIMARY SETTLEMENT CENTERS
MAIN CURRENTS OF PENETRATION AND SETTLEMENT
PANAMÁ

MAP 17

CARIB
ARAWAK
CHIBCHA
BORO
CARIB
JIVARO
ARAWAK
CUZCO
TUPI
GÊS
BOTOCUDO
GUARANI
ABIPONES
ARAUCANIAN
PUELCHE
ALIKULUF
TEHUELCHE
YAHGAN
ONA
0 SCALE 500
MILES
SOUTH AMERICA
SELECTED INDIAN CULTURES
GREATEST EXTENT OF INCA EMPIRE
SEDENTARY CHIBCHAS

MAP 18

of population. In the history of settlement in the four hundred years since the Portuguese first planted successful colonies on the coast of South America, three products, in turn, have dominated a period. Each period has been characterized by the spectacular rise of a commercial product, by the sale of this product in an expanding market and the collection of promoter's profits, and by the eventual decline of prosperity owing to increasing competition from areas of production outside Brazil, where people were willing to invest in "the planting of the trees." Each of Brazil's great products has led to the development of one specific region, and has given rise to an area of concentrated settlement around an urban nucleus. As one product after another has passed its zenith and begun its decline, the population has moved on to new frontiers, or remained decadent. The chief products which have thus punctuated Brazilian history and have colored the Brazilian map are sugar, gold, and coffee. In addition there have been minor interludes neatly set off in time and space—dominated by rubber, cacao, oranges, and other products.

The early decades of the colonization of Brazil by the Portuguese, however, were not associated with any of these commercial developments. The first settlement was established in 1502 at Salvador in the state of Bahia. But the Portuguese found no sources of gold and gems comparable to those of India, and no rich native civilizations which invited pillage. Brazil was neglected, because at the beginning of the sixteenth century Portugal was a poor country with a population which probably did not number more than a million; and for many decades she had all she could handle in the development of her connections with India and the other parts of the East. Brazil was neglected until the encroachments of the French and the Spaniards made it imperative for Portugal to establish colonies on the American coast, or to relinquish her claims. The division of the coast of Brazil into *capitanias*, each under the direction of a person selected by the Portuguese crown, led to a very uneven distribution of settlements, for those capitanias which came under the direction of capable organizers and administrators flourished, while others which came under the direction of men of lesser ability were often not settled at all. A successful colony was founded at São Vicente, near the site of Santos, in 1532, and another at Olinda, near the site of Recife in the state of Pernambuco, in 1537; Recife itself was not founded until 1561. Meanwhile a mission was established on the site of the present city of São Paulo in 1554—the first of the Brazilian settlements on the highlands.

The three chief primary settlement centers from which the Portuguese carried forward their conquest of Brazil were São Paulo, Salvador, and Recife (Map 17, Page 32). These are the places which correspond to Mexico City, Cartagena, Lima, and Asunción in Spanish America. Rio de Janeiro, founded on its present site in 1567, was at first only a fortress and naval base for the protection of the coast, and not at all a primary settlement center.

Sugar Colonies

The rapid rise of the commercial production of sugar in Brazil took place late in the sixteenth century. Sugar cane was introduced in 1532 and planted around São Vicente; but not until the second half of the sixteenth century did the spectacular rise of this new product begin and then it was the Northeast, centering upon Salvador, which prospered. A considerable difference appeared early between the colonists who came to São Vicente and São Paulo, and those who came to Salvador and Recife. According to Freyre the Portuguese who settled in the Northeast included a considerable proportion of wealthy people, many of whom came from the north of Portugal and had long been accustomed to the direction of large estates. The people who settled at São Vicente and São Paulo were mainly from the south of Portugal—mostly poorer people who did not possess enough capital to go to the aristocratic colonies of Bahia and Pernambuco. The Northeast was also much closer to Europe and to Africa than was São Vicente. Distance in the days of small sailing vessels was of greater significance in human affairs than it is today. At any rate, it was the people of the Northeast who were able to buy Negro slaves, to build sugar refineries, to clear the land, and to plant sugar cane; the people of São Vicente, with their Indian slaves, were unable to share in any important way in the prosperity of the sugar period. The plantation owners of the Northeast soon found themselves selling on a rapidly expanding market, and producing at costs which, after the initial investment, were very low. During most of the seventeenth century, the Northeast of Brazil was the world's chief source of the new and increasingly popular food product, sugar from cane.

So profitable did the sugar-producing area of the Northeast become that it invited conquest by other European powers. In 1624 the city of Salvador was occupied by the Dutch. Although they were soon forced to withdraw from Salvador, the Dutch succeeded in occupying Recife and in spreading their control of the Brazilian coast all the way from the northern border of Bahia to the Amazon. The Portuguese colonists, however, returned to the attack and, without help from Portugal, pushed the invaders back step by step until, in 1654, they recaptured the city of Recife. This was a very important event for Brazil. The co-operative effort necessary to retake Salvador and Recife built certain loyalties and traditions which explain in part the present solidarity of the Northeast as a region.

Gold

While sugar production was bringing wealth to the people of the Northeast, especially in the states of Bahia, Pernambuco, and Paraíba, the settlers in the south were enjoying no such prosperity. The people of São Paulo were poor; they had discovered no source of wealth within their means to exploit; yet they were not at all content to accept this situation. From São Paulo a series of semimilitary expeditions went forth into the interior of the country. These expeditions were called *bandeiras*, and the members of the expeditions were called *bandeirantes*. The first objective was to find gold—which had already been discovered in many of the stream gravels of the country south of São Paulo. But gold in the South proved to exist only in small quantities, and the bandeirantes had to seek other forms of wealth to exploit. They found Indians; large numbers of the native peoples, having first been brought together around the mission stations, were carried into slavery. Intermarriage with the Indian women became common, and the area occupied by the explorers from São Paulo soon had a considerable proportion of half-breeds—a racial type which in Spanish America is called mestizo, but which in Brazil is called *mameluco*.[1] The bandeirantes traveled slowly over the vast interior of the continent, pushing the borders of Brazil far to the west and to the south. Searching restlessly for slaves, gold, or any other sources of wealth, they grazed their animals on the savannas and even stopped to plant and harvest crops on the way. These hardy adventurers established the colony of Colonia on the shores of the Plata opposite Buenos Aires in 1680; they pushed westward to the Paraguay north of Asuncíon; they even roamed into the Northeast, into the scrub-forest country (Map 17, Page 32) inland from the sugar colonies. Finally, in 1698, they discovered rich gold-bearing gravels in the central part of Minas Gerais (Map 14, Page 23) on the headwaters of the Rio São Francisco. Shortly thereafter, other gold discoveries were made: at Cuiabá in Mato Grosso in 1719; and near the former capital of Goiaz in 1725. In Minas Gerais, in the country a little to the north of the gold fields, diamonds were discovered in 1729.

The discovery of gold and gems, especially the discoveries in central Minas Gerais, came at a time when the prosperity of

[1] The word *mestiço* in Portuguese refers to any person of mixed blood, often mixed white and Negro.

the sugar planters of the Northeast had passed its zenith. Declining yields on soils which had been cultivated for many years, and increasing competition from other areas were decreasing profits in the Brazilian region. It is not in the Brazilian tradition, under such circumstances, to aim at greater production through the use of better agricultural practices. Income in the Northeast was spent to raise the standard of living of the aristocracy, not for investments which might lower the cost of production per unit. That would be "planting the trees." Brazil suffered, moreover, from the curse of great area; virtually limitless area meant the ever-present possibility of moving on to new lands and of exploiting new resources; it meant the lack of any compelling reason for the intensification and stabilization of economic life in any one region. When gold was announced in Minas Gerais, the result was a gold rush, in which not only Paulistas and Portuguese from the home country participated, but also many former sugar planters of the Northeast who came bringing their slaves.

The gold period started early in the eighteenth century, reached its peak of development between 1752 and 1787, and was definitely over by the beginning of the nineteenth century. During this time Minas Gerais was transformed from a wilderness into a well-populated agricultural, pastoral, and mining region, dotted with many small towns, and with its rural districts partitioned among a relatively small number of landlords. The settlement of this part of Brazil led to the development of Rio de Janeiro as a port, for this place came to be the chief outlet for the gold, and the chief urban nucleus of the new region of settlement. Great quantities of gold were sent back to Portugal, greatly to the profit of the king and of the mine owners in Brazil. But little of this prosperity was shared by the workers of Minas Gerais. By the beginning of the nineteenth century the best sources of gold and diamonds had been exhausted, and Brazil was ready for a new form of speculative development.

Coffee

Recent Brazilian history has been dominated by the commercial production of coffee, and this activity is concentrated in the state of São Paulo, inland from the city of that name. Like the sugar-cane planters, the people of São Paulo found themselves providing a very large proportion of the world's supply of a new commodity which was rising rapidly in popular favor. Coffee planting started around Rio de Janeiro and at other places on the coast from Santos to the Amazon; but by the end of the first quarter of the nineteenth century there was a definite concentration of coffee in the Paraíba Valley, inland from Rio de Janeiro. From this district, coffee planting spread westward into São Paulo State—a movement which was increasingly rapid after 1850. Most of the European immigrants who came to Brazil after 1850 went to the new coffee lands of São Paulo, with the result that the new region of concentrated settlement was occupied by a very different kind of people from those of the older sections of Brazil. Coffee supported the rise of the great city of São Paulo. Now, in the modern era, São Paulo has become the leading center of manufacturing industries in all of Latin America.

Other Commercial Products

Meanwhile, other agricultural or forest products were leading to the rapid development, followed by the equally rapid decline, of other parts of Brazil. Rubber created havoc in the Amazon valley, rising to a mighty crescendo of speculation and wild spending in 1910, then declining to a very minor position among the world's products after 1912. Cotton, cacao, various wild fruits, nuts, dyes, and other substances led to minor and local flurries of speculation at various times and places. The collection of maté leaves in the Araucaria forests of Southern Brazil is one of these. In each case Brazil, after a period of feverish growth, was forced to yield to other sources of supply, where more intensive methods of production were applied. The result, in Brazil, has been a lack of stability of settlement.

Immigration

Not until the nineteenth century did the population of Brazil increase rapidly. Birth rates were relatively low, and infant mortality was very high because of bad hygiene and the lack of nourishing foods. The immigration of Negroes in the Northeast built up there the densest population of any part of Brazil. In fact, as late as 1870 half of all the Brazilians lived in this region. Early in the nineteenth century the German geographer Alexander von Humboldt estimated that the population of Brazil was composed of about 920,000 whites, about 1,960,000 Negroes, and about 1,120,000 Indians and mixed Indians and whites—a total of only 4,000,000 near the end of three centuries of settlement!

A rapid increase in the population of Brazil took place during the period of new European immigration after 1850. Since 1822, when Brazil became an independent country, about five million immigrants have arrived, most of them since 1900. But not all of Brazil was equally affected by this stream of new arrivals: over half of them went to São Paulo State, where coffee was demanding the services of an army of workers.

This stream of immigrants was made up mostly of Europeans. About 34 per cent were Italians, 30 per cent were Portuguese, 12 per cent were Spaniards, 3 per cent were Germans, and the remaining 21 per cent included many different nationalities. There are today a little under two hundred thousand Japanese in Brazil—also mostly in São Paulo State. After 1918 the proportion of Italian immigrants dropped to almost nothing, while Poles and other people from eastern Europe and the Japanese have increased rapidly.

Colonies of the South

The first people to penetrate the southern part of Brazil, the part south of the São Paulo Coffee Region, were the bandeirantes who made use of the prairies for the grazing of cattle and mules. Later, in 1824 in Rio Grande do Sul, and in 1850 in Santa Catarina, colonies of German farmers were established. In these states, however, the immigrants were not tenants or wage workers on large estates, but small landowners, occupying and cultivating their own properties. In the course of time, these colonies were added to by new groups of Italians and Poles.

The outstanding fact regarding the settlements of southern Brazil is that they have started to expand. The clusters of people in the three southern states of Brazil (Map 15, Page 30) are all growing rapidly, and, with little new immigration to support them, frontiers of pioneer settlement have appeared around the margins of the original nucleuses and new colonies have budded off from the older ones, but without any decrease in the density of population in the original centers. This is a condition which is discovered in only four parts of mainland Latin America, two of which have already been described—the Antioquia Region of Colombia, and Middle Chile. In the midst of a country with shifting patterns of population, handicapped by scarcity of numbers in the face of a vast thinly occupied area, the expanding settlements of Southern Brazil are of special importance and significance to Brazil.

As a result of the rate of population increase in the south, and of the arrival of immigrants in São Paulo, the population of Brazil as a whole has started to increase at a more and more rapid rate. In 1872 there were about ten million Brazilians; by 1920 there were well over thirty million; and at present it is estimated that the number of people in Brazil is a little more than forty million.

The Cities and the Sertão

Before turning to view more closely the relations of people to the land in the various regions of Brazil, one more important fact concerning the distribution of people must be presented. No other Latin-American country illustrates more strikingly the enormous contrast which exists between urban centers and the sparsely populated areas beyond the zones of concentrated settlement. Brazil's cities, like those of other countries, have been making very rapid gains in population and in manufacturing development since the beginning of the First World War. Both Rio de Janeiro and São Paulo have more than a million inhabitants. The impact on the shores of South America of ideas developed in Europe and North America is supporting the growth of great, progressive cosmopolitan centers which appear superficially to be more an expression of conditions outside of the continent than of conditions within it. In these cities new architectural forms are making their appearance and large groups of people, whose lives are now ordered on the urban pattern, are thinking and acting more and more like city people throughout the Occidental world. Industrial society is so new, so much in contrast to the traditional life of the country, and the city people have adopted attitudes and objectives so different from those which have moved the Portuguese and their descendants since before the discovery of America, that some Brazilian writers now insist that the "real" Brazil is not to be found in the cities at all. The real Brazil, they say, is only to be found in the back country—in the thinly peopled wilderness beyond the frontiers of concentrated settlement; in the land which the Brazilians call the *sertão*.[2]

The sertão is not a wilderness in the sense that it is made up of unexplored territory. Actually it has been tramped over, lived in, its resources exploited, and its landscapes modified in

[2] Pronounced sair-tong'. The plural is *sertões*, pronounced sair-tó-aish.

many ways over the course of more than four centuries. The sertão forms a sort of penumbra around the margins of the effective national territory: a transition zone of shifting population, but one in which a way of living has become established which has withstood the forces of change over hundreds of years. Aside from groups of people temporarily engaged in seeking for gold, the economy of the sertão is essentially pastoral—the grazing of herds of cattle on the open range. Scattered throughout the vast area of the sertões there are small groups of people clustered more or less permanently around ranch headquarters or in small towns. Contact with the regions of concentrated agricultural settlement is made through annual fairs held in border towns: beyond the frontier of close settlement the pastoral sertão extends indefinitely inland; its area can be roughly, but not exactly, delimited as the zone with a population density between two and ten per square mile.

The pastoral inhabitants of the sertão are not like the Brazilians in the cities or even those in the agricultural areas. They are almost pure Portuguese with a mixture of Indian. They are essentially democratic, knowing no rigid class distinctions, for the ranch owners look, act, dress, and live like their workers. They are a fiercely independent people, courageous, resourceful, and superstitious; but they are so widely scattered or gathered in such small groups that they cannot support the cost of those numerous things which bring a society forward from a pioneer life to one which can be described as civilized. Here it is likely that the pioneer way of life is permanently established.

To the Brazilian who lives in or around the cities, the sertão is a land of mystery. Its influence on Brazilian economic, political, and artistic thought is profound. The clusters of people along the coast are isolated from each other by this great thinly populated territory. For hundreds of years people have believed that a vast wealth of resources was lying dormant in the interior, and groups of settlers have gone out to seek this

Brazilian form of El Dorado; yet the only permanent settlers in the sertão, the only people who have been able to establish a permanent workable connection with the land, are the widely scattered herders. These settlers are not to be thought of as a fringe of pioneers engaged in the first rapid occupation of new lands in advance of a moving frontier: they are, rather, the fragments of population left from the many groups which have attempted to enter and utilize the riches of the interior; they represent a very old, stabilized society in a land long occupied.

We return, then, to our problem: why are there so few people in Brazil? The answer is not to be found only in those areas where concentrated settlement scallops the eastern border of the country. The answer must also be sought in the regions beyond. Perhaps the persistence of the tradition of collecting the fruit without planting the tree is, itself, a reflection of large area, of which so great a part is sertão. For more than four centuries the Brazilians have been struggling to break that sequence of cause and effect—a sparse population, the resulting predominance of destructive exploitation, and the resulting failure of the system to support more people. For more than four centuries the sertão has absorbed almost every effort to intensify the economic life; after all this time Brazil is still an empty land. But now there are expanding colonies in the South, and there are cities.

Chapter III

THE NORTHEAST

THE NORTHEAST [1] plays a part in Brazilian national life which is somewhat similar to that played by New England in the national structure of the United States. Some of the first colonies of Portuguese in Brazil were planted on the coast of Bahia and Pernambuco, around the primary settlement centers of Salvador and Recife (or near-by Olinda). Bahia and Pernambuco were the most prosperous states in Brazil during the sugar period. Back of the sugar plantations of the coast there developed a pastoral sertão. Although the sugar industry of the Northeast has long been decadent, the descendants of the planting aristocracy continue to exert a powerful influence on Brazilian political and intellectual life, for this region has produced more than its share of leaders. In no other part of Brazil, moreover, are the inhabitants to such a degree conscious of regional loyalty in addition to state loyalty.

The Northeast is not, however, a simple unit. Within the area between Salvador (in Bahia), Teresina (in Piauí), and Cape São Roque there are two strongly contrasted parts, and these parts are differentiated not only by the physical character of the land but also by the racial composition, and fundamental traditions of the people. First, there is the Northeast

[1] The Northeast, as defined in this book, includes the states of Piauí, Ceará, Rio Grande do Norte, Paraíba, Pernambuco, Alagôas, Sergipe, and parts of Maranhão and Bahia (Map 14, Page 23).

of the sugar plantations, the part which forms a belt along the coast between Salvador and Natal. Rainfall in this zone is dependable. The thick semideciduous forest characteristic of the rainy tropics has largely been cleared away, exposing the deep, dark-red soil which develops on crystalline rocks under such a forest. Plantations are large and devoted to the cultivation of sugar cane. The workers are mostly Negro and mulatto who are dominated by a small group of white plantation-owning families. There are important differences between the parts of this sugar region which focus on Salvador and the parts which focus on Recife; but altogether, the zone of the sugar plantations stands in striking contrast to the "other Northeast."

This other part is the Interior, bordering the coast north of Natal. It is a land of recurring droughts, of scrub forest standing on a soil which is hard, sandy, and light-colored; a land devoted largely to the pastoral life, but with little islands of agriculture where water is dependable. The Interior is occupied by people of Portuguese or Portuguese-Indian origin, only very slightly mixed with Negroes. Throughout the long course of Brazilian history these two Northeasts, the Coast and the Interior, have been closely linked by a common tradition, yet at the same time they have remained as sharply contrasted as black and white.

THE LAND

The essential difference between the two parts of the Northeast existed before the arrival of the Europeans, although the border which separates one from the other was sharpened by the process of settlement. The fundamental contrast is one inherent in the character of the land itself.

Surface Features

The three basic elements which combine to make up the surface character of the Brazilian Highlands are all represented in the Northeast (Map 2, Page 6). The basement of crystalline rocks, once covered with strata of sandstone, is now partly exposed, forming a surface of gentle slopes. This surface varies in height from a thousand to fifteen hundred feet above sea level in the northern part of the state of Bahia to only a few hundred feet above the sea in Ceará. Scattered over the crystalline uplands there are many low knobs, groups of hills, and ranges of low mountains—only the largest of which can be shown on the map (Map 2, Page 6). These are all remnants of erosion and denudation, standing above the general level of the hilly upland because of their superior resistance to the destructive action of air and water. The third surface element is the cover of sandstone strata, now partly stripped off by erosion. The eastern limit of the main body of the sandstone plateau forms a prominent east-facing cuesta which runs north and south along the border between the states of Piauí and Ceará. East of the main cuesta, however, there are mesa-like outliers, capped with sandstone. The largest of these is the Chapada do Araripe.[2]

In a zone of varying width along the coast the crystallines have been covered with relatively young layers of sand and clay, now solidified into sandstone and shale. The sandstone and shale are of more recent origin than the thick sandstones of the interior plateaus. The coastal stratified zone begins in Ceará, and narrows as it passes Cape São Roque and approaches Recife. It extends well inland in northern Bahia, surrounds the bay of Bahia, and thence runs southward as a narrow belt along the coast of southern Bahia. The streams which cross this coastal zone have cut through the upper sandy layers, leaving

[2] For persons trained in physiography it is interesting to note that this crystalline upland of the Northeast, sloping gently toward the coast of Ceará, north of Cape São Roque, is one of the few examples known in the world of a peneplain which is still essentially in place. The arrangement of the drainage, too, is of interest. The rivers, apparently, were established in their courses on the overlying sandstone, but as this cover was stripped off the rivers became superimposed on the underlying crystallines. One of the best descriptions of these surface features is given by Pierre Denis.

low mesas, or *taboleiros*, standing above the valleys. These mesas are dry because of the porosity of their sandy soils. Along the valley bottoms, however, the underlying shale has been uncovered, and in the bottoms of the deeper valleys, even the crystallines appear; these valleys offer the best cropland of the coastal zone. The taboleiros stand about 200 feet above sea level in the district just south of Cape São Roque; but in Bahia they are more than 600 feet high.

A geologically recent submergence of the coast has drowned the mouths of the rivers both around the bay which gave Bahia its name, and around São Luiz in the state of Maranhão, which lies just beyond the border of the Northeast as here defined. Most of the coast line is made up of offshore bars and lagoons which are filled with a dense growth of mangrove. The bars, north of the Rio São Francisco, have been cemented by chemical action of the lagoon waters to form stone reefs; an opening in one of the reefs, permitting access to the quiet lagoon behind it, provides a small natural harbor for the port of Recife.

Climate and Vegetation

The fundamental contrast between the two parts of the Northeast, however, is a result of climatic differences and of resulting differences in the natural vegetation and soil. The coast south of Cape São Roque receives regular rains, brought by the cold air masses as they push far to the north in the southern-hemisphere winter. Recife, for example, receives an average annual rainfall of about sixty-five inches, most of which occurs between April and July. This coastal zone of abundant rains extends inland for only about forty or fifty miles in Pernambuco, but becomes wider and wider toward the south. On the coast northwest of Cape São Roque, São Luiz de Maranhão receives an average annual rainfall of about eighty-five inches, most of which occurs between January and June, as in the eastern part of the Amazon Basin. These rains, we may recall, are brought by the indraft of warm, moist air from the equatorial North Atlantic. Between eastern Maranhão on the west and the coast of Pernambuco on the east lies a triangular-shaped zone of irregular rainfall, subject at intervals to floods and droughts.

Friedrich Freise has made an important study of the drought area of the Northeast, and has produced what he calls a map of "calamities" (May 13, Page 22). He finds three little areas where the rainfall average is very low, but where during the period from 1835 to 1935 there were more than fifty years of flood or drought. Other parts of the area show varying tendency to recurring calamities. He finds that, in so-called good years, about 90 per cent of the rain in the drought area falls between December and April or early May. Generally the rains start in October—the first showers being known as the *cajú* rains, because the tree, which produces the edible cajú nut, buds forth with new leaves and flowers at this time. In the rainy season the moisture is brought in violent showers of brief duration and of small extent. The whole rainfall of a month may be brought by four or five violent showers, all occurring within a few days of each other.

In bad years several irregularities may appear. Sometimes a whole year may pass in certain localities without any rain at all. Sometimes there are rains in December and January, but none after that. In other years there may be no rain from January to the end of March, followed by excessive downpours in April and May. Any of these departures from the normal results in disaster for the farmers, and if several abnormal years come in succession, there may be a widespread failure of the pasturage on which herders must depend.

The natural vegetation of the Northeast reflects these climatic contrasts. The zone of heavy, dependable rains along the coast was marked by a dense semideciduous forest, becoming an evergreen tropical rain forest in southern Bahia (Map 19, Page 50). Tropical rain forest also covers the land in

Maranhão. Between lies the *caatinga*, a scrub-forest type which is adapted to the irregular periods of deficient moisture. In

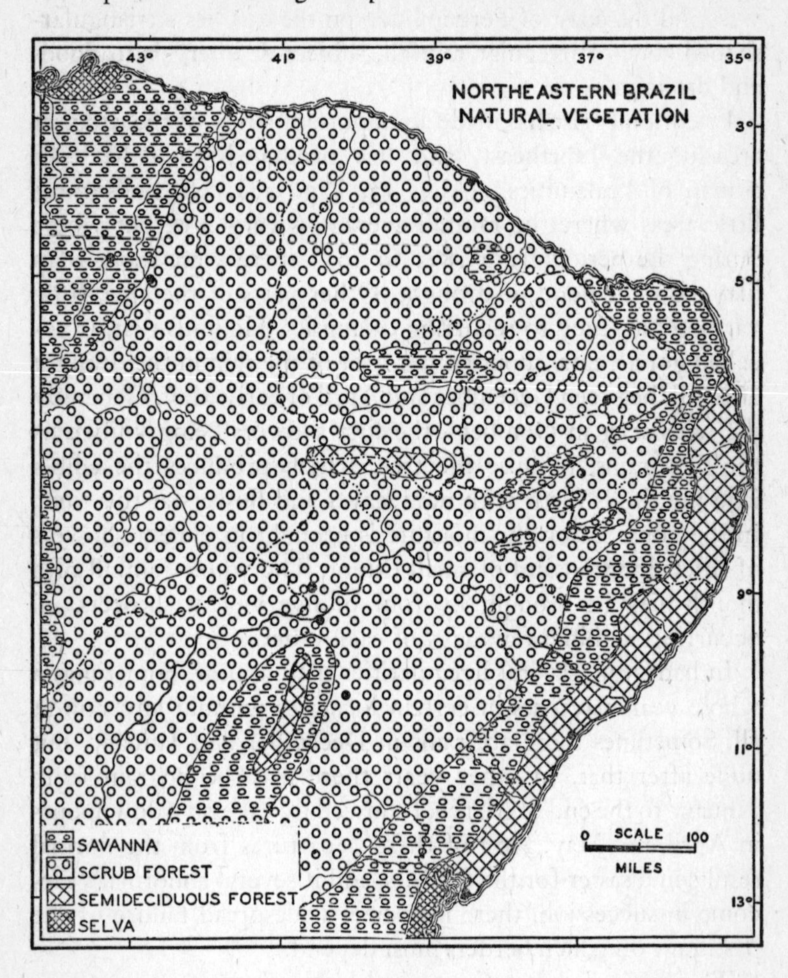

MAP 19

normal years the rainfall is by no means deficient, and the caatinga in many places forms a dense growth. Leaves are shed during drought, thus enabling the trees to survive. Large areas of the caatinga have been cleared for charcoal or simply burned to make more room for the growth of pasture grasses. In most parts of the region the margins of the streams are followed by the usual fringe of galeria forest, but in the drier spots where the streams dry up completely in the dry season, and form only pools of salty water even in the rainy season, there is not even this fringe along the stream banks. However, in certain localities within the region there occur almost pure stands of trees of considerable potential economic value in the modern world. The palm which produces Carnauba wax, important in the manufacture of such things as phonograph records, is one of these; there is also the tree which produces Oiticica oil, a possible substitute for Tung oil in paint and varnish manufacture, which is found in the galeria forests especially of Rio Grande do Norte and Ceará.

SETTLEMENT

The earliest colony along the coast of Brazil was established at Salvador, in Bahia. In the first decades of the sixteenth century the only product of the Northeast was dyewood from the semideciduous forest. The dyewood was taken to Lisbon where it was found to be similar to Brazil wood, which was commonly in use for dyeing in the middle ages. The name "Brazil" had already been applied to some islands which were supposed to lie in the Atlantic, and it was easily extended to the new land after dyewood was discovered there. During the first decades of settlement in Bahia, the colonists learned from the Indians how to grow tobacco; this part of Brazil has been famous for its production of high-grade tobacco for more than four hundred years.

Sugar Plantations

After a few decades, however, the Portuguese began to sense the possibilities of profit from the commercial production of sugar cane. This Moorish crop, already familiar to the Portuguese through their experience with cane plantations in the Madeira Islands, gave excellent yields in the coastal region around Salvador and Recife. The most productive sugar-cane soils were those developed on the crystalline rocks under the semideciduous forests. The sandy taboleiros of the immediate coast were of little agricultural value, and the yield of cane dropped off rapidly as one pushed farther inland beyond the inner edge of the tall forests. The deep soils on the crystalline rocks, enriched by a humus content exceptional in rainy tropical soils, were extraordinarily productive when they were first put to use. Forest clearing and cane planting spread rapidly, especially in two districts: around the bay in the state of Bahia, a district known as Recôncavo; and inland from Recife in the state of Pernambuco.

After 1538 in Salvador and after 1574 in Recife, Negro slaves were imported in large numbers. From then on, the population of the sugar region of the Northeast comprised four classes: the Indians, who survived in considerable numbers only in Bahia; the Negro workers on the plantations; the Portuguese landowners who drew a sharp color line against intermarriage with the black people; and the poorer people of Portuguese descent who were not landowners, many of whom took Indian or Negro wives, and most of whom settled in the towns and cities as small traders or fishermen. On the plantations, or *fazendas*, the wealthy landowners built themselves substantial homes of stone and cement, erected churches, and set up the big *engenhos*, or sugar mills. In contrast to the *casa grande*, or the home of the plantation owner, were the miserable *senzalas*, or slave quarters, built of mud and thatch.

The sugar lands were soon occupied by a relatively dense population. As the children of the first plantation owners grew up and married, they were established on new plantations, with new engenhos, often utilizing virgin land in the same valley as the parental estate. Little by little the plantation area was extended until it covered all the good soils, and perhaps even pushed for short distances into the bordering scrub forest. Nevertheless, the striking contrast in vegetation and rainfall dependability led to the development of a sharply defined frontier, and to the growth of compact settlement in the agricultural area. Had this first zone of settlement been located in a position where the semideciduous forests and good soils extended indefinitely inland, it is quite possible that the population density necessary to support the cost of a civilized way of living for the aristocracy could not have been built up. In this case the importance of a rather striking natural contrast was enhanced in the course of settlement by a people whose way of living was not adapted to the sertão.

Settlement of the Sertão

The first people to push westward into the sertão came from the towns and cities of the sugar region. In the rural districts of the coast there was no room for a white worker, and for many life in the towns was intolerable. Some of these poorer people who came to the Northeast were newly converted Jews, or *christãos novos*, who, like the settlers in Antioquia, were seeking a refuge in the New World. Many of the Portuguese who were too poor to own land and felt themselves ill adapted for life in the towns, moved out beyond the frontier into the sertão. With herds of cattle to provide them with food and with something to sell, they were sufficiently nomadic to avoid the worst effects of droughts and floods. These pastoralists established estate headquarters and used the wide expanse of grazing land in the scrub forests with little attention to property lines. The chief areas of pastoral activity were in the state of Ceará, inland from Fortaleza, and along the lower and middle course of the Rio São Francisco, in the state of Bahia. Contacts with the sugar colonies were made chiefly through the fairs held at frontier towns, of which the most important were at Feira de

Sant'Anna in Bahia, and at Campina Grande in Paraíba. Meanwhile, a few spots of agricultural settlement appeared in the midst of the sertão—at the northern base of the Chapada do Araripe, in the vicinity of Jardim de Seridó, around the low mountain groups south of Fortaleza, and in small areas elsewhere. These settled spots have persisted to the present time (Map 20, Page 55); they still produce chiefly food and other materials for the use of the pastoral people.

Life went on, therefore, along very different lines in the two contrasted parts of the Northeast. Yet the contacts between the sertão and the sugar plantations were not so remote that the mystery of the wilderness failed to be impressed on every child brought up in the centers of concentrated settlement.

Decadence of the Sugar Plantations

The process of decadence in the sugar plantations, which set in about the beginning of the eighteenth century and has continued to the present, has been a long and irregular one. When gold was discovered in Minas Gerais, and diamonds shortly afterward, the profits to be made in sugar were no longer so great that this new form of speculation did not have its immediate appeal. Between 1710 and 1720 there was a strong movement out of the Northeast, especially out of Bahia, in which many plantation owners moved southward with their slaves, following the valley of the Rio São Francisco to its headwaters in the mining region of Minas. From 1729 to 1745 the movement was revived, leading to the newly opened diamond fields of northern Minas Gerais and southern Bahia. It is estimated that 500,000 people left the sugar lands of the Northeast before the middle of the eighteenth century. Between 1780 and 1790, there was another big exodus of owners with their slaves, involving some 150,000 people, according to Freise, this time to the state of Maranhão, where a new coffee frontier was being established. Early in the nineteenth century some 100,000 people left the Northeast for the new coffee frontier in the Paraíba Valley, inland from Rio de Janeiro.

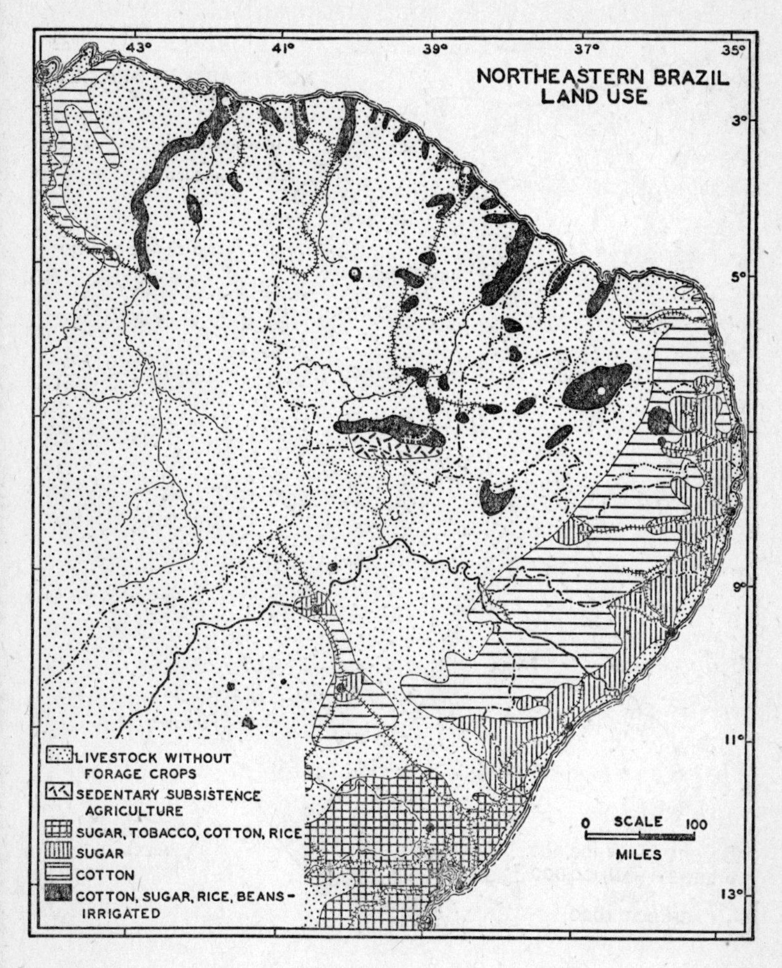

MAP 20

All these emigrations, however, did not permanently reduce the number of people in the agricultural part of the Northeast (Map 21, Page 56). As plantations of sugar cane were abandoned, or held for sale at low prices, people from the sertão moved in, occupying chiefly the outer zone of the agricultural

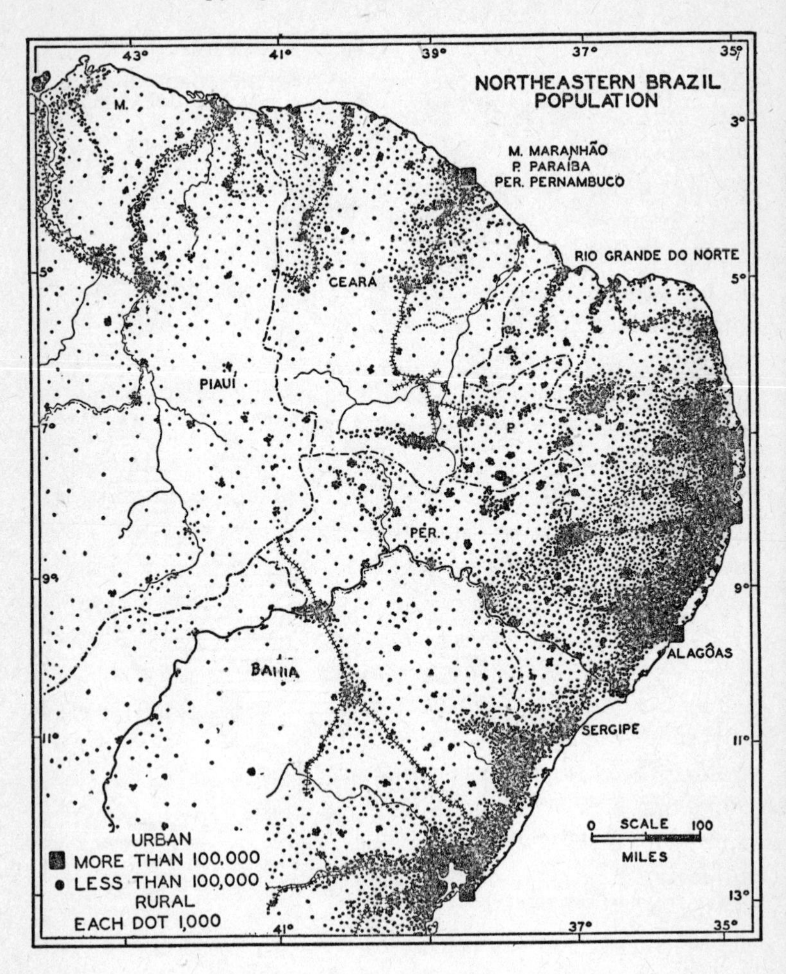

MAP 21

area. In most cases these newcomers were people who had previously farmed in the sertão, and the crop they brought with them was cotton. The low population density of the sertão was continued as a result of the process of decadence and abandonment in the neighboring zone of the plantations.

Meanwhile the sugar industry was being changed from one which competed for a place in the international markets, to one which survived on the domestic market behind a tariff wall. Two events after the middle of the last century combined to eliminate Brazilian sugar from an important place on the world markets. The first was the establishment of large-scale sugar production in the West Indies. Sugar mills there, equipped with new types of machinery, and receiving cane from a large surrounding area over a system of railroads, were able to reduce the costs of production far below those of the inefficient engenhos of Brazil. The second was the emancipation of slaves in 1888, which dealt a final blow to the old plantation system of the Northeast.

During the past fifty years the sugar of the Northeast has gone almost exclusively to domestic markets; but the domestic market has been a rapidly growing one and has been amply protected by tariffs against imported sugar. Brazilians consume large quantities of sugar per capita, for with each cup of coffee —and the average Brazilian drinks many cups of coffee every day—four or five spoonfuls of sugar are used. Rapid increase of population in the Southeast and in São Paulo created a new market for the sugar planters of the Northeast, and helped to prolong the existence of an industry already decadent. Other competing areas of sugar production in Brazil have gradually cut down the share of the Northeast, until, in 1937, the state of São Paulo alone accounted for more than half the supply.

Meanwhile the economic organization of the sugar lands of the Northeast has been transformed. The old plantations with their landowning aristocracy, their slave or tenant workers, and their small-scale mills, or engenhos, have gradually disappeared. Companies organized as commercial enterprises have bought many of the plantations and now cultivate them with wage workers hired from among the tenants of the old estates.

On these new plantations the cane from a wide area is brought to new, modern, large-scale sugar mills, or *usinas*. Where sugar production survives today in the Northeast, it is on this new basis.

Cotton in the Northeast

While the sugar industry was going through this long slow process of decadence, a new crop was appearing in the Northeast and was taking its place among the leading exports of Brazil. This was cotton. Cotton is planted in many small scattered areas throughout the sertão from Maranhão to Bahia; but the chief cotton region is on the margin of the former sugar lands in Pernambuco, Paraíba, and Alagôas. The first expansion of cotton planting in the hinterland of Recife took place about 1750, as people from the interior began to move into the region of the sugar plantations. Since cotton can be grown where there is less rainfall than is required for sugar cane, the margin of the agricultural land moved farther inland, into the scrub-forest area, and the frontier lost some of its sharpness. The territory around Jardim de Seridó came to form a transition zone between the predominantly black, very densely populated sugar area, and the white, but thinly populated sertão. The North American Civil War brought about a great rise in cotton planting in Brazil; and when the peak of this period of production was reached in 1871–72 the Northeast accounted for about 85 per cent of the cotton exports of Brazil. In that crop year, over 350,000 bales were sent to foreign markets.

Unfortunately the statistics of cotton production do not always make clear the fact that two very different kinds of cotton are produced in the Northeast. From the drier parts of the sertão comes the Brazilian "tree-cotton," which has a long, silky and very strong fiber. This type of cotton is very much in demand, especially for the construction of automobile tires. The largest volume of cotton from the Northeast, however, is a short staple variety like the upland cotton of North America, a product which runs directly into competition on foreign markets with supplies from areas where production is generally cheaper than it is in the Northeast.

Cotton, like sugar, has failed to provide the basis of a stabilized economy in the Northeast. With the increasing competition on the world market of the less expensive cotton from North America, Brazilian short-staple cotton was gradually confined to the domestic trade. The big droughts of 1877 to 1879 brought disaster to the cotton planters, and contributed to the large migrations of people in 1878 to the rubber forests of the Amazon. In the modern period when cotton is consumed in increasing quantities in the textile factories of São Paulo, a relatively small proportion of the short-staple variety comes from the Northeast. Of all the cotton produced in Brazil, however, the Northeast accounts for about half.

The people of the Northeast have been seeking other products to supplement the failing sugar and cotton. The most promising developments seem to lie in the cultivation of the palm which gives Carnauba wax, or the tree which gives Oiticica oil, or the Mamona plant which gives castor oil. Most of these waxes and oils are still collected from wild sources. There are many plans for the establishment of plantation production, and some little progress has been made. The relatively dense population of the old sugar region would suggest that an abundance of labor could be found, but the capacity of these people for work is said to be low because of the prevalence of bad health conditions.

Characteristic Fazenda of the Agricultural Northeast

The large estates which in Brazil are known as *fazendas* have certain peculiarities which distinguish those of one region from those of another. The fazendas of Pernambuco, Paraíba, and Alagôas in the agricultural zone inherit many of their features from the colonial days of sugar prosperity. On a few of the estates the casa grande is still occupied by descendants of the sugar aristocracy who cling to the genteel rural life of an era which ended with the emancipation of the slaves. The majority of the landowners, however, no longer reside on their estates. The senzalas, in which the agricultural workers of the earlier period lived, are no longer in common use. The tenants on the typical fazenda of the Northeast occupy scattered, isolated homes, dispersed over the land as widely as possible, and are more permanently attached to particular estates than is common in Brazil as a whole. At the present time, the laborers who are hired by the day to work for the large usinas are brought together from homes widely scattered over the plantations.

In the cotton area of the Northeast the tenants are less permanently attached to the land than in the sugar area. The homes they occupy are as widely scattered as elsewhere in the hinterland of Recife; but the tenant families come and go with little idea of forming permanent connections. The large landowners, as in Argentina, are, first of all, cattlemen. They find that in order to prepare pasturage for cattle they must clear the brush; and they find that the best way to clear the brush is to contract with tenants for the temporary use of a part of the fazenda for agriculture. Each large estate in the cotton area, therefore, has some of its land each year planted to cotton by tenants, who in some cases pay no rent, and whose part in the system is essentially to prepare the land for use as pasture. As in the case of the Argentine grain farmers, these producers of cotton can increase or decrease their crop with a minimum of dislocation or financial loss.

Bahia

The section of the Northeast which lies within the hinterland of Salvador has certain peculiarities which distinguish it from the country north and west of the Rio São Francisco. This territory includes the states of Bahia and Sergipe. It is notable that since the emancipation of the slaves in 1888, the district of Recôncavo around the bay of Bahia has enjoyed a renewed prosperity. In fact, this area is distinctly unusual in this respect, for the former slaves in other parts of Brazil have not showed much energy in reconstructing the economy of the regions in which they form a considerable proportion of the inhabitants. Whether this is due to inherent laziness, lack of stimulation from the climate, bad health, or bad diet, or a combination of all of them, is difficult to say. Nevertheless, it is important to note that the Negroes of Bahia are not of the same origin as most of those elsewhere in Brazil. According to Arthur Ramos, Brazilian student of the Negro question, the black people of Bahia are mostly Sudanese, whereas those of other parts of the country are Bantus. At any rate, the descendants of the slaves in the Recôncavo district have shown uncommon energy in rebuilding the agriculture of the area. The land is now divided into small farms, worked by Negro and mulatto owners. The crops grown include sugar cane, tobacco, cotton, and rice, together with such native food crops as manioc. Salvador is still of importance as a source of tobacco of good quality.

Because of this relatively prosperous group of Negro farmers in the Recôncavo district, the state of Bahia as a whole has a larger proportion of Negroes and mulattoes than any of the other divisions of the Northeast. According to Brazilian estimates, the Northeast as a whole is occupied by a population which is 36 per cent white, 12 per cent Negro, and 51 per cent mulatto, with only 1 per cent Indian and mameluco. In Bahia, however, only 33 per cent of the inhabitants are white, 19 per cent are Negro, and 47 per cent are mulatto.

Salvador is not only the focus of the densely populated Recôncavo district, but also of a wider area beyond. A railroad has been extended across the sertão to Joazeiro, above the falls on the Rio São Francisco (Map 20, Page 55). Between Joazeiro and Pirapora in Minas Gerais (Map 3, Page 7) the São Francisco is navigable, and small steamers collect the few products of this vast area from many little ports along the river. At least the northern part of the São Francisco Valley lies within the hinterland of Salvador.

Cacao District of Bahia

An important cacao district along the coast of southern Bahia and northern Espírito Santo (Map 22, Page 63) [3] is also tributary to Salvador. Ilheus, the chief port of southern Bahia, was one of the very early towns to be established in Brazil (1532), but Indian raids during the sixteenth and seventeenth centuries left the Portuguese clinging to only a few places that could be defended from the interior. Not until the middle of the eighteenth century (1746) was cacao planted in the country back of Ilheus; then the warm and rainy climate of this region proved to be so ideally suited to the cacao tree that, from then on, the plantations have been expanded little by little. Since 1890, especially in more recent years, the expansion has been rapid, and in 1930 this region produced 95 per cent of Brazil's cacao. In fact, southern Bahia is now second only to the Gold Coast of Africa among the world's cacao producers, accounting for 19 per cent of the world production in 1939.

The land suited to the planting of cacao is restricted to a zone parallel to the coast and some fifty to a hundred miles in width. As in the part of the Northeast which lies north of Salvador, the deep soils developed on the crystalline rocks have proved to be more productive than the porous, sandy soils of the taboleiros. At Ilheus the crystallines extend eastward to the ocean, producing one of those harbors with sugarloaf mountains so characteristic of the Brazilian coast. Only around Ilheus does the zone of cacao plantations reach the sea; elsewhere it begins some twenty to thirty miles inland, either on

[3] The cacao district cannot be said to belong to the Northeast as the Brazilians understand that region. It is included here only because of its position in the economic hinterland of Salvador.

the crystallines, or on the alluvial terraces of the river valleys.

On the western side, the cacao district is restricted by the rising slopes of the Great Escarpment. This striking feature of the Brazilian coast reaches its northern limit just south of Salvador. In Bahia it is made up of a series of parallel escarpments forming a zone of increasing elevation toward the interior. Since the cacao tree does not do well above 600 feet, the extension of the plantations inland is limited to the deep, and mostly narrow, river valleys.

Plantation practices in Bahia are notably extensive and exploitive. In spite of experience gained on a few well-run plantations, on which sustained yields have been maintained for more than a hundred years, most of the plantations continue productive for only forty or fifty years. Contrary to the advice of experts, most of the plantings are made on land from which the selva has

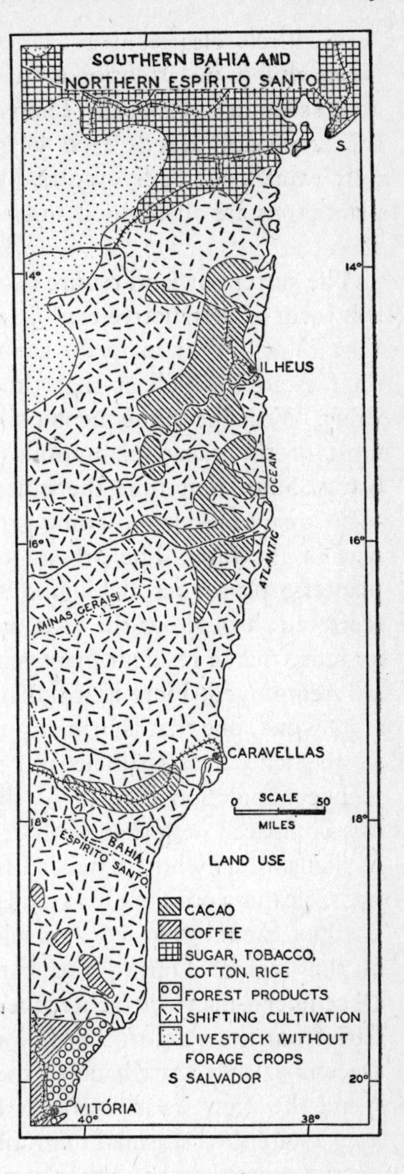

MAP 22

been entirely cleared away. Once planted, the young trees are given almost no attention until they come of bearing age—after seven or eight years. Thereafter, instead of clearing away the brush and weeds each year, this kind of work is done only every four or five years. When yields decline, the older plantations are abandoned and new ones are set out on virgin soils.

The system of land tenure is one of the important causes of this form of destructive exploitation. During the period of the First World War many of the plantation owners mortgaged their estates, which at that time were increasing rapidly in value. With the subsequent collapse of values after the war, most of the cacao plantations came into the hands of the banks. Since that time there have been few resident owners—no aristocratic landowning group remains on the land, even part of the time. The present owners are business men, not planters; properties belonging to one man may be widely scattered throughout the area, and on each plantation perhaps no more than a resident manager and a few workers are regularly employed. Here is speculative and destructive economy at its worst, one that is bringing temporary and unstable activity to such places as Ilheus and Salvador.

The population density of this cacao district is unusually low compared with that of other cacao-growing regions. Most of the laborers who are needed for the work of harvesting the pods, cleaning out the cacao seeds, and transporting the finished product, are migrant workers who do not remain permanently in the region. During the harvest season—from April to December—many men enter the cacao district, coming in large part from the sertão of the Northeast. About the middle of December they start back to the interior, always planning to spend the New Year season at home. This regular and now long-established seasonal migration of workers links the cacao district more than any other agricultural area of the Northeast to the people of the sertão.

The Pastoral Sertão

The coastal regions of the Northeast are in striking contrast to the Interior—the sertão. The sertão is a land subject to drought and flood—a land of natural calamities. It is a pastoral country, in which the predominantly white population derives the major part of its food from meat, in contrast with the agricultural coast lands, where a population which is more than half black subsists principally on a vegetable diet. The people of the sertão are individualists, energetic and resourceful; but they are a people who resist any change in the way of living which, over centuries, has provided the greatest measure of security in this uncertain habitat.

The line between the agricultural zone and the pastoral zone is a sharp one. In fact it has an exact legal definition. The line of separation is called the *travessão*. On the coastal side of this boundary, anyone who wishes to use his land for pasture is required by law to erect a fence to keep his animals from roaming over the unfenced crop areas. On the interior side of the boundary, lands to be used for crops must be fenced; the pastures remain entirely open. During the last fifty years the rise of cotton cultivation has had the result of moving the travessão farther into the interior, broadening the coastal zone devoted to agriculture: but beyond the line of demarcation, now, as in the past, lies the sertão.

In the pastoral sertão many of the estates are operated in common by a group of people, rather than as individual holdings. In some cases the original grants of land were *sesmarias*, given by the Portuguese king. The numerous descendants of the first owners inherit the right to pasture a certain number of cattle on the undivided estate, and other people, in the course of time, have purchased such rights. To divide the estates among the heirs would greatly decrease the security in a land subject to droughts. Where a man establishes a home and makes use of a specific piece of land for a period of thirty years, individual ownership is legally recognized; but, in the sertão, settlement of this degree of permanence is limited to the wet spots.

Throughout the sertão variable amounts of land are devoted each year to the production of food crops. During good years, small openings in the scrub forest, carefully protected from grazing animals by brush fences, are planted to maize, beans, and other vegetables, watered by natural rainfall. In dry years these little gardens are ruined and there is a shortage of food. Even in good years, however, the people of the sertão use crops only to supplement their diet of meat.

In a few spots, on the other hand, the sertão is suitable for permanent agriculture under irrigation, and these spots are densely occupied by a farming people (Maps 20 and 21, Pages 55 and 56). A large cluster of farming people is located at the northern base of the Chapada do Araripe, where springs emerging from the cliffs bring water to support fields of cotton, sugar, and rice and other food crops. For a long time the somewhat wetter lands around Jardim de Seridó have been utilized for the production of cotton. Another important concentration of farming is on the Serra de Baturité, near Fortaleza. Here, and in several smaller wet spots near by, agricultural products are raised chiefly for consumption by the herding people, including coffee and sugar which is made into brandy (*caxaça*). Small agricultural areas producing in part for the cattle herders are also to be found along the Rio São Francisco, and at the base of the mountains in central Bahia. Here cotton and sugar are raised for export. There is a close economic relation between the scattered pastoral people and the agricultural people, who are grouped together in clusters.

The curse of the sertão, for both pastoralists and farmers, is the repeated calamities of flood and drought (Map 13, Page 22). During the early centuries of settlement, there were so few inhabitants that the herders could escape the worst effects of these disasters. During the eighteenth century the shifting of settlers from the sertão into the outer margins of the agricultural region repeatedly reduced the population pressure of the interior. Not until the nineteenth century were so many people living in the sertão that the problem of surviving the calamities became critical. Since then floods and droughts have commonly been followed by a vast influx of refugees into such coastal cities as Fortaleza, where they remain until conditions in the interior improve.

Between 1877 and 1879 the interior of Ceará was visited by one of the most prolonged droughts in its history. The economic life of the whole interior was disrupted, and great numbers of refugees came to the cities. Fortaleza grew in a short time from a town of 30,000 people to one of 125,000, and the problem of feeding so large a number became critical. It was at this time that the rubber boom was getting started in the Amazon forests, and the demand for rubber gatherers far exceeded the possible supply of workers in that region. In 1878 about 54,000 people left Ceará to gather rubber along the far stretches of the Amazon and its tributaries. Most of these people never returned; today the old rubber sections of the Amazon are largely occupied by the scattered descendants of people who came originally from Ceará.

Similar but less spectacular emigrations occurred during other years of drought, especially in 1915 and 1932. Commonly the Northeasterner who migrates to other parts of Brazil leaves only temporarily; if it is possible for him to return to his native land he does so. Most of these migrations have had no permanent effect in reducing the population of the Northeastern sertão.

The first steps to be taken by the Brazilian government to attack the problem of the droughts were made between 1880 and 1889 by the Emperor Dom Pedro II. During the last decade of the empire he had a number of earth dams, lined with stones, constructed along the watercourses of the area with the intention of conserving the water and protecting the valleys against flood. But the plans were faulty; the dams were soon washed out or the reservoirs filled up with silt.

The attention of the federal government was again directed to the Northeast when, in 1910, a special commission began to study the causes and effects of the droughts. The *Inspetoria Federal de Obras contra as Secas* undertook to make a thorough inventory of the area—to collect weather records, to make maps, to study the distribution and quality of the water supply, and to chart the existing character of the vegetation cover and the land use. The result has been a fine series of maps and publications dealing with various aspects of the region.

On the basis of these studies a number of steps have been taken to diminish the worst effects of the calamities. Nearly a hundred reservoirs, some built by the municipalities, some by the federal government, have been constructed. Considerable difficulty has been encountered, however, by the failure of the inhabitants to co-operate in the use and maintenance of systems of irrigation. Most of the water-control works which had been built before 1910 were privately owned units of small size. To expect the highly individualistic people of the sertão to work together for the public control of water was expecting too much.

In addition to reservoirs and flood-control works many miles of automobile roads have been constructed. Motor trucks can now be hired by the planters to bring the bales of cotton to the railroads, and most of the long-distance transportation away from the railroads is now done in this manner. Mules still furnish the chief means of bringing the farm products short distances to the local markets.

Here, then, are the two Northeasts: one facing the problem of a decadent agricultural system; the other facing the results of recurring natural calamities. Here we have been able to examine a region in which the peculiarly Brazilian relationship between a speculative agricultural zone and a bordering sertão has had its first, and perhaps its most typical, development.

The sertão of the Northeast remains Brazil's chief problem area. Freise's recommendation is not encouraging: "Perhaps those periodic calamities, which not only affect the northeastern states but have their repercussions throughout the life and economy of all Brazil, could be at least mitigated, if not overcome, by a controlled and methodical evacuation of the regions most frequently hit by drought, by limiting reservoir construction to those areas where the incidence of drought is not so severe, and by shifting agricultural activities to such special crops as are really suited to semiarid country." On the other hand, many Brazilians believe that the sertão, if properly supplied with water for irrigation, perhaps from the São Francisco, could be made into an especially productive land for tropical crops.

The agricultural part of the Northeast faces entirely different problems. There is no need to evacuate its population which, dense as it is when measured by Brazilian standards, is by no means too dense for the possibilities of effective support. If many of the inhabitants of the sugar region are apparently lazy, apathetic, and content with miserable conditions of life, this may well be due to prevailing illiteracy, bad hygiene, and inadequate diet. Disease and malnutrition exact a heavy toll of the people of the Northeast; but these are conditions which have been recognized and will eventually be attacked. Many writers familiar with the Northeast insist that there is nothing eugenically wrong with the population, and that better sanitation and diet would counterbalance the enervating effects of the continuously warm and humid climate.

Meanwhile the Northeast continues, chiefly through its upper classes, to exert a strong influence on the rest of Brazil. The descendants of the planting aristocracy have contributed more than their share to the formulation of the political, artistic, and intellectual values of the Brazilian civilization. Unfortunately for the Northeast, these leaders are in increasing numbers drawn away from their homeland to take up residence in the capital city of Rio de Janeiro, where Brazilian life now finds its highest expression.

Chapter IV

THE SOUTHEAST

ON THE SHORE of Guanabara Bay in the southeast of Brazil there is a city which started as a defense post to guard a thinly populated sector of the Portuguese realm but which has grown in size and in the extent of its influence until today it has become the focus of everything Brazilian. The breath-taking beauty of the site on which this city has been built places it among the scenic wonders of the world. But not until the visitor stops to look beneath the things which first impress the eye is the full significance of this place revealed. For the city is not an exotic growth, like something which, cast up by the sea, has taken root on the shore: it is a product of all the vast extent of territory and all the varied activities of the people who occupy nearly half of the South American continent. There is a reflection, for those who understand, of every part of Brazilian life: of the boundless optimism of those who seek new speculative wealth on the frontier; of the deep hopelessness of those who live in poverty in the areas of decadence; of the gay sunshine of tropical coasts and the somber mysterious shadows of great forests; of the lost settlers of the sertão, those scattered, isolated victims of vast area; and of the great cities where the newest concepts of crowded urban living have come to Brazil from across the water. All these facets of Brazil are reflected in the city on Guanabara Bay—the city which is called Rio de Janeiro.

Rio de Janeiro, capital of Brazil, is more than just the urban nucleus of one of the zones of concentrated settlement. Today the city is far bigger than the productivity of its immediate hinterland would justify. Yet the settlement of the Southeast

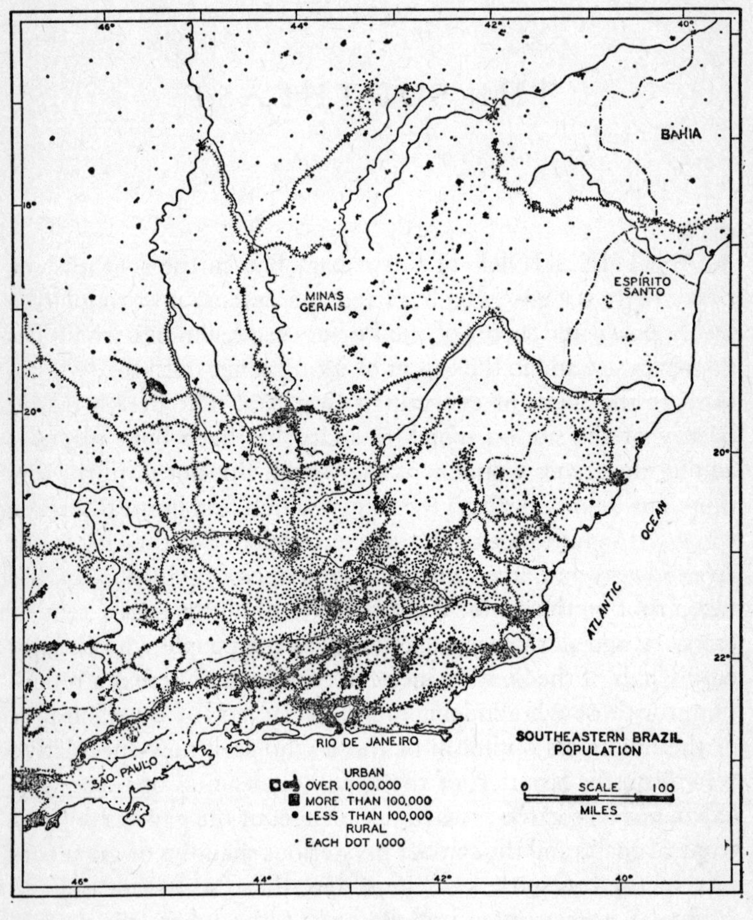

MAP 23

gave Rio de Janeiro its start, and the roads of this region, and of the sertão beyond it, still lead to the shores of Guanabara Bay.

The zone of concentrated settlement, which we call the

Southeast for want of a better regional name, is not a unit in the minds of the inhabitants. No such regional consciousness is found in this part of Brazil as is found in the Northeast. The people think of themselves as belonging to one of the several states: Rio de Janeiro State, Minas Gerais, or Espírito Santo (Map 14, Page 23). Yet the states do not coincide exactly with the outlines of the areas of settlement (Map 23, Page 72). The whole northern half of Minas Gerais lies in the sertão. The western part of Minas Gerais—the part known as the *Triangulo* —belongs to the area focusing on São Paulo city, and the eastern part of São Paulo State—the part known to the Brazilians as the *Norte*—lies within the hinterland of Rio de Janeiro.

Within the states or parts of states which are thus combined in a region of settlement, the variety of local contrasts is greater than in the Northeast. One of the outstanding characteristics of the Southeast is the intricate arrangement of its surface features, and the absence of any wide natural focus of lines of travel.

The population of the Southeast is scattered in small, isolated units, and is loosely attached to the land. The settlers who came to the region first in search of gold remained to gain a living from agricultural and pastoral activities. But the story of the long process of readjustment since the decline of gold mining is a complex one. Again and again new speculative forms of land use have been introduced. Each time this has happened there has followed a period of hectic expansion accompanied by rapidly rising values and an influx of population, and then a period of sudden collapse, decadence, and abandonment. Always, at the end of each speculative cycle, the land has been returned to pastoral uses. The present pattern of scattered settlement, the multiplicity of small towns, the grass-covered terrain which was once forested, the spots of new and thriving development —none of these features in the Southeast can be understood without a knowledge of the cross-currents of settlement and resettlement which have moved back and forth across a stage so ill adapted for the play.

THE LAND

The physical background of the land is itself one of great diversity. The Southeast is made up of many little natural areas each more or less distinct from the others. The intricacy is due chiefly to the surface configuration; the climatic conditions and the cover of vegetation, compared with those of the Northeast, exhibit wider zones of transition and fewer striking contrasts.

Surface Features

The surface features of the Southeast consist chiefly of a complex arrangement of crystalline hilly uplands and low mountains (Map 1, Page 4 and Maps 3 and 24, Pages 7 and 75). There are almost no large level areas except in the two deltas along the eastern coast—those of the Rio Doce and of the Rio Paraíba. Small valley flats, terrace remnants, and isolated bits of high-level surfaces otherwise deeply dissected are scattered throughout the area. Only far in the interior are any remnants of the nearly level cover of sandstone strata to be found.

The mountains of the Southeast stand above the general surface of the crystalline hilly uplands. Most of these mountains are massive and rounded, owing their existence to beds of resistant quartzite or other types of crystalline rock which are less easily decomposed than the granites and gneisses. The highest peak in Brazil is the Pico da Bandeira (9,462 ft.), located on the border between the states of Minas Gerais and Espírito Santo (Map 24, Page 75). Another relatively high range is the Serra dos Orgãos, just northeast of Guanabara Bay. High mountains also occur in the massive Serra da Mantiqueira, on the southwestern border of Minas Gerais, just north of the Paraíba Valley. Only in these three places, however, do mountains rise above the upper limit of trees, which in this part of Brazil is found between 6,200 and 6,500 feet above sea level.

SOUTHEASTERN BRAZIL
0
100
200 Miles
0
100
200 Kilometers
48°
46°
44°
42°
40°
20°
22°
Rio Paranaiba
Uberaba
Rio Grande
Rio São Francisco
Belo Horizonte
Itabira
Rio Doce
R. Doce
Ouro Preto
Vitória
Pico da Bandeira
Ribeirão Preto
Rio Pomba
Juiz de Fora
Paraíba R.
Campos
Paraíba R.
Dos Órgãos
Petropolis
Pico de Itatiaia
Piracicaba
Campinas
Taubaté
Rio Tiete
Niteroi
Rio de Janeiro
Sorocaba
São Paulo
Santos
Elevations in meters
Low mountains
Tableland of central Minas Gerais
Inner lowland of São Paulo
Diabase cuesta
Tableland of western São Paulo
Coastal lowlands
Coastal terraces
Crystalline plateaus
Raisz

Map 24

In the central part of Minas Gerais, the long, unbroken range known as the Serra do Espinhaço reaches elevations only of 5,500 or 6,000 feet.

Block mountains which are likewise not high enough to stand above the tree line form a belt of rugged terrain between the crystalline hilly uplands of the interior and the coast all the way southward from southern Bahia. This is the Zone of the Escarpment which is crossed by two rivers rising in the hilly uplands of the interior,—the Rio Doce and the Rio Paraíba. The Rio Doce rises in eastern Minas Gerais, some of its headwater tributaries coming from the Serra do Espinhaço. It passes in a deep and flat-bottomed valley through the block mountains in the state of Espírito Santo. Through the valley of this river an approach of uniform gradient is offered all the way from the Atlantic to the eastern side of the Serra do Espinhaço—the only passage of its kind through the Zone of the Escarpment to the interior which is to be found between Salvador in Bahia and Porto Alegre in Rio Grande do Sul.

The Rio Paraíba offers a much less satisfactory line of travel. Its valley is wide, with extensive floodplains and terraces, all the way from the big bend of the Paraíba, a short distance east of São Paulo city (Map 3, Page 7) to Entre Rios, located almost due north of Rio de Janeiro. Between Entre Rios and the beginning of the delta above Campos, the Paraíba descends turbulently for about a thousand feet through a narrow rocky gorge. The wide middle part of the Paraíba Valley runs parallel to the coast, not into the interior, and it is bordered both to the north and to the south by block mountains. A northern tributary to the Paraíba, the Rio Pomba, has excavated a wide amphitheater in the hilly uplands of southeastern Minas Gerais (Map 27, Page 92), but the inner margin of this amphitheater is a steep and almost unbroken cliff, a thousand feet in height, which separates the Pomba basin from the highlands of the interior.

We can understand the difficulty of travel in the Southeast more clearly if we consider the profile of a route from the coast near Rio de Janeiro northward to the crystalline hilly upland of central Minas Gerais (Map 3, Page 7). Along the immediate coast there is an outlying block mountain, separated from the front of the Great Escarpment by a zone of low country. A break in the coastal mountains permits the sea to come in through a narrow opening. This is the famous entrance to the bay on which Rio de Janeiro is located—an opening guarded by the typical knobby peak, the Sugar-Loaf, formed wherever in the rainy tropics crystalline mountains are exposed to the wash of waves at their base. Guanabara Bay, however, is bordered by mountains only at its entrance: most of the shores of the bay are low, swampy, and fringed with mangrove. The lowland, known as the *Baixada Fluminense*,[1] is not flat—it is composed of low rounded hills, shaped like half oranges.

The northern edge of the Baixada Fluminense is sharply terminated by the base of the Great Escarpment. East of Petropolis this escarpment is surmounted by the Serra dos Orgãos, and passes in this section are much higher than those farther to the west. In the vicinity of Petropolis the passes are between two and three thousand feet above the sea. In the northwest corner of the Baixada Fluminense, however, there is one pass which requires a climb of only 1,463 feet. From the crest of the Great Escarpment the descent to the Paraíba Valley —here a little over a thousand feet above sea level—is not difficult.

The Paraíba Valley offers an easy route of travel from the pass westward toward São Paulo; but for one who wishes to reach Minas Gerais the valley can only be considered a barrier. Beyond it, to the north, the ascent to the hilly upland, even if one travels to the east of the Serra da Mantiqueira, is by no

[1] Baixada is pronounced by-sháh-dah.

means easy. The general level of the hilly upland in southern Minas Gerais is between 2,600 and 3,200 feet, with the higher elevations in the Rio Grande upland of the southwest.[2]

Climate and Vegetation

The climatic features of the Southeast have a rather surprising simplicity. The effects of altitude, to be sure, are reflected in the lower temperatures, and in a vertical change in the character of the vegetation on the higher mountains. The narrow coastal fringe has temperatures characteristic of most tropical east coasts. They are not excessively high at any time of the year, and, especially in winter, are often surprisingly low owing to the passage of cold air masses. High humidity, however, does increase the unpleasantness of the hotter part of the year, especially in places which are sheltered from the compensating effect of the wind. During the summer months the wealthier people of Rio de Janeiro seek the lower temperatures (nine degrees lower) and the more active social life of the community at Petropolis, on the crest of the Great Escarpment. The temperatures of the interior are lower than those of the coast, especially on the higher Rio Grande upland of southwestern Minas. Belo Horizonte, on the northwestern side of the Serra do Espinhaço, averages a little over 72° in its warmest month and about 62° in its coldest month.

[2] The details of the surface features are even more intricate than the broader pattern. Throughout this part of Brazil the details of ridges and valleys are controlled by two major fault trends. The faults are not recent, for this is not a region of frequent earthquakes. But they have become zones of weakness which are quickly excavated by the rivers. One system of faults runs from north-northeast to south-southwest; the other crosses the first, running from east-northeast to west-southwest. The excavation of valleys and scarps along these faults results in the formation of an exceedingly complex pattern of angular block mountains of rhombic shape. These two dominant trends appear not only in the minor landforms, but also in such major surface features as the Paraíba Valley, the Serra da Mantiqueira, the trend of the Great Escarpment, and even the trend of the coast on either side of Cabo Frio.

The rainfall, too, has a relatively simple distribution over southeastern Brazil. On the slopes of the Great Escarpment, and on the sides of the mountains near the coast, rainfall of more than 80 inches is recorded in a number of scattered localities. Over most of the area, however, the amount remains with little variation between 40 and 60 inches. Throughout this area, also, the rainfall maximum comes during the summer months, and the cool season is relatively dry. Not until one reaches the northern and western side of the Serra do Espinhaço does he encounter a dry season of real moisture deficiency, for nearer the coast even the winter season has a considerable number of rainy days.

These climatic characteristics are reflected in the natural vegetation of the Southeast (Map 25, Page 80). To reconstruct the actual details of the distribution is not always easy, for over much of the region the original cover has been entirely changed during the period of European settlement. The coastal zone, the front of the Great Escarpment, and no doubt some of the very rainy spots on the mountains farther inland were covered originally by a dense rain forest which proved to be a very considerable barrier to Portuguese penetration. The southern and eastern parts of the highlands were covered with a semideciduous forest which extended inland as far as the Serra do Espinhaço; and even today this forest covers large areas of the Rio Doce Valley and of the mountains of Espírito Santo. The Serra do Espinhaço itself as well as the São Francisco Basin to the west of it was covered, and still is, largely with scrub forest, except in the south where the use of wood for charcoal has practically destroyed the last vestiges of the original forest. The line between the scrub forest and the savanna is not at all sharp, but the line in southern and western Minas Gerais, between semideciduous forest and savanna, was apparently a very distinct boundary—perhaps sharpened as a result of the common practice of burning the savanna. The savanna, covered with scattered thickets of scrub forest and threaded by galerias along the streams, extended southward almost to the Rio Paraíba, and apparently some of the flood-plain of the Paraíba was covered with grass. The northern

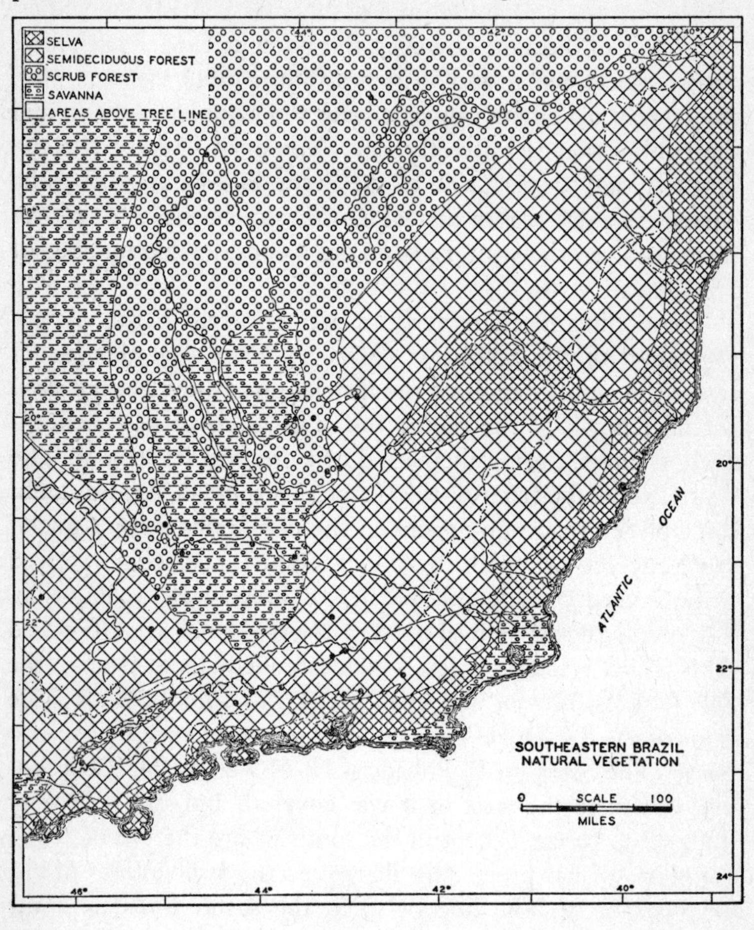

MAP 25

slopes of the Serra da Mantiqueira were grass-covered. In the southwestern part of Minas Gerais the forest boundary turned sharply northward, and forests covered the mountain slopes along the border between Minas and São Paulo as far north as the Rio Grande.[3]

COLONIAL SETTLEMENT

Such is the nature of the Southeast, a land in which a very important part of the story of Brazil has been enacted. This is the land with the heart of gold and the breast of iron; but it is a land not easy to penetrate, and not easy to move about in, for its surface and its forests are barriers to easy travel, and there is no natural focus of routes.

At first the highlands of the Southeast remained less well known than many more remote parts of Brazil. When Rio de Janeiro was finally established on its present site after the French had been dislodged in 1567, its function was that of a defense point, not that of a nucleus from which colonization of the interior was contemplated. In fact, a site was selected on the shores of Guanabara Bay which was difficult to reach from the interior, in order that the fortress might have additional protection from possible attack.

The first exploring party to reach the highlands ascended by the easiest possible route—not from Rio de Janeiro, but through the valley of the Rio Doce from Vitória farther east. This great natural highway to the interior might have played a very different role in the course of settlement had it not been occupied by a group of exceptionally warlike Indians—the Botocudos (Map 18, Page 33). These savage tribes resisted the white men, and, like the Araucanians of Chile, took advantage of the white man's lack of knowledge of the forest to retard the advance of the Portuguese. Although the coast of Espírito Santo and southern Bahia was colonized very early, the only settlements which survived the attacks of Indians were Vitória, on an island, and Ilheus, on a site which could easily be

[3] The Portuguese terms for these vegetation types are: Forest in general, *mata;* Rain forest, *selva;* Scrub forest, *caatinga;* Savanna, with scattered trees, *campo cerrado,* without trees, *campo limpo.*

defended from the interior. Most of the coast between Campos and Salvador was abandoned, and even today this section of Brazil remains a great empty space on the population map (Map 23, Page 72), and the Rio Doce has not developed into an important line of travel to the interior.

It was not until 1698 that Minas Gerais became important. In that year bandeirantes from São Paulo discovered gold in the stream gravels of the southern part of the Serra do Espinhaço. Until that time, however, they, like the rest of the Portuguese, generally neglected Minas. The chief routes into the interior ran northward from Itu and southward from Sorocaba. People from São Paulo had also pushed northeastward into the upper part of the Paraíba Valley, where Taubaté became the chief town.

The Gold Period

The gold which was the chief cause of the rapid settlement of the Southeast after 1698 was found at many scattered localities throughout Minas Gerais, but chiefly in the central area around the southern part of the Serra do Espinhaço. Although there are veins of precious metal in the rocks of this range, the mining of the eighteenth century was entirely in the stream gravels. Many towns were established near the places where mining proved to be especially profitable. One of the most important of these towns—the place which soon became the political center of this part of Brazil—was Villa Rica (now known as Ouro Preto). Other major mining centers included Mariana, Sabará, and São João del Rey (Map 3, Page 7). After the discovery of diamonds in 1729 near Tijuco (now known as Diamantina) there was a rush of new settlers still farther toward the north.

The people who poured into Minas Gerais came chiefly from three places. A large number were new immigrants from Portugal, mostly not men of means but adventurers seeking a quick road to wealth. Many Paulistas entered Minas also, and during the early years of the eighteenth century they even fought for the political control of the territory. The Paulistas were defeated, but their numbers continued to swell the ranks of the gold seekers. There were also considerable numbers of former plantation owners from the Northeast, especially Bahia, who, with their slaves, moved into the new zone of exploitation. Villa Rica supplanted Salvador as a place of great wealth; gold supplanted sugar.

To estimate the amount of gold produced in this region is difficult, owing to the lack of records. The "royal fifth," which was returned to the crown of Portugal, gives some clue. The total amount was probably considerably less than that which has been taken from California in the years since 1849. But it was sufficient, during the period from 1700 to 1800, to make Brazil the leading gold producer of the world, accounting for about 44 per cent of the gold produced during that century.

Colonial Roads

With the discovery of gold and diamonds and the beginning of the settlement of Minas Gerais, the question of an outlet for the region became important. The desire of the Portuguese government to maintain its control of gold exports and, perhaps, the fear of raiders, led to the selection of one port of shipment and the prohibition of shipment from any other port. Several possible routes to the coast from central Minas Gerais were available. The most direct way, and by far the easiest one in terms of grades, would have followed the Rio Doce eastward to Vitória; but, as we have said, the presence of warlike Indians in that territory made it one to be avoided. The way northward to the Brazilian capital at Salvador required not only a long river trip on the São Francisco, but also a difficult overland journey from Joazeiro to the coast. The obvious advantage of attaching this newly discovered gold district to the established political center of Brazil had to be given up.

The selection of Rio de Janeiro as the port of shipment for the gold was by no means inevitable. Perhaps if the Paulistas had been able to establish their claim to the political control of Minas Gerais, the main roads to the coast would have been built to São Paulo and Santos. At first, much of the gold was carried by mules over the route to Taubaté, and thence directly southeastward to a little port on the coast. The most direct route from Villa Rica to a place on the coast south of Cabo Frio led to the shores of Guanabara Bay, and this easily defended naval base had the additional advantage of protection from pirates. When the seat of government was moved to Rio de Janeiro in 1763, this town had already gained pre-eminence as the chief port of Brazil.

The route from Villa Rica to Rio de Janeiro, as we have seen, is not an easy one, and the course followed by the road which was completed in 1719 illustrates certain important characteristics of Portuguese settlement. To the Portuguese, forests presented a much greater barrier to travel than did steep slopes. The Portuguese routes of travel, therefore, can be understood more clearly when they are compared with a map of forests than when compared with a map of slopes. In starting northward from Rio de Janeiro, the necessity of cutting and maintaining a road across the Baixada Fluminense was avoided by transporting goods across the bay and up the small, mangrove-fringed streams as far as the shallow-draught boats could be floated. From the river landings the shortest route to the base of the Great Escarpment was taken. Since mules did the work of carrying, the height and steepness of the climb meant less than the directness of the road: consequently the low pass from the northwest corner of the lowland, which was relatively distant from Guanabara Bay and off the most direct route to Minas, was never utilized as an important line of travel until railroad engineers in the nineteenth century became interested in finding easy grades over the mountains. The chief passes of the colonial period were all more than two thousand feet in elevation; the main road to Minas passed the site which was used later for the resort town of Petropolis.

The crossing of the Paraíba was near Paraíba do Sul (PS on Map 3, Page 7), which became one of the larger towns of the valley. Beyond this, the road climbed onto the highlands by the most direct route. It led by way of Barbacena to Villa Rica, with a branch from Barbacena to São João del Rey.

In addition to this main axis of penetration, roads were also built in other directions from Rio de Janeiro. One led to Campos, on the delta of the Paraíba, where cattle were pastured on the open savannas along the coast (Map 25, Page 80). A more important road, however, led directly from the port of Rio de Janeiro to São Paulo. It also neglected the low pass over the Great Escarpment, ascending and descending several ridges to follow the more direct route by way of Bananal to the Paraíba Valley, and thence to São Paulo. Beyond the big bend of the Paraíba a steep climb from this valley into the São Paulo Basin was necessary. Over these two roads an important part of the meat supply for the people of Rio de Janeiro was driven—some of the animals coming all the way from the prairies of the southern states. All three roads out of Rio de Janeiro became the important axes of settlement of the Southeast; and the places where side roads branched off from the main ones, or where the roads crossed through passes or over rivers, were the places where the first commercial towns were planted. Although these old roads no longer exist, pieces of them are in a sense preserved in the main streets of the little towns.

Villa Rica was a thriving center of more than 60,000 people during the gold period. Although it took two weeks or so to reach it on horseback or muleback from Rio de Janeiro, the large amount of wealth concentrated in the hands of those whose luck had been good resulted in the creation of much luxury and splendor in this center. Many churches and many palatial homes were built. These were decorated with some very fine examples of colonial carving and painting. Only in the last few years has the Brazilian government recognized the historical value of these old churches and buildings and created a service for their preservation. Ouro Preto today is a national monument, filled with the relics of that amazing period.

Decadence

The gold fever lasted for about a century. All through the interior, stream gravels and hillsides which were found to contain gold were worked over by placer methods. Even today there are many spots which remain desolate wastes, miniature, man-made badlands, where the earth was torn and furrowed in the frantic search for the precious metal, and then abandoned. But between 1800 and 1830 there was a rapid decline in gold seeking. The richer placer deposits had been worked over, and other parts of the world were producing gold at lower cost. Except for certain vein-mining enterprises, to be described later, and except for sporadic attempts to rework the old deposits, gold mining in southern Minas Gerais was at an end.

The people, whose sole means of support had been mining, were forced to find another basis for existence, or to move away. They did both. During the first third of the nineteenth century, there was a large emigration from Minas Gerais. It is impossible to estimate the number of people actually involved, but the results of this movement may be observed in the present character and distribution of people throughout the neighboring regions. A great many Mineiros (people of Minas Gerais) returned to the Paraíba Valley in São Paulo State, where, at that time, the planting of coffee was just entering the period of speculative expansion. Many of the planters who established themselves, in the middle of the nineteenth century, around Ribeirão Preto (Map 4, Page 8) were formerly proprietors of gold mines in Minas. Most of those who went to São Paulo carried with them a considerable capital won from the gold fields. The poorer people who possessed a sufficient love of the unknown, headed northward and northwestward into the sertões. People from the mining districts were chiefly responsible for the thinly scattered pastoral settlement of the whole southern part of the São Francisco Basin, and for the movement of pastoralists on westward into Goiaz.

These movements of emigration had a profound effect on the character of those who remained in Minas Gerais. The more successful people moved on into São Paulo, attracted by the opportunities for quick wealth on the coffee frontier; the more adventuresome people moved out into the sertões; those who remained were, in general, those who had been less successful and who lacked the peculiar quality of mind that leads some men to seek the unknown. If today the inhabitants of rural Minas seem to remain apathetic in the face of innovations and improvements, perhaps the process of selection which went on after the gold period may in part account for it.

During the last hundred years the history of the Southeast has been punctuated by repeated attempts to re-establish some basis of speculative profit. Most of these endeavors proved for a time, and in certain localities, to be successful. But one after another the speculative cycles of sugar and coffee ran through the period of maximum development and then rapidly declined. The more recent cycles of rice and orange cultivation are still in process of development. But the stabilized and fundamental support for the people of Minas remains the grazing of cattle for meat and dairying. Before turning to a discussion of these agricultural cycles and of the pastoral base, we must examine certain elements of the pattern of settlement.

PATTERN OF SETTLEMENT IN THE SOUTHEAST

The present pattern of settlement in the Southeast is the result of processes continued over more than two centuries. The period of gold prosperity saw people spread widely over the central and southern part of Minas Gerais. New boom towns grew up near the rich gold-bearing gravels, and these survived as small agricultural centers after the period of mining came to an end. Each cycle of agricultural development brought a new arrangment of people on the land. Each boom development brought a wave of settlers to those places which were physically suited to the new crop, which were sufficiently accessible, and which were occupied by landowners ready and able to make the necessary investment in equipment. New types of mining activities and the development of industries in some of the cities led to other concentrations of people. The pattern of settlement remains notably unstable, with only a loose attachment of people to place.

The rural population of the Southeast is fairly dense. In southern Minas Gerais and the neighboring parts of São Paulo and Rio de Janeiro the rural density is not much less than 100 per square mile, and in central Minas it is between 25 and 60. Yet one who travels by rail through this region gains the distinct impression that the land is thinly populated: one passes through great distances of apparently empty country, used only for pasture.

The Fazenda Mineira

One reason for this impression of low population density is the arrangement of people on the typical large estate of Minas Gerais—the *fazenda mineira*. In many respects this traditional form of rural settlement is similar to the sugar fazendas of the Northeast. The tenants are widely dispersed over the countryside in isolated homes, as much hidden from the homes of their neighbors as possible. The boundary lines which separate one large estate from another are commonly drawn along the ridge crests or stream divides, leaving each little valley as the undivided property of one owner. Where the crops are concentrated in the valleys, as in the Northeast, this arrangement is quite satisfactory; but it seems ill advised in a hilly country like Minas, where the agricultural lands—at least those devoted to tree crops like coffee—are restricted to the hillsides. Where roads and railroads follow the undissected remnants of the upland surface, as is the case in many parts of southeastern Minas, the estate buildings, and the scattered tenant homes in the valleys are all hidden from the traveler who does not depart from the main routes.

Not all the rural workers of Minas Gerais, however, are dispersed in single-family homes over the countryside. A very large proportion of the rural people are gathered together in rural villages. It is a custom of long standing for the large landowners to make gifts of small sections of their estates to the church. The express purpose of such a gift is to establish a town, dedicated generally to a saint and administered under the direction of the church. While there is a certain religious prestige to be gained by such a grant, it is obvious that economic profit will also accrue, if only because of the supply of workers gathered together in the neighborhood. When crops are to be cultivated as a part of the process of replacing worn-out pastures with new pastures, or when other jobs need to be done, here is a reserve of laborers ready to be called on. When one landowner has established a *patrimonio*, as such grants are called, it frequently follows that other landowners, not to be outdone, set up other patrimonios not far away. Many of the rural workers of Minas are now grouped in these small, scattered villages.

The appearance of the small rural villages, which are extraordinarily numerous throughout this part of Brazil, is not very pleasing. The center is invariably a small church, facing a bit of open ground known as the *praça* (the Portuguese equivalent of the Spanish *plaza*). The village praça, however, is usually only a grassy space, crossed by paths worn by the unregulated going and coming of the inhabitants. The houses are huddled together around the margins of the praça, or perhaps, in the larger villages, are strung out along the roads which converge on the church. In either case, the houses are built as close together as possible, as if their owners were fearful of the vast

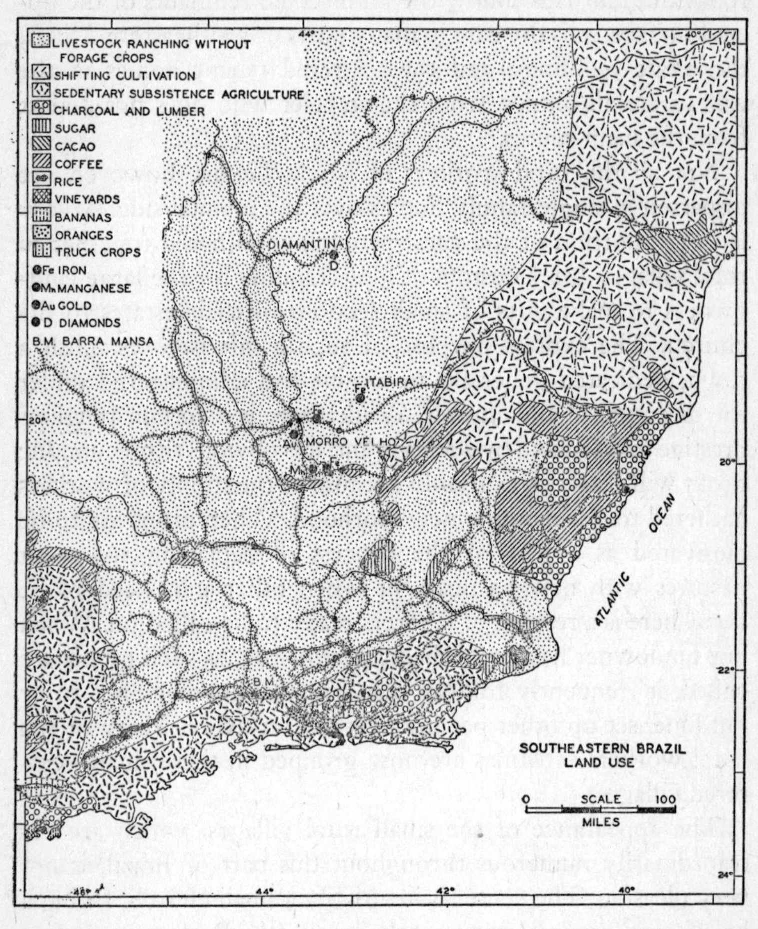

MAP 26

empty spaces beyond. The buildings are comfortless structures of "daub and wattle"—that is, of mud daubed on a framework of poles—with mud floors and leaky tile roofs. The passage of the years is marked by many unrepaired cracks and openings both in walls and roof. The people who live in these camp-like, unhygienic structures, and who do so little to improve their conditions of living even within their homes, cannot be expected to form any very close attachment to the land. The question may be raised, but not easily answered, whether this prevalent attitude toward the rural home and the rural life is a cause or a result of the instability of settlement.

That so many people live either in complete isolation on the fazendas or in these small scattered village communities is one of the fatal weaknesses of settlement in this part of Brazil. Where a population is so widely disseminated in small groups, great difficulty is found in covering the costs of building and maintaining roads, schools, or the many other services and institutions which contribute to the establishment of a civilized way of living. Illiteracy, poor hygiene, primitive methods of agriculture, lack of material comforts in the home—all are partly the result of isolation; and the isolation is in part the result of this scattering of the rural people in groups which are too small.

Railroad Lines

Another reason for the impression which a traveler in the Southeast gains of a relatively sparse population, is the fundamental lack of integration between the railroad system and the pattern of settlement. The Southeast is served by one of Brazil's two chief railroad nets. Yet a close examination of the relation between the railroad lines and the centers of population reveals a notable lack of adjustment, and throws additional light on one of the basic symptoms of instability.

Railroad development in the Southeast began near Rio de Janeiro and spread inland. The first railroad in Brazil was built in 1853 to connect one of the small landing places on the northern side of Guanabara Bay with the base of the Great Escarpment. Soon after this, another railroad was built across the lowland from Rio de Janeiro to the base of the escarpment near the only low pass. This became the first section of the government-owned railroad, known as the *Central do Brasil.* The main line of the Central now makes use of the low pass over the Great Escarpment and reaches the Paraíba Valley at Barra do Piraí (Map 26, Page 90). The main line then turns

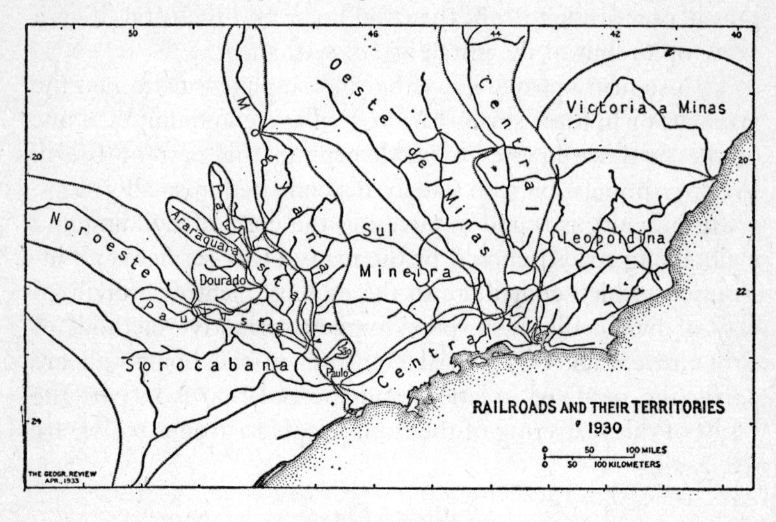

MAP 27

(Courtesy of the *Geographical Review*, published by the American Geographical Society of New York.)

eastward to Entre Rios before starting the difficult ascent into Minas Gerais. It passes through Juiz de Fora, Barbacena, and Belo Horizonte. A long projection from Belo Horizonte extends northward into the sertão to reach the head of navigation on the Rio São Francisco at Pirapora. A branch of the Central runs up the Paraíba Valley from Barra do Piraí to the great bend of the Paraíba, where it climbs steeply to the São Paulo Basin and reaches São Paulo city. On either side of the main line of the Central, other railroads cover southeastern and southwestern Minas Gerais (Map 27, Page 92).

Most of these railroads, from a North American or European point of view, do not constitute efficient, modern means of transportation. The main line of the Central to Belo Horizonte and the branch to São Paulo are built on a broad gauge of five feet six inches; but the other lines are all on a one-meter gauge. Most of them are single-track lines, cheaply constructed, and poorly maintained. In order to reduce to a minimum the heavy cost of building cuts, fills, bridges, and tunnels the lines wind about over the slopes with only a very few sections of straight track and with many steep grades. The wood-burning locomotives struggle painfully up the hills, or clatter noisily down the declines accompanied by clouds of dust and showers of sparks. These railroads serve a region which, for the most part, has only small quantities of goods to ship in or out. They both reflect this state of affairs and contribute to its continuation. Their rates are so high that some potential traffic is sent by other means of conveyance; yet these rates are necessary to cover the high cost of maintenance where traffic is so light. When the trains stop at a station, the traveler is able to hear the "music" of rural Minas—the shrill, discordant squeak of the ungreased axles of oxcarts which still carry a considerable proportion of the goods transported in the interior. There has not been in the Southeast such a happy co-ordination of railroad building and wheat farming as that which made the fortunes of so many people in the Argentine Humid Pampa.

Railroads and Towns

The lack of integration between the railroad system and the pattern of settlement in Southeast Brazil becomes more apparent when we consider the location of towns with reference to the railroads. Many of the towns were first established with reference to the colonial roads—either at river crossings, or road junctions, or at the ends of passes, or at other points of special significance on roads built for horses, mules, and oxen.

Since the railroads generally cannot follow these old routes very closely because they cannot negotiate grades which are so steep, the main railroad junctions are in many instances remote from the road junctions. Changes in the pattern of settlement resulting from the construction of railroads may be observed in many parts of the Occidental world—old towns remote from the new lines of circulation declining in population in favor of new towns which spring up along the railroads; the formation of double towns, a railroad town to serve a near-by road town; or, in many cases, the extension of the older towns to form a continuous built-up connection with the new means of transportation. But in Brazil these transformations are taking place slowly. Most of the old towns have maintained their importance, even when they are reached only by branch lines of the railroads, or by no railroads at all. Many are the important rail junctions at which urban development is either small or even entirely lacking. Many are the stations along the main lines where automobile busses gather to meet the trains and to carry passengers over poor roads to large towns located perhaps a mile, perhaps five or ten miles away. And still the commonest means of shipping goods is by the slow oxcart.

Railroads, we may surmise, do not play a very large part in the economic life of the region—as large a part as the railroads of North America or of Europe play in the economic life of those continents. One sign of this lack of integration is the prevalence of small-scale manufacturing establishments. Rates of transportation are so high that relatively inefficient plants can sell to local markets from which the goods manufactured at lower cost elsewhere are excluded. In this region the economist can study at the present day an economic life which has passed into the realm of history in most parts of western Europe.

Nevertheless, the inevitable transformation of the pattern of settlement and of the economic system in the Southeast has made a start. In the Paraíba Valley, upstream from Entre Rios, most of the older towns originally established along the colonial roads at points where river crossings were easy have also been reached by the railroad. In recent years many new industrial plants have been built to serve more than a local market. The first hydroelectric plant in Brazil was built in 1889 in Juiz de Fora, which has since become an important manufacturing center. Several mining communities in the Serra do Espinhaço also make use of the rail connections, and steel manufacturing plants at Caeté and Sabará are dependent on the rail lines not only for the shipment of their product, but also for the supplies of charcoal which keep them running. Similarly, in the southwest of Minas Gerais, on the northern slopes of the Serra da Mantiqueira, there are several communities where rail connections are essential for the economic life: these are resort towns where mineral springs and cooler air attract the well-to-do people of Rio de Janeiro and São Paulo for vacation and rest—such places as Caxambú, Lambarí, and Poços de Caldas (Map 3, Page 7). These few places, which for one reason or another are closely integrated to the railroad system, stand in striking contrast to the prevailing lack of such integration in most parts of the Southeast.

Belo Horizonte and Ouro Preto

The transformation of the settlement pattern in the interior of the Southeast has appeared in no more striking form than in the transfer of the state capital of Minas Gerais from the old colonial town of Ouro Preto to the entirely new city of Belo Horizonte. Ouro Preto is a typical Portuguese town. Its unplanned, narrow, winding streets of irregular width are flanked by buildings built close together. It lies sprawled across the slopes of a narrow mountain valley in the midst of the Serra do Espinhaço, on a site so hilly that not only was the railroad unable to reach it, but also any expansion and modernization of the city was next to impossible. In 1896 the political center of the state was moved to a new place where a city had been planned with wide streets and a pattern similar to that of Washington, D. C. Ouro Preto is rich in historical tradition, an art center with fourteen churches which are fine examples of colonial architecture, and which contain important paintings and sculptures. But today Ouro Preto is occupied by fewer than 10,000 people, who live surrounded by the empty shell of buildings which once housed more than 60,000. Belo Horizonte, on the contrary, occupies a site on the northern side of the mountains where a wide sweep of the highland offers ample space for expansion. New government buildings, new residences, new industrial plants give this city an atmosphere entirely different from that of the traditional Brazilian cities. The new capital has grown rapidly; in 1920 there were some 55,000 people in it, in 1929, 109,000, and in 1938 it had a population of 208,000. This city is more modern in its planning and in some of its architecture than are most of the cities of North America.

The new site chosen for the political center of Minas Gerais was selected with scant attention to the geographic realities. To be sure, it is located not far from the center of the state; but it is not only remote from the center of the inhabited part of the state, but it is separated from that part by the Serra do Espinhaço (Map 23, Page 72). Most of the people of Minas Gerais live east and south of this mountain range, whereas Belo Horizonte, located north and west of the barrier, stands almost literally on the margin of the sertão.

LAND USE IN THE SOUTHEAST

The present patterns of land use in the Southeast, like those of population and lines of circulation, are the result of several cycles of speculative growth and subsequent collapse. The basic form of land use is pastoral, and this has provided the one permanent economic support for the settlement of the Southeast since the end of the gold period. Meanwhile, however, a succession of agricultural cycles has appeared. Each cycle is initiated by the rapid spread of commercial planting in one locality—usually a locality which has the advantage of accessibility to a market or a port. Quickly the opportunity for profits is seized by the people of other localities and the new form of land use is expanded far beyond the limits of the area where the cycle originated. Increased competition from new plantings and decreased yields in the older plantings result in a decline in the original area, and in some cases even in the movement of settlers away from it. Sugar cane was the crop of the first of these cycles, spreading from centers about Rio de Janeiro and Campos. The coffee cycle began in the Paraíba Valley and spread both into other parts of the Southeast and also westward into São Paulo State. More recently the Paraíba Valley has been the scene of boom developments in commercial rice production, and in the planting of oranges. The strategic location of the Paraíba Valley between Barra do Piraí and Jacareí, forming the main line of travel between Rio de Janeiro and São Paulo, together with the suitability of the floodplain and terraces for a variety of crops, has made possible the development of several of the agricultural cycles in this nuclear area. In the valley, a relatively dense population was already gathered before the start of the gold period, and during the gold period much of the food consumed in Minas Gerais came from this region. With the decline of mining activities many of the Mineiros had returned to the Paraíba Valley. An ample supply of cheap labor was therefore available in a region which had all the advantages of easy accessibility to rapidly expanding markets. Now, the first signs of jute planting have appeared—perhaps initiating still another speculative cycle; and in this valley the Brazilians are now planning the construction of a large-scale steel plant. The Paraíba Valley has played the role of nuclear area in the economic history not only of the Southeast but also of São Paulo.

The Sugar Cycle

The earliest of the speculative cycles to develop in the Southeast was the cultivation of sugar cane. Sugar was not a new crop in this part of Brazil, for it had been grown since early colonial times in the lower areas along the coast. Wealthy sugar growers owned plantations around the outskirts of colonial Rio de Janeiro, and the name engenho is preserved in many of the sections of the city—for example, Engenho Novo, one of the northern suburbs. By the end of the sugar period there was a considerable amount of production coming from large plantations around Rio de Janeiro and Campos. According to figures given by João Antonil in 1711, the state of Rio de Janeiro in that year produced almost as much sugar as the state of Pernambuco.

For a time the new gold fever retarded the expansion of cane plantations. With the decline of gold mining many of the owners of large estates in the interior turned to the production of sugar cane. Especially in the valley of the Rio Pomba in southeastern Minas Gerais, sugar cane became a crop of major importance. The higher parts of the upland which were too cool did not share in this cycle, but most of the lower valleys, even in the mountainous sections, were utilized for cane.

Several factors contributed to the decline of sugar planting in the Southeast. One was perhaps the large and growing market for beef in Rio de Janeiro, which, with the transportation facilities available, had to be supplied from near-by sources in order to satisfy the Brazilian preference for freshly killed meat. Another was the impoverishment of the soils, after years of hard use, especially the light soils of the Paraíba Delta. Still another reason, according to Deffontaines, was the almost complete deforestation, for the production of sugar or alcohol requires a plentiful supply of cheap fuel. At the present time, sugar production in the Southeast has been greatly reduced in the face of the booming sugar district of São Paul State. The landowners have turned their cane fields back into cattle pastures; a large number of people formerly employed in the cane fields have emigrated to other parts of Brazil. Only on the southern part of the Paraíba Delta and in the Pomba Valley are small areas still devoted to sugar cane.

The Coffee Cycle

Coffee was the second crop to achieve such importance in the Southeast that it attracted new settlement, and drew people away from the other parts of the country. The coffee plant had been grown around Rio de Janeiro and in the Paraíba Valley since about 1774, but its value as a commercial crop came only with the rise of a market for coffee in the cities of Europe and North America in the early nineteenth century. The first area of rapid expansion of coffee planting was in the Paraíba Valley, especially on the higher terraces and lower mountain slopes of the southern side of the valley whence the product could easily be sent out over the road to Rio de Janeiro. People came from various parts of Brazil to swell the current of migration to this new region of prosperity, and many were those who moved into the Paraíba Valley from the decadent gold-mining towns of interior Minas Gerais. The peak of production in the Paraíba Valley was reached soon after the middle of the century. From about 1860 down to the present, the coffee plantations of the Paraíba Valley have continued to decline, and are now almost entirely gone. There never had been much care of the trees or the land, and the wasteful method of planting coffee in vertical rows only on the slopes—which agricultural specialists do not advise—resulted in a gradual decline of yields. The competition with better favored areas in São Paulo State sealed the doom of the coffee fazendas of the Paraíba Valley. More and more of the area was utilized for pasture.

Coffee was planted widely over the southern part of Minas Gerais, especially the southeastern part, as well as in the Paraíba

Valley. After the freeing of the slaves in 1888, for a decade the state government attempted to bring in agricultural immigrants by offering subsidies of various kinds, as was being done with much success in neighboring São Paulo, but the conditions of life on the fazendas of Minas, especially the low wages, and the fact that the tenants were located in scattered and isolated homes, did not appeal to the prospective immigrants. In spite of the effort, therefore, the main current of European immigration never affected Minas Gerais significantly. The coffee plantings, whether because of inadequate care, or because of poor soils, or both, little by little declined in yield and were abandoned. The life of the plantations was extended perhaps longer than might otherwise have been the case by various schemes introduced by the growers of São Paulo to maintain the price of coffee. Today a small amount of coffee still filters out from eastern Minas Gerais and from the bordering mountain districts of Espírito Santo and Rio de Janeiro. The greater part of the land, however, has been returned to grass pasture for the grazing of herds of cattle.

It was the shipment of coffee to Rio de Janeiro that stimulated the first railroad construction in Brazil. In 1873 the tracks of the Central cleared the barrier of the Great Escarpment. By 1875 the main line had been extended to Juiz de Fora in southern Minas, where there was considerable activity in coffee planting; and by 1877 the branch line was built along the Paraíba Valley to São Paulo city. But by that time it was too late; the coffee plantations of the Paraíba Valley were already on the decline, and coffee production was moving elsewhere.

The Rice Cycle

The development of a specialized rice district in the middle Paraíba Valley marks the appearance of still another agricultural cycle. Rice is one of the major items of diet of the Brazilian people, and is widely grown as a subsistence crop for local use. It would have been strange indeed if a district of specialized rice production had not appeared to supply the large and growing urban populations of Rio de Janeiro and São Paulo. As it happens, there is a section of the Paraíba Valley which is physically well suited to this crop and which borders the branch of the Central running between the two metropolises.

The middle part of the Paraíba Valley, from the big bend of the river not far from São Paulo city to the beginning of its gorge east of Entre Rios, remains broad and open between the bordering ranges of mountains (Map 3, Page 7). Its bottom, however, is not entirely flat. On either side it is lined with a series of terraces, somewhat dissected by tributaries to the Paraíba which in places have cut the loose terrace gravels into very rough and hilly terrain. At intervals the terraces, which stand some 50 to 100 feet above the river, advance toward the center of the valley, carried on the shoulders of buried ridges of solid rock. In these places the river flows over small rapids, bordered by high terraces on either side. Upstream from each of these narrows, the terraces retreat, leaving a wide zone of swampy floodplain through which the river meanders. The floodplain at these wide points is between five and ten miles across.

The first settlement of the Paraíba Valley avoided the floodplain, and even the flatter parts of the terraces. Brazilians have always preferred the hilly locations on which to plant tree crops. The coffee plantations, therefore, were mostly back from the center of the valley. But the little towns which were strung along the road between Rio de Janeiro and São Paulo were commonly located near the narrow places, where the valley could be crossed without entering the floodplain swamps. Three of the larger towns were connected directly southward by mule trails to little ports along the coast, and actually found these outlets cheaper than the longer route to Rio de Janeiro. With the decline of coffee, the Paraíba Valley also declined in population; and the coming of the railroad cut off the little remaining activity at the ports.

The use of the floodplain for the cultivation of rice on a commercial scale began in the period between 1918 and 1920. Much earlier a bit of swampy land near Taubaté had been cleared and used for rice with excellent results, but the product was consumed only locally. In 1918, however, high prices for rice in São Paulo and in Rio de Janeiro, together with the enterprise of some immigrants who came to the valley through São Paulo, resulted in a boom period of speculative development. Land values began to soar as more and more of the floodplain area was cleared and planted. The fortunate owners became wealthy; in a few years most of them had departed to share in the delights of life in São Paulo or Rio de Janeiro, leaving their estates in the hands of tenants, who also for a time were able to make good incomes both for themselves and for the owners.

Several features of this district of concentrated rice production serve to illustrate the fundamentally exploitive character of Brazilian land use. In the first place, the most important factor governing the selection of land on which to grow rice has been accessibility to the railroad. In a zone along the southern side of the floodplain, the rice fields are almost continuous, and, here, are close to the line of the Central which follows the edge of the southern terrace. Varying physical qualities of the floodplain soil or of the supply of water are disregarded—in other words, there is no sign of close adjustment of the patterns of land use to the varying character of the land. Then, too, there is no attempt to control the supply of water beyond a minimum of drainage ditches. The somewhat irregular natural floods of the Paraíba are used to cover the growing rice; if the flood fails, the rice is not covered; if the flood is too high, the rice cannot be harvested. There is no reservoir upstream, no public diversion canal, none of the hydraulic works one expects to find in a district specializing in the production of rice. We have heard so much of the intensive methods of the Oriental rice growers that we forget that rice can be grown also with very much less work.

raça in Salvador, capital of Bahia, where the royal palms compete in beauty with the towers of old churches.

A view in Salvador, showing the elevator which provides quick transportation betw
the upper and lower cities. *Above:* a typical scene in the sertão of Ceará during
dry season.

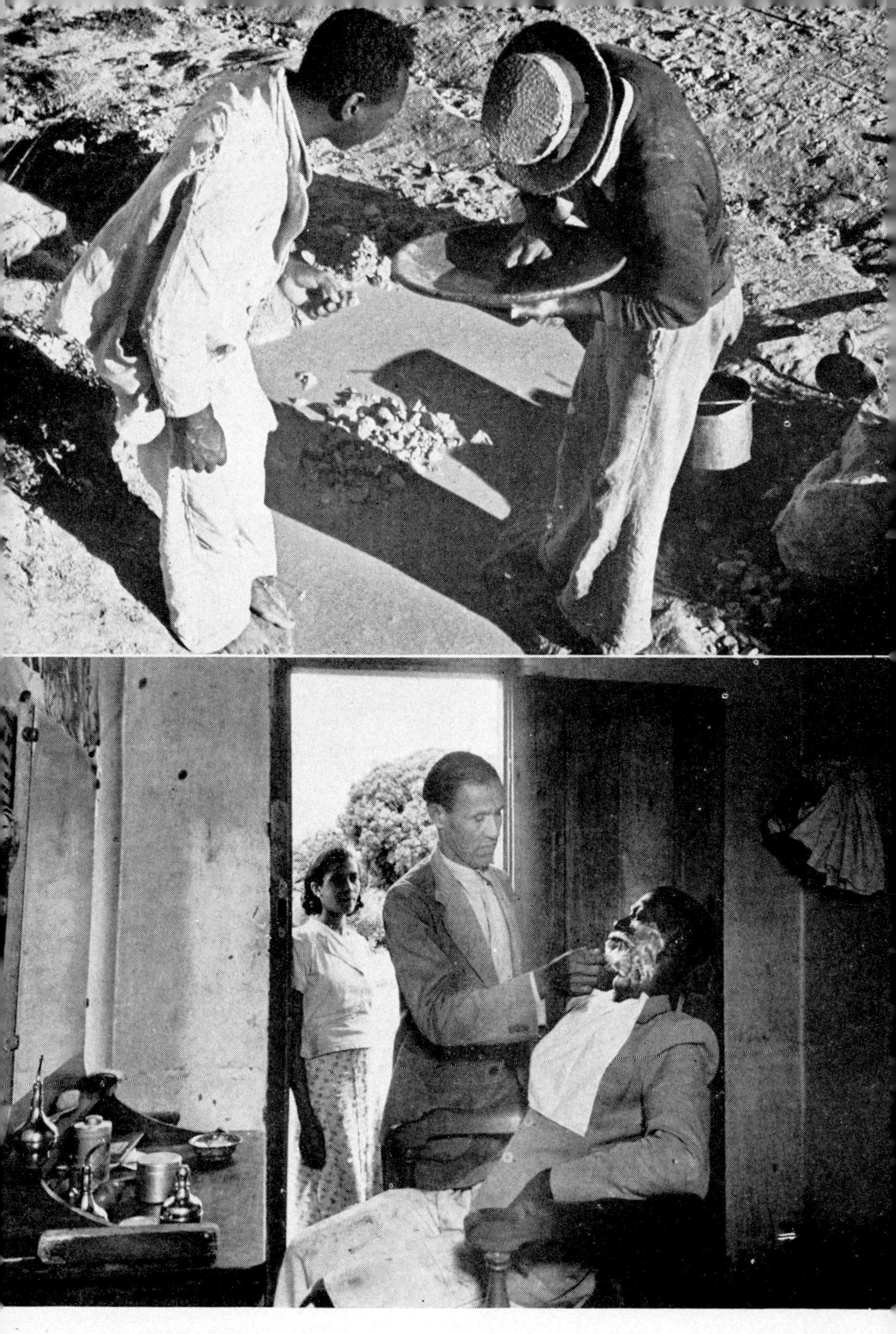

arber shop in the interior of Minas Gerais, which does much the best business when the gold panners (*above*) have good luck.

Two small towns in the interior of Minas Gerais. Entre Rios on the Rio Paraíba, wh
the main railroad line turns northward toward Juiz de Fora; and (*above*) the town
Coimbra, set in the midst of the hills, where the small houses crowd about the *praça*
the roads leading to it.

Of course the yields per acre are low. In the rice district there are fewer than 100 rural people per square mile; and there is no reason to suppose that they are more permanently established than were the coffee growers before them. In fact, a new boom crop has now appeared. This new crop will not occupy the floodplain of the Paraíba where rice is grown, but it may induce some of the rice growers to seek the greater profits of the new enterprise. The new crop which is sweeping the Southeast is the orange.

The Orange Cycle

New plantations of oranges have appeared suddenly during the last five years. On the sides of the hills in the lowland near Rio de Janeiro, orange trees planted in vertical rows have now replaced the bare grassy slopes terraced by the feet of grazing animals. On the hills which border the line of the Central in its course through the Paraíba Valley, orange plantations are appearing where once there was coffee. Oranges are replacing cotton and coffee in parts of São Paulo State, too, for at the moment this new production is booming, and, without regard to the quality of the land or the possible stability of the production, every one who can possibly plant oranges does so. The objective is quick profits—not the establishment of a stable form of rural life. Here the tree is planted, to be sure, but there is little else done to it beyond harvesting its fruit.

The domestic market is small, for the traditional Brazilian diet does not include much fruit. In São Paulo city, it is true, there is a notable increase in the popular consumption of oranges. But the bulk of the crop must find its way to a foreign market. In 1927 Brazil as a whole produced only 360,000 boxes of oranges; but by 1937 the production reached 5,000,000 boxes, and oranges ranked fifth among Brazil's exports. About a quarter of them went to Argentina, where the Brazilian oranges were able to compete with the fine Argentine and Paraguayan varieties. How long this current of trade can continue without invoking tariff barriers remains to be seen. About half the Brazilian production went to England, where the southern-hemisphere oranges reach the market at a time of the year when supplies from the northern hemisphere are low. The whole business is too new, and the markets are too recently found to merit any prediction regarding the stability of orange cultivation. But if it is not stable, the loss in Brazil will be at a minimum, for there has been a minimum of investment. If this is just another speculative cycle, then the workers in these new plantations will migrate elsewhere to the next boom region.

Use of the Land for Pasture

Always in the background of any speculative agricultural development there is the possibility of a return to the use of the land for pasture. Through the centuries cattle have provided the one steady source of income, although, of course, it is a moderate income, and in the grazing areas there are no rapidly rising land values. Yet a surprisingly large proportion of southern Minas Gerais and the neighboring parts of Rio de Janeiro State are devoted exclusively to pasture. Many parts of the formerly forested country have been so completely denuded of trees that the landscape in the dry season reminds one of the hillier parts of western Texas. In not a few sections, the pastures have been so heavily grazed that they are being seriously attacked by soil erosion. Nor is the carrying capacity of the land permanently benefited by the common practice of burning the grass in September, at the end of the winter dry season.

The pastures of the Southeast are used for beef cattle and for dairy cattle. Places located near a road or a railroad over which milk can reach the city of Rio de Janeiro in not more than eight hours are generally devoted to dairying. This is roughly a zone with a radius of not much more than 125 miles from the city. Beyond this zone there are several communities where Swiss immigrants have taken the lead in the manufacture of cheese.

Unfortunately the Brazilian cattle are poor milk producers, and a better selection of stock would require greater investment in the care of the pastures. As in the Argentine Humid Pampa, the poorer scrub cattle are able to survive where better breeds could not.

Beef cattle are grazed on most of the pastures of the Southeast. Range animals from the more distant places, perhaps from the sertão, are brought to the better pastures of the once forested country where they are fattened. Cattle are driven on the hoof to the fattening pastures, and then shipped by rail to the consuming centers. The slaughterhouses of the larger cities are greedy; and because of the desire for fresh rather than refrigerated meat, the supply must be regularly maintained.

Deffontaines has described a form of tropical transhumance in the mountain regions of the Southeast. During the rainy summers the animals are either driven, or drift without much care, into the higher parts of the Serra da Mantiqueira, chiefly to avoid the floods and the insect pests which are especially annoying at this season at lower altitudes. They remain on the high pastures from September or October until May or June when the failure of the water during the dry winter season forces them back to the lower altitudes.

Shifting Cultivation of Food Crops

On most of the fazendas of the Southeast, whether they are devoted to the grazing of animals or to the production of a commercial crop, certain areas are given over to the production of food for local consumption. These areas are temporary and are shifted from year to year. They are worked by renters who make small payments to, or share a part of their crop with, the landowners. The food crops are chiefly maize, rice, beans, bananas, and manioc. The little patches of land devoted to these crops are scattered without regard to slope or position. Observed from the air the complete lack of adjustment between the small fields and the land itself or the pattern of roads and villages is striking. The lands devoted to these crops look as if they had been thrown like pieces of paper from an airplane and had become fixed wherever they chanced to fall.

There are two reasons for the haphazard arrangement of food crops. The first reason is that the cultivation is shifting and not permanent. With this method of farming, the soil continues to yield well only for two or three years, after which the garden patch is abandoned and permitted to return to grass or brush, while a new spot is selected for cultivation. The second reason is that the hoe rather than the plow is the chief implement. For hoe cultivators, any slope up to as much as 35° is just as arable as level land would be, and certainly much easier to work on. A change to plow cultivation would introduce a great change in the significance of slopes in terms of human use, and would greatly reduce the area of arable land in a country as hilly as the Southeast of Brazil.

Over a long period of time, the shifting cultivation of food crops, together with the practice of burning the brush to make more pasture, has resulted in the complete destruction of the forest. Through the centuries the land which seems so empty has actually been used again and again, until its productivity is all but exhausted. The disastrous results of long-continued destructive exploitation of land resources by a shifting population are here exhibited in the emptiness of the rural landscape and in the poverty of the rural people.

Centers of Agricultural Progress

There is another side to this rather dismal picture, however. Modern agricultural schools offer instruction by thoroughly competent staffs to those who wish to avail themselves of the opportunity. The new Escola Nacional de Agronomía is located in the Baixada Fluminense not far from Rio de Janeiro. In rural Minas Gerais two agricultural colleges are of special importance because of their location in the midst of agricultural and pastoral communities. One is located in Viçosa in the southeast and the other in Lavras in the southwest.

New agricultural practices are spreading around all these centers. Better breeds of cattle and better techniques in caring for the animals are being adopted. Plows drawn by oxen are beginning to replace the hoe and motor trucks are replacing oxcarts. The traditional Brazilian practice of planting tree crops in vertical rows on the hillsides, which is the easiest practice where the hoe is used but which leads to the maximum of soil erosion, is being attacked by the demonstration on experimental farms that trees do better in horizontal rows. The beginning of a new era for the farmers of the Southeast is making its appearance around these modern agricultural colleges.

COLONIES OF SMALL FARMERS IN THE SOUTHEAST

In contrast to the traditional forms of rural settlement in the Southeast are the attempts made under government direction to start colonies of small farmers, working their own lands. Attempts of this sort date back to the early nineteenth century. In 1818, for example, a group of Swiss were given lands near Nova Friburgo in the Serra dos Orgãos. Unfortunately this colony never prospered, chiefly because of its isolation from any possible market for its surplus products. From a maximum of some 1,600 persons, the number dwindled to not more than a dozen families. Nevertheless, these Swiss immigrants are responsible for the start of cheese production in many of the communities of Rio de Janeiro and southern Minas Gerais, and for many of the delicious brands of cheese sent regularly now to the city markets.

Another group of colonists established since 1900 in the Serra da Mantiqueira has not been any more successful. Germans, Italians, and French were brought to Brazil with government aid and given lands in this mountain region north of the

Paraíba Valley. Most of the original settlers have drifted away, and some of their settlements are now completely deserted. Isolation is chiefly responsible for this failure also; for isolation imposed the necessity for self-sufficiency, and self-sufficiency made impossible the kind of prosperity and material gain which the immigrants desired.

A more important current of pioneer, small-farmer settlement was directed to the mountains of Espírito Santo. The coast of this state was one of the earliest parts of Brazil to be occupied by the Portuguese; but the settlements were so continuously subjected to the attack of warlike Indians that the Portuguese were forced to abandon all but a few defensible spots. In the nineteenth century a considerable part of the forest lands of western Espírito Santo was cleared and planted with coffee by the large landowners moving in from Minas Gerais. But the zone in between these two areas of Brazilian settlement —between the coastal towns and the coffee fazendas of the western border—remained unoccupied.

As the Indians were little by little subdued through contact with the Brazilians, this mountainous and heavily forested country in central Espírito Santo was open for European colonization. At first, from about 1840 to 1850, the colonists were chiefly Austrian and German; from 1877 to 1899 was the period of Italian colonization, which accounted for some 65,000 persons, a little less than double the estimated number of Germans; in more recent years, Poles have added a different element to the settlers. In each case the land was divided into small properties, about 125 acres each; and the newcomers built substantial homes and did their own work. They planted maize, rice, manioc, and coffee, depending on the latter crop for a cash return. Where the mountain settlements were too high to produce coffee, they have for the most part been abandoned: but coffee during the nineteenth century brought its growers enough profit to enable the colonies at lower altitudes to become prosperous.

Prosperity from coffee, however, did not mean stability. After a few years the coffee plantations of Espírito Santo, being cultivated by the inadequate methods in use throughout this part of Brazil, began to show declining yields. The large financial rewards to be derived from coffee production on virgin soils, together with the abundance of new lands near by, made available by the pacification of the Indians, was too much for the stability even of the small proprietors. Not only have the children of the first settlers moved on toward the north, but also many of the original settlers moved to new clearings. A frontier of new settlement has crept steadily northward toward the Rio Doce; but, since the current of new immigration was greatly reduced after 1914, this frontier has become a hollow one—that is, its advance is accompanied by the depopulation or the abandonment of the older settlements behind. These older clearings were in many instances rented by Brazilians who utilized them for cattle pasture. In 1926 a new bridge over the Rio Doce at Collatina opened the way to the sparsely settled country to the north, where the descendants of the Botocudos now practice a shifting cultivation of subsistence crops. Settlement has gone forward in this area, again with coffee as the chief crop. So this peasantry of small farmers, yielding to the lure of speculative profits from the use of virgin lands, has itself become migratory.

Another section of the Southeast where small farmers have been established on the land has a brighter future. The lowland back of Guanabara Bay, with its half-orange-shaped hills and its tidal swamps, was never an important area of settlement. It was a matter of comment among the travelers to Brazil during the nineteenth century that most of the food supply for Rio de Janeiro city came from a great distance: from Campos, from São Paulo, from Minas Gerais. There were only a few sugar estates on the more favorable sites; a few coffee plantations which were later used for cattle. The demand for charcoal for use in cooking in the city resulted in the rapid destruction of the forest; but the lowland was so empty of permanent settlers that it has often been described as a sertão.

In 1935 the federal government began work on an ambitious plan to drain and clear the swamps which border Guanabara Bay. Dikes and gates permit the escape of water from the rivers at low tide, but bar its return at high tide. Mangrove is being cleared away, and a considerable area of rich soil reclaimed. On these new lands, with malaria and other diseases of the tropical swamps now under control, small proprietors will be established on lots averaging less than ten acres each. Some of the settlers already occupying the first sites are Brazilians from the city of Rio de Janeiro; there are small numbers of immigrant Europeans and Japanese also included in the first group of colonists. This project seems to have advantages of access to a large market which the other colonial schemes have lacked.

MINERAL INDUSTRIES IN THE SOUTHEAST

Agricultural and pastoral settlement in the Southeast, then, has not led to the establishment of any large numbers of people on the land with anything like permanency or stability. But the Southeast possesses other resources than those of soil and vegetation. This region also has a remarkable store of minerals, of which gold is by no means potentially the most important. Although the decline of the placer gold workings left many of the earlier settlements of Minas Gerais stranded, this decline was not the result of the exhaustion of the minerals but only the playing out of the more obvious and accessible deposits. There is still a wealth of gold and diamonds, and in addition there are many other minerals of vital importance in terms of modern large-scale industries. Perhaps these mineral resources may lead to the development of a stabilized pattern of settlement where farming and stock-raising failed.

One of the sources of gold, indeed, has continued to support a stabilized mining community for more than a century. This is the famous Morro Velho mine, which was opened up by a British company in 1834 and has been continuously in operation ever since. It is located in the Serra do Espinhaço, a short distance south of Belo Horizonte, at a place where a most unusual ore body was discovered. Morro Velho has the distinction of having one of the two deepest mines in the world: its shafts have followed a rich gold-bearing vein to a depth of more than 8,000 feet. At a depth of 6,726 feet, the rock in the shaft had a temperature of 121°, and it was necessary to build an air-cooling plant to permit operations at lower levels. Yet the richness of the ore has provided a steady income in spite of increasing costs. Near the entrance to the mine is the little town of Nova Lima (10,000 population)—a long stabilized community of company employees, including a group of resident British managers and technicians.

Iron

Brazil's outstanding mineral reserve, however, is its extraordinary supply of iron ore. Something like thirteen billion tons of ore are to be found in the southern and eastern parts of the Serra do Espinhaço, chiefly in that part drained by the headwaters of the Rio Doce. This reserve was estimated about 1935 to constitute 23 per cent of all the iron ore of the world. Furthermore, it is one of the richest known deposits. With an iron content ranging from 50 to 65 per cent, and with very few impurities (phosphorus, for example, only .02 per cent), this ore is richer than most of the iron deposits today in use in the industrial regions of Europe and North America. There can be no doubt that Brazil possesses iron reserves of such quantity and such quality as to place her foremost among the nations in this resource. Furthermore, all of these ores are so disposed that they may be mined by simple quarrying, without expensive tunnels and shafts.

The value of the iron ore to Brazil, however, remains to be seen. The Brazilians were aware of the existence of iron in their country as early as 1590, a century before gold was discovered in Minas Gerais, but no special value could be attached to so large a body of ore until the world found a use for it. It was not till the middle of the nineteenth century that there was any great demand for iron ore, and in this age of revolutionary chemical and metallurgical inventions nothing is less certain than the future of any mineral. There will be no certainty regarding the wealth iron ore may create for Brazil until the wealth has been created.

Up to the present time the ores of Minas Gerais have scarcely been touched. When their quantity was first announced in 1910 by the North American geologist Orville Derby, then head of the Brazilian Geological Survey, there was a scramble for mining concessions. The Brazilians themselves secured some of the concessions, but claims to the largest ore bodies were established by British, North American, French, and German capitalists. The largest single ore body, located near the town of Itabira (Map 26, Page 90), is now in the possession of the Brazilian government.

Up to the present time there has been no large-scale mining in Minas Gerais, but small-scale operations have long been carried on. Several steel plants are located near the mines, notably at Sabará and Caeté (Maps 3 and 26, Pages 7 and 90). The total production of these small companies in 1937 amounted to 98,000 metric tons of pig iron, 71,000 tons of soft steel, and 76,000 tons of hard steel. Since the Brazilian market for steel and pig iron is between 300,000 and 400,000 tons each year—chiefly for re-enforcing rods for concrete structures, or wire, sheets, tubes, and rails—the domestic production can satisfy only a small proportion of the total demand. The small-scale steel plants, however, turn out a high-grade product. For fuel they depend on charcoal, and with the passing years the forests which are cut for this purpose must be sought at greater and greater distances. All the operators, in an industry where a shutdown means disaster, fear the possible traffic jam on the Central which would cut off their charcoal supply. The Eucalyptus plantations which have been set out in many parts of the Southeast have not provided a solution to this problem, so rapid is the consumption of wood.

In 1940 the Export-Import Bank of the United States granted a loan to Brazil for the development of a modern domestic steel plant. The engineers in charge of the project are now at work building the mills in the Paraíba Valley, a little west of Barra Mansa. The ore is to be brought over the Central from mines in the southern part of the Serra do Espinhaço 235 miles away. The Brazilians hope to be able to make use of domestic coal. In the state of Santa Catarina there is low-grade coal which can, however, be made into coke in spite of its high ash and phosphorous content. The fuel is to be shipped by boat to Rio de Janeiro and other small ports near by, and thence by rail over the Great Escarpment to the steel mills. So pure are the Brazilian iron ores that the usual ratio of coal to iron can be reversed —making it possible to use more iron ore than coal in the steelmaking process. The problem remains to bring the railroad lines up to the standard of effectiveness which will permit the uninterrupted shipments of raw materials and fuels.

The location proposed for the new steel plant in the Paraíba Valley is an excellent one in terms of the domestic market for steel. About 45 per cent of the steel will be used in São Paulo and about 30 per cent in Rio de Janeiro; the remaining 25 per cent will be consumed in other parts of Brazil which are most easily reached by steamer through Rio de Janeiro. The prospects are bright for the establishment of a stabilized industrial community in the Paraíba Valley, and for the development of the surrounding rural areas for the production of food for the urban workers. Perhaps this marks the beginning of a new era for the Southeast, and for Brazil as a whole—an era of steel and heavy industries.

The export of iron ore on a large scale, however, will probably not take place by way of the Central. The great iron deposit at Itabira will be more easily shipped out by way of the Rio Doce valley. Recently the Brazilian government has purchased the concession for the railroad in this valley and the rights to the Itabira ore body. Mining on a vast scale is planned and will be started as soon as the machinery is available. The railroad is being rebuilt to carry heavy ore trains; at the port of Vitória new docks are being built to handle the huge tonnages of ore which will soon be shipped from there. The demand for this high-quality Brazilian ore both in Europe and in the United States is increasing rapidly as the high-grade northern hemisphere ores near exhaustion. Returning ore boats will bring coal to Vitória. Plans are already being made for the use of this coal in new heavy industries to be built in the Rio Doce valley.

Other Mineral Operations

The Southeast of Brazil contains also a wealth of other minerals, mostly concentrated in and about the Serra do Espinhaço. This part of Minas Gerais, for instance, is one of the world's leading sources of manganese—one of the hardeners of steel. Manganese mines have long been in operation, but the majority of the mines have been opened up since the beginning of the First World War. Most of the manganese deposits are in the southern part of the Serra do Espinhaço, along the line of the Central; shipment is by way of the Central to Rio de Janeiro. Manganese exports, even in the peak years of the First World War, did not involve such tonnages as might result from the potential iron-ore developments.

Central Minas Gerais also contains workable ore bodies of zirconium, chromium, molybdenum, nickel, tungsten, diamonds, beryl, and quartz crystals. In fact, it is the only source in the world of commercial quartz crystals for electrical use. The diamonds, in the modern period, are used almost exclusively for industrial purposes, not as gem stones. The presence in this part of Brazil of large supplies of the ferroalloys, or hardeners of steel (manganese, chromium, nickel, molybdenum, and tungsten), is a matter of great importance to the United States, which, in spite of its extraordinary mineral wealth, does not possess important quantities of these essential items.

The minor minerals, however, are relatively insignificant in terms of population and settlement. Only where mining and manufacturing are to be developed on a large scale are considerable numbers of people likely to be attached to the land, even temporarily. The other mining operations require the services of relatively small numbers of people, and the number employed in the mines fluctuates unpredictably with the conditions of the world market.

THE SERTÕES OF THE SOUTHEAST

The Southeast, like the Northeast, has its frontier of concentrated settlement, and beyond the frontier its sertões. The sertões of this part of Brazil include the São Francisco Valley in northern Minas Gerais and southern Bahia, and also some of the land west of the São Francisco in the central state of Goiaz. This vast extent of territory is occupied by a scattered and predominantly pastoral people, with a density of population between two and ten per square mile. Most of the northern part of the area was peopled by frontiersmen from Bahia in the eighteenth century, and the southern part was entered during the early nineteenth century by people scattering from the declining gold fields of Minas Gerais.

The only product to reach the outside world regularly from the sertões has been cattle. The inhabitants live a seminomadic existence around the widely scattered ranch headquarters, having few contacts with the outside world except those provided by traveling salesmen, or *mascates*, mostly Syrians, who come with mule loads of manufactured articles. Cattle are driven overland to the fairs which, as in the Northeast, are located on the edge of the more densely settled country. Those in Minas Gerais which have had a steady importance are held at Tres Carações and Campo Belo (Map 3, Page 7).

The advance of the railroad into the sertões has had the effect of depopulating the surrounding country. As the narrow-gauge line of the Central advanced northward beyond Belo Horizonte, with the distant objective of Belém, the railhead acted like a magnet, drawing to it people who before had been widely scattered. At the present time Pirapora, on the São Francisco, is the railhead. This little town of 4,000 inhabitants is now growing, partly through the arrival of settlers from all the vast territory around it.

Great things are expected of the valley of the São Francisco. Good authorities assert that there is a huge area where soil and climatic conditions are ideal for cotton. Some cotton is actually produced today in small, isolated plantations near the river. A fleet of river boats operates between Joazeiro and Pirapora, giving access to the many small villages along the way. From the north comes salt secured by the evaporation of salt water from springs located near Joazeiro. Januaria is an important community, for the salt, landed at this point, is carried by muleback over all the state of Goiaz. From southern Minas Gerais a small trade in coffee, maize, manioc, and lard is carried northward to the São Francisco in exchange for the salt, cattle, and cotton that move southward. Yet it is difficult to agree with the optimistic citizens of Pirapora that the advantages of this valley are soon to be realized, drawing to it a great influx of colonists. The physical advantages of the area for cotton may be all that is claimed for them; but the market for cotton is anything but certain and the source of the colonists is not apparent. Still, it is one of the characteristics of the sertão that great things are always about to take place and sometimes they do!

RIO DE JANEIRO

Perhaps nowhere in South America is the contrast between city and country sharper and more vivid than between the hinterland of the Brazilian Southeast and Brazil's magnificent capital, Rio de Janeiro. In contrast to the emptiness and poverty of much of the interior of the Southeast, Rio de Janeiro is one of the most strikingly beautiful cities in the world. Established originally where the knobby ribs of the coastal mountains border the western side of Guanabara Bay (Map 24, Page 75), the city now occupies several narrow lowlands between projecting rocky ridges. It has extended both northward into the lowland back of the coastal mountains and southward to the crescentic beaches of white sand which are festooned from headland to headland along the Atlantic. During the period since the beginning of this century, the old, unhealthful, unimproved Portuguese city, which reminded one of an overgrown rural village, has been transformed into a metropolis. Fine new docks now border the bay; the mangrove swamps, once infested with fever-carrying mosquitoes, have been cleaned away, and along the margin of the water a stone seawall has been built, with a wide tree-lined avenue between it and the first row of buildings. In the downtown section, at one end of the famous Avenida Rio Branco, a group of new office buildings, constructed on modern lines, has made its appearance; and along the nearest of the Atlantic beaches, in the Copacabana District, modern-style apartment buildings and hotels face the open ocean. Against the background of green, forest-clad mountains, bare rocky cliffs, and blue water, the city presents an unforgettable picture in a frame of unparalleled design.

Not all of the city is beautiful, however. Rio de Janeiro has its poor districts, its slums, some of them located on the tops of the rocky ridges which overlook the throbbing business district, or the gay beach at Copacabana. The 1,664,000 people who live in the urban area include many who are crowded into miserable homes, and who have little opportunity to appreciate the magnificence of the picture of which they are a part.

The modern-style skyscrapers strung along the bay or along the Atlantic give the impression that this growth is not something that has sprung from the land, but rather something which has come from across the sea. Investigation confirms the impression. Rio de Janeiro made its start, to be sure, during the great gold period of Minas Gerais, when it was selected as the outlet for the wealth of the Southeast. But when the capital of Brazil was transferred from Salvador to Rio de Janeiro in 1763, and especially when, in 1808, the Portuguese king, fleeing from Europe, made Rio de Janeiro the capital of the whole Portuguese world, the little town with its muddy or dusty streets, and its bad record for fevers, began to extend its influence far beyond the limits of its immediate hinterland.

In the modern period, Rio de Janeiro has actually left its immediate hinterland far behind. The hinterland of the capital city today is all of Brazil. Located midway between the clusters of people grouped along the coast in the Northeast, and those grouped along the coast in the southern part of Brazil (Map 15, Page 30), and located also close by the economically most productive state of São Paulo, Rio de Janeiro has become the hub of commercial exchange for all these widely scattered communities, but its connections are *by sea;* coasting steamers, in fact, carry by far the greater proportion of Brazil's whole domestic trade. Of all the imports to Brazil from foreign countries in 1938, 41 per cent came to Rio de Janeiro. Some of these foreign goods were later shipped by sea from the capital to other ports in the north or in the south. Of the coastwise trade of the country, Rio de Janeiro accounted for about 20 per cent of the imports and 30 per cent of the exports. No small part, therefore, of the continued growth of Rio de Janeiro into a commercial and industrial metropolis of nearly two million people is the result of the fact that the great majority of Brazil's more than forty million inhabitants live near the sea, not inland.

Because Rio de Janeiro was chosen as the capital, as well as because it is pre-eminent in economic advantages, much of the wealth of Brazil has been concentrated there. The interests of the nation focus on the capital, and to the capital come the leaders of business, politics, and art. Like the picture in a crystal ball, Rio de Janeiro mirrors the complete Brazilian scene, from the throbbing activities of the cities to the utter desolation of the sertão.

Chapter V

SÃO PAULO

ONLY A LITTLE MORE than two hundred miles southwest of Rio de Janeiro is another city of more than a million inhabitants—São Paulo. There are fewer than fifty such cities in the whole world, and only four which are located in low latitudes, two in India and two in Brazil. We can understand how Rio de Janeiro might have attained its great size, for, as we have said, in it are focused the interests of the people scattered over the whole of Brazil—not only the political interests of the nation but also the commercial, intellectual, and artistic. On first thought São Paulo might seem to be just another example of the trend toward a multiplicity of urban centers which we found to be characteristic of the Southeast. Yet cities of over a million are not created simply by decree; they achieve such numbers only as the result of the operation of social and economic forces. The processes which have led to the rise of this second metropolis and of the cluster of people in its immediate hinterland are of great importance to students who are seeking an answer to the riddle of an empty Brazil.

The cluster of people, of which São Paulo city is the urban nucleus, is of recent origin, and only since the middle of the last century has it wielded a predominant influence in Brazilian economic affairs. In the historical background is that great trilogy of wealth-bringing products—sugar, gold, and coffee. The story of São Paulo is the story of the sweep of coffee across the state, and of the consequences of that most recent wave of speculative exploitation. The beginnings date back to the early decades of the nineteenth century, to a period when "coffee shoppes" had become a fad in England, and when coffee was being advertised as the cure for a long list of diseases. The new beverage gained swiftly in popularity. Again, as in the case of the spread of the sugar market centuries before, Brazil began to produce at the very beginning of a rising market, and went on to capture the larger share of the international trade. This is a commercial situation in which a maximum of profits are to be made by the producers with a minimum of investment in production. In the decade between 1870 and 1880 Brazil was furnishing about half of the world's supply of coffee; since 1900 each year it has furnished from 65 to 75 per cent; and in the meantime the total annual production of coffee in the world has increased from 8,000,000 bags between 1870 and 1880, to 25,000,000 bags between 1930 and 1940.

In this enormous increase in coffee production, the state of São Paulo has played a leading part. This one state has produced between 65 and 70 per cent of all the coffee in Brazil; and, as a result of the economic prosperity of the great era of expansion, this one state has furnished from 30 to 40 per cent of the revenue for the federal treasury of Brazil. São Paulo was the scene of a rapid increase of population, a rapid advance of the frontiers of agricultural settlement, and a rapid increase in land values on the advancing frontier of coffee production. The pioneer movement has continued to the present time. Of all the regions of concentrated settlement in Brazil, therefore, São Paulo is far in the lead in terms of commercial prosperity and financial and political influence.

São Paulo does not show that closeness of adjustment between people and place which one would expect if prosperity is in any way related to stability of settlement. Here in São Paulo, to be sure, we are not dealing with a region of declining population in a stage of decadence, for the population is still growing, and there is still the optimism of the frontier; nor are we dealing with a people who are backward in their agricultural or industrial techniques, for the Paulistas are famed for their readiness to adopt new devices and methods; nor are we dealing with a region which is isolated or difficult of access, for São Paulo is better off in its roads and railroads than is any other part of Brazil. Furthermore, the people are predominantly European with much less mixture of Indian and Negro elements than is found in the regions previously considered. Nevertheless we find in the midst of this expanding, vigorous center of Brazilian economic life the same looseness of attachment between people and land, the same temporary and destructive exploitation of the soil, the same shifting patterns of population, the same hollow frontier. But all these things are developed here on a bigger scale and the processes of change are going on more rapidly.

THE LAND

The land on which these events are taking place is arranged with a pattern somewhat more convenient for the needs of the inhabitants than was the case in the Southeast. There is the familiar combination of crystalline uplands, low mountains, and tablelands of stratified rock as in other parts of the Brazilian Highlands, but the design of all these elements is much simpler than that of the Southeast. Along the low coast the climatic conditions are those of the rainy tropics, but in the highlands distinctly lower temperatures are experienced. In the southern part of the state, the beginning of the zone of transition appears between areas suited to tropical plants and areas from which such plants are excluded because of low temperatures and frosts. São Paulo also has the *terra roxa*.

Surface Features

Immediately back of a narrow zone of wet lowland along the coast, the Great Escarpment rises to elevations between

2,600 and 2,900 feet (Maps 4 and 24, Pages 8 and 75). Generally the Atlantic margin of the Brazilian Highlands is composed of a wide zone of block mountains and narrow structural valleys, descending by a series of steps from the unbroken upland to below sea level. This is the situation in Espírito Santo and in Rio de Janeiro; and it is also the situation in the southwestern part of São Paulo State, where the angular valleys of the Zone of the Escarpment are threaded by the tributaries of the Rio Iguapé. But from a point somewhat southwest of Santos northeastward approximately to the border between the states of São Paulo and Rio de Janeiro, the Great Escarpment forms one unbroken slope from the edge of the upland to the sea. This is the section to which the name Serra do Mar was originally applied. Where the Iguapé brings down to the coast a heavy load of waste material worn from the eroded edge of the highlands, the foot of the Escarpment is bordered by a narrow alluvial lowland, rearranged by the waves and shore currents into long curving beaches of white sand backed by mangrove-filled lagoons. Santos is built at the easternmost end of this lowland fringe. Where the single slope of the Great Escarpment descends directly to the water's edge and is drained only by short torrents, so little alluvium is brought down that the bays and promontories are largely unmodified by bars and spits, and the island of São Sebastião remains separated from the mainland. The Bahia de Sepitiba, on the border between São Paulo and Rio de Janeiro, is open to the Atlantic, with only the beginning of a sand bar forming on its eastern side.

Above the Great Escarpment the upland, which is drained by the tributaries of the Rio Paraná, has a conspicuously even skyline, especially striking as one reaches the crest of the Serra do Mar above Santos and enters the gently sloping hill country of the São Paulo Basin (Map 4, Page 8). The valleys on the upland are broad and generally swampy along their bottoms; the interfluves rise in broad sweeping curves to the uniform summit elevation of about 2,600 feet above the sea. A few ranges of low mountains, or strings of mountain knobs, stand above this general level, and one such range separates the basin of São Paulo from the interior of São Paulo State. Between the São Paulo Basin and the Paraíba Valley there is a sharp drop: the Central Railroad which connects São Paulo with Rio de Janeiro by way of the Paraíba Valley descends about 550 feet in fifteen miles as it leaves the São Paulo Basin.[1]

Only the eastern and southern parts of São Paulo State lie within the area of crystalline rocks. On the inland side of the range of mountains which separates the São Paulo Basin from the rest of the state there is only a narrow band of crystalline upland. Beyond this the granites and gneisses disappear beneath a covering of stratified rocks, the layers of which dip gently toward the west and north. Map 4, Page 8 shows the northern end of the great Paraná Plateau. Geologically this plateau is a structural basin of sedimentary rocks with layers of diabase (see also Map 1, Page 4). The older sedimentary layers which rest on the crystallines are easily eroded by the streams. As a result, where these layers outcrop they have been excavated to produce an *inner lowland*, and the streams which descend into this inner lowland from the edge of the crystalline upland do so over falls and rapids. Along the margin of the crystallines in São Paulo there is a string of towns, such as Sorocaba, Itú, Campinas, and Mogi-Mirím, where the relationships are similar to those of the "fall-line" towns of

[1] Persons interested in the physiography of Brazil should note the river capture which has taken place east of São Paulo city. The São Paulo Basin is drained by the Rio Tietê, which crosses through a gap in the mountains northwestward toward the Paraná. In recent geologic times, the streams which now form the headwaters of the Paraíba were tributaries of the Tietê. The big bend of the Paraíba is the result of the capture of these headwaters by the stream which flows eastward to reach the Atlantic near Campos (Map 24, Page 75). The eastern part of São Paulo State which was thus transferred to the Paraíba drainage is now a conspicuously even-topped upland, with its summit level about the same as that of the São Paulo Basin; the valleys have been deeply incised in intrenched meanders below the upland surface.

southeastern United States, except that the rivers are flowing inland rather than toward the ocean.

Among the various layers of rock which cover the granites and gneisses in the Paraná Plateau, some are more resistant than others. In the midst of the inner lowland, for instance, there are certain strata which are enough stronger than the formations on either side of them to hold up a belt of low hills along their outcrop. But the inner lowland is sharply terminated in the north and west by the steep face of a cuesta, capped by almost vertical cliffs of diabase. This rock, which is of volcanic origin, was originally laid down in molten sheets either on the surface or squeezed between layers of rock near the surface. Being so much more resistant than the sedimentary rocks around it, the outcrop of diabase, throughout this part of Brazil, is marked by steep cliffs; and because the diabase layer dips toward the north and west, like the other rocks in the western part of São Paulo, the steep face of the cuesta is always toward the south and east athwart the lines of traffic. In southern São Paulo the general level of the inner lowland is between 1,900 and 2,200 feet above the sea; but the top of the diabase cuesta, like the top of the crystalline upland, rises some 600 feet higher. The cuesta is sharp and continuous where it enters São Paulo from Paraná, and is interrupted only in its northward swing where the northwest-flowing rivers have cut water gaps through it. In northern São Paulo, the diabase cuesta crosses the inner lowland and borders the crystallines, here standing above the general level of the hilly upland to the east. Since the diabase in the north is much broken by faults, the cuesta appears in detached pieces.

From the crest of the diabase cuesta the land slopes gently westward toward the Rio Paraná. Although the southern part of the Paraná Plateau is mostly composed of diabase at the surface, in São Paulo this rock appears only in a narrow band where its outcrop forms the cuesta. Most of the Paraná Plateau in western São Paulo is made up of sandstones resting on the diabase, with the latter exposed only in the valley bottoms (Map 1, Page 4). Wherever the rivers encounter diabase in their channels they form rapids.

Soils

The soils of São Paulo State are closely related to the underlying rock. On the crystalline upland a reddish clay soil, known as *massapê*, is formed similar to that found throughout eastern Brazil where the crystallines are exposed under a semi-deciduous forest cover. Among the soils of the Paraná Plateau, the *terra roxa*,[2] formed on the outcrops of the diabase, is the best known. This is a deep, porous soil containing considerable humus, which can be easily recognized by its dark reddish purple color. When it is wet it becomes so slippery and sticky that travel over it is very difficult, and in dry weather it gives off a powdery red dust which stains everything it touches. On the outcrops of sandstone, a light-colored, sandy soil is formed, known as *terra arenosa*. These popularly recognized soil types are being given scientific definition and will soon be mapped by the new soil survey of the state.

Soils cannot properly be described in general terms such as good or bad, fertile or infertile. Fertility is always in relation to the use intended for the soil. The terra roxa, for example, is excellent for coffee trees, especially as its porosity allows the roots to penetrate far into the ground. Its chemical composition, however, is such that, for cotton, it is an inferior soil, for the plant tends to form branches and leaves instead of fiber. Detailed technical studies by soil specialists and agronomists are needed in any agricultural region to determine which soils and which techniques are best suited to bring desired results. One important point regarding many of the soils of São Paulo has recently been set forth: that is their tendency to erode rapidly, especially when they are used without fertilizer for

[2] *Roxa*, in Portuguese, means "purple": it is pronounced ró-shah.

the production of cotton. When the terra roxa is allowed through bad agricultural practices to dry out at the surface it is especially liable to erode badly during the next heavy rain.

Climate and Vegetation

São Paulo as a whole is a region of abundant moisture. Along the coast the amount of cloudiness and rainfall is great. One of the rainiest places in Brazil is found on the slopes of the Great Escarpment and of the Zone of the Escarpment. An average of nearly 150 inches is recorded on the Serra do Mar between Santos and São Paulo. The zone of heavy rains, however, is narrow; São Paulo city, less than thirty-five miles from Santos, receives an average annual rainfall of only 56 inches. Most of the state receives between 50 and 60 inches (Map 8, Page 15), and only the Great Escarpment and the Zone of the Escarpment are likely to remain sparsely inhabited because of excessive moisture.

A very important change occurs in the regimen of the rainfall along the southern boundary of São Paulo. In the south there is no winter dry season such as is found generally throughout the highlands of tropical Brazil. A little south of Sorocaba a rather sharp line separates the area of winter drought from the area of year-round rain.

Temperatures show marked differences between the coast and the interior of São Paulo. At coastal stations like Santos the temperature is moderately high, ranging from 66° in winter to 75° in summer. On the higher parts of the plateau average temperatures are some ten degrees lower. At São Paulo city the coldest and warmest months average 58° and 69° respectively. Toward the west and north in the interior of the state the temperatures increase; in the valley of the Paraná the average of the coldest month is above 65°.

There is an important temperature boundary as well as an important rainfall boundary in southern São Paulo and north-

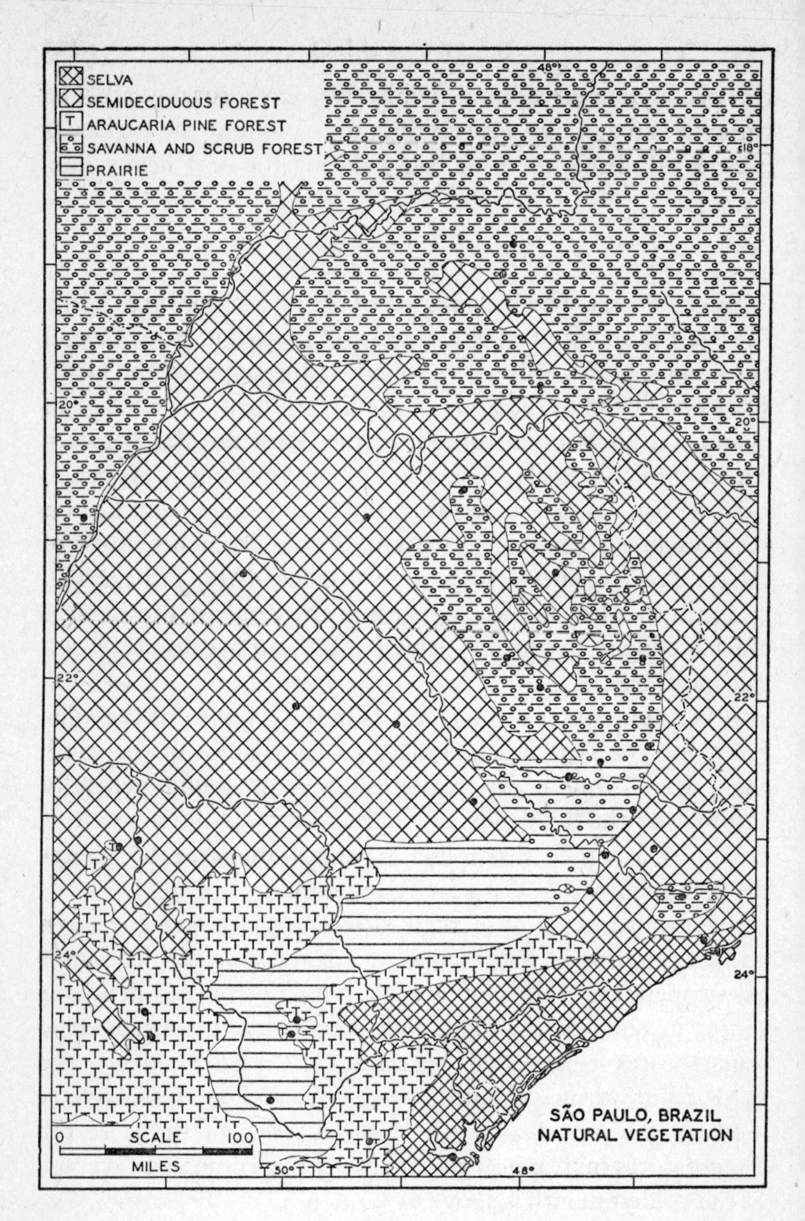
SELVA
SEMIDECIDUOUS FOREST
ARAUCARIA PINE FOREST
SAVANNA AND SCRUB FOREST
PRAIRIE
48°
18°
20°
20°
22°
22°
24°
24°
0
SCALE
100
MILES
50°
48°
SÃO PAULO, BRAZIL
NATURAL VEGETATION

MAP 28

ern Paraná. The northern limit of frosts occurs there. Frosts occur at times in the higher mountains of the Southeast, in Minas Gerais, but south of the latitude of Sorocaba they come frequently enough to make the planting of tropical crops somewhat hazardous. In the boundary area frosts occur only in the higher valleys and on south-facing slopes. In northern Paraná, frosts come almost every year, but they are distributed in patches or frost pockets, interspersed with many frost-free spots. In middle Paraná there are no frost-free spots on the plateau, and freezing temperatures are experienced every winter. Frosts do not occur along the coast, nor in the Paraná Valley and its deeper tributaries.

The various climatic features which have been described are nicely reflected in the pattern of the natural vegetation (Map 28, Page 128). Along the coast and on the rainy slopes of the Escarpment there is a dense tropical rain forest composed of broadleaf evergreen species with many epiphytes and lianes. In the cloud zone of the upper part of the Escarpment the trees are moss-covered and the ground is almost constantly soaked with moisture. On the highlands, however, forests and grasslands are intermingled. Semideciduous forests once grew luxuriantly on the slopes of the mountains and over most parts of the crystalline upland; dense forests marked the outcrops of diabase to such a degree that some of the early travelers in that region said that a map of forests was a map of the geology. Semideciduous forests, becoming denser toward the west, covered the whole of western São Paulo down to the Rio Paraná. This river formed and still forms an amazingly sharp vegetation boundary, for immediately west of it begins the scrub forest in which there are many open patches of savanna.

Within the forested areas of São Paulo State there were numerous grassy openings. The São Paulo Basin, itself, was originally grass-covered, with trees only in the rainy zone near the crest of the Escarpment and on the surrounding mountains. The inner lowland was occupied by savanna with scattered scrubby trees and with galeria forest along the streams. South of Sorocaba, however, where there is no longer a dry season, the savannas were transformed by degrees into pure grass prairies, which the Brazilians call *campo limpo*. These prairies continue southward into Paraná.

The tropical semideciduous forest mixes with the midlatitude forest of Paraná in a wide zone of transition in northern Paraná and southern São Paulo. The forests to the south are composed of Araucaria pine with an undergrowth of broadleaf species not unlike the pine-oak forests of the southern Appalachians. Where the frosts occur irregularly pines grow in those places which have frosts once in every ten years or so; the semideciduous forest is evidence that the place is frost-free.

SETTLEMENT BEFORE THE COFFEE PERIOD

The first permanent settlement on the highlands of Brazil was a mission founded in 1554 on the site of the city of São Paulo. Many settlements had already been made along the coast and, in the Northeast, the coastal zone was beginning to witness the rise of the sugar-planting. No route from the coast to the highlands anywhere south of Salvador offered greater ease of penetration for the colonial Portuguese than the one from São Vicente (near Santos) to São Paulo. Not only was this part of Brazil inhabited by fewer and less hostile Indians than the region between Cape Frio and Salvador but the physical barriers to penetration of the interior were narrower here than they were anywhere else. A single ascent led from the coast to the upland, but, what was more important, the forest belt in this section was narrowest (Map 12, Page 21). To be sure, this ascent offered no advantages like those of the broad valley of the Rio Doce; but the Portuguese were less interested in an easy climb than they were in avoiding heavy woods. When a road was built over the Great Escarpment to São Paulo it made the ascent not by the easier grades now followed by the São

Paulo Railway, but over the very nose of a steep spur where the forest was a little less dense than in the ravines on either side. At no other point along the coast between Salvador and southern Brazil could the barrier of rain forest be crossed in so short a distance. Less than thirty miles inland the settlers came upon the open campos of the São Paulo Basin. Unlike the North American pioneers who built their homes in the woods and shrank from the open prairies, these Portuguese settlers felt secure only when they had emerged from the forest. The São Paulo mission was founded on the lower terraces overlooking the swampy valley of the Tieté in the midst of country covered with tall grass and scattered thickets of scrub trees.

The people who came to São Vicente and São Paulo were not wealthy. Anyone in Portugal with private means or with any standing at court went to Salvador or Recife; others came to São Paulo. They were a vigorous, energetic, adventurous people, and, coming mostly from the south of Portugal, they inherited no small amount of Moorish restlessness and lack of stability. They could not afford Negro slaves and the Indians were poor workers; nor was the land in the São Paulo Basin productive of wealth-bringing crops. So they began to look for other sources of wealth.

The Bandeirantes

For more than a century expeditions from São Paulo pushed into the interior of the continent, searching restlessly for sources of profit. A glance at the map (Map 17, Page 32) will indicate the enormous extent of territory they covered. From the shores of the Plata to the banks of the Amazon, the bandeirantes tramped through the endless sertões pasturing their herds of cattle. They stopped here and there to pan the stream gravels for gold or to plant temporary fields of maize. They mated with the Indian women and increased their numbers by hordes of mameluco children. They were not gentle people, these bandeirantes. Wherever they found

Indians grouped together around one of the Jesuit missions they carried them away to be sold into slavery. When there were battles to be fought, or dangers to be encountered, the bandeirantes were ready and eager. Their expeditions were more than simply exploring parties: they constituted a way of living for a restless people in a land which, for them, contained few resources they could turn into wealth. They pushed the boundaries of Brazil far to the west of the original line of demarcation between Spanish and Portuguese territory (about 50° W. Long.). Few are the parts of this vast domain which have not been lived in, picked over—in a sense, ransacked; many little communities now lost in the great interior of Brazil had their origin in expeditions which remained in the wilderness instead of returning eventually to São Paulo. Not until gold was discovered in Minas Gerais in 1698 and in Mato Grosso in 1719, did the wealth for which the bandeirantes had been searching at last come to some of them.

Sorocaba

The rise of the gold-mining communities of Minas Gerais, however, did not bring great prosperity to São Paulo, although many of the Paulistas were attracted to the new source of wealth. The large and growing population of the Southeast did offer a market for cattle and mules. In the sertões of the west and south cattle were permitted to graze and breed almost without care, and mules were raised especially in Rio Grande do Sul and the Banda Oriental. It is interesting that on the two sides of the continent there should have developed the same sort of mule and cattle trade, with trails leading northward to the centers of settlement from the remote prairies east and west of the Paraná-Plata. On each side, one town achieved major importance as the scene of the annual livestock market: Sorocaba, a litle west of São Paulo, played the same role for eastern South America that Salta played for the western part.

Every year during June and July Sorocaba was crowded

with people. Herders brought mules and cattle from the far south or from Mato Grosso; buyers came not only from Rio de Janeiro and Minas Gerais, but also from distant Bahia and Pernambuco. During most of the period from the early seventeenth century until the railroads appeared in the late nineteenth century, Sorocaba remained the outstanding example in all of Brazil of a market town located on the border between the sertões and the regions of denser population along the coast.

THE SPREAD OF COFFEE OVER SÃO PAULO

At the close of the gold period, about 1800, São Paulo and the little towns around it were still on the border of the sertão. They formed the southwestern outposts of the area of relatively dense population which, as a result of the gold prosperity, had developed in the hinterland of Rio de Janeiro. São Paulo, Sorocaba Campinas, and the other little towns of this part of the state were the not very prosperous urban centers of a not very prosperous pastoral and agricultural area, in which the fazendeiros, or fazenda owners, cultivated a few acres of maize and sugar cane, but derived most of their income from the sale of beef cattle. There was little then to differentiate this region from the other parts of the Southeast, of which it was essentially a part. When, in the early nineteenth century, coffee began to be grown in the Paraíba Valley, some of the planters around Campinas and Sorocaba added this crop to their small plots of maize and sugar cane. In the São Paulo Basin itself temperatures were too low for coffee.

In 1847 a forward-looking landowner from the vicinity of Limeira took a radical step. He had been cultivating the usual crops with Negro slaves, but realizing that slavery as an institution was doomed, he undertook, with government aid, to bring to his estate some eighty families of German peasants—four hundred persons in all—who were established as tenants, or *colonos*.

At first the change was slow, but the fifteen years between

1885 and 1900 witnessed the sudden transformation of the São Paulo region from an outlying part of the Southeast, to a new and independent region of settlement, focusing on the city of São Paulo and the port of Santos. This sudden transformation was the result of three developments which were so closely linked that to separate cause from effect is almost impossible. The three developments were the increase of the European and North American market for coffee; the spread of coffee over São Paulo State; and the rapid immigration into São Paulo State of millions of Europeans. The result of these three developments was the profound alteration of both the Paulista landscape and the Paulista way of living.

Immigration

The figures of the population of the state tell the story. In 1872 there were about 837,000 inhabitants, located chiefly in the Paraíba Valley, and in the mountains and hilly uplands of the territory around Campinas, Sorocaba, and São Paulo. In 1890 there were 1,384,000 people, and the frontier of new coffee planting was beginning to roll north and west. By 1900 the population of the state had nearly doubled, reaching 2,280,000. The increase continued, reaching 4,500,000 in 1920, 6,500,000 in 1934, and an estimated 7,131,000 in 1938.

The rapid increase of population was the result of immigration which both caused and was caused by the increasing prosperity of the region. During the whole period from 1827 to 1936, São Paulo received 2,901,204 new arrivals,[3] but only 53,517 of these had come before 1886. In the fifty years from 1887 to 1936 the average annual immigration was nearly 57,000. In each of the years 1891, 1895, 1912, 1913, and 1929 the number of immigrants exceeded 100,000; but in 1903, after the first small financial crisis of the coffee region, and in 1918, after the First World War, the number dropped below 20,000. Only in

[3] Figures from Estado de São Paulo, "Movimento migratorio no Estado de São Paulo," *Bol. da Directoria de Terras, Colonias e Immigração*, Vol. 1, 1937: 31–158, and "Cincoento anos de Immigração," *Bol. do Ministerio de Trabalho, Industria e Commercio* (Rio de Janeiro), April, 1937: 301–314.

© Charles Perry Weimer

Coffee beans being spread on the drying platform, interior of São Paulo state; *above:* coffee pickers delivering their harvest for measuring.

The outer harbor of Santos, looking toward the sea, and (*above*) the port and of Santos, the world's largest coffee shipping center.

© *Charles Perry Weimer*

Martinelli Building and one of the main business streets in São Paulo. The National City Bank of New York is at the end of the street on the left.

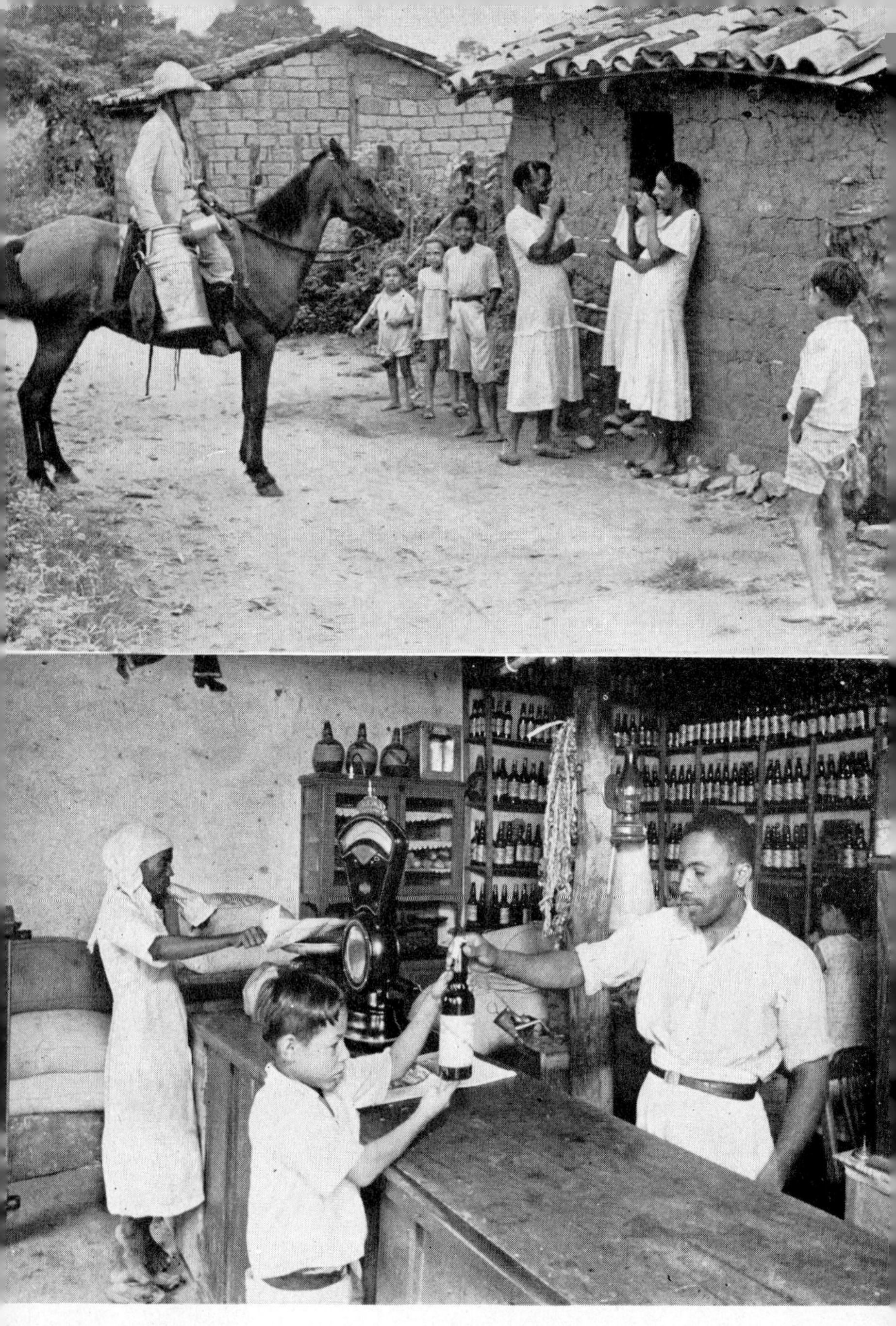

Two scenes from the back country: a village store where the little fellow is buying a bo
of Antarctica beer, manufactured in São Paulo; *above:* the milkman is picking up so
village gossip.

one year, 1915, did the departures outnumber the arrivals, but during the whole period about 48 per cent eventually left Brazil. During all this time Brazil as a whole received about 4,600,000 immigrants, a somewhat smaller number than entered Argentina. São Paulo's share of this immigration was about 60 per cent.

Many nationalities and races were involved in this migration. As in Argentina in the same period, Italians were the most numerous, coming in maximum numbers from 1890 to 1900, and again just before 1914. Since 1918 the number of Italian immigrants has dropped very greatly. After Italians, in total numbers, came Portuguese, Spaniards, Germans, Japanese, Russians, Poles, Austrians, Turks, Lithuanians, and others. Between 1918 and 1935 there was a large immigration of Japanese.

Most of the Japanese and many of the Germans went to the State of São Paulo, which also received immigrants from other parts of Brazil. The rise of São Paulo as a region of speculative agriculture led to much emigration from the older regions of settlement in Brazil. The number of Brazilians who came to São Paulo was exceeded only by the number of Italians. The state of Bahia contributed the largest number of Brazilian immigrants to São Paulo, with the state of Minas Gerais second. The accompanying table gives the number and proportion of immigrants between 1827 and 1936 who came to São Paulo State:

IMMIGRANTS TO SÃO PAULO STATE—1827 TO 1936[4]

Nationality	*Number of people*	*Percentage*
Italians	942,903	32.50
Brazilians	494,834	17.06
Portuguese	413,161	14.24
Spaniards	386,613	13.33
Japanese	177,551	6.12
Others	486,124	16.75

[4] From "Movimento migratorio no Estado de São Paulo," *loc. cit.*

Compared with the migration of Europeans into North America during this same period those who went to Brazil and to Argentina were only a trickle. The question can still be asked, "Why did so few people go to Brazil?" A part of the answer to this question is offered by the conditions of life on the *fazenda paulista*, and also by the objectives of the Europeans who were led to migrate in such numbers to the New World. It is probably a mistake to believe that the majority of the immigrants came because they desired freedom from oppression, or religious liberty. Most of them came because they had heard that in America one could become rich.[5] In North America some did become rich, but in South America, in Argentina and in Brazil, the immigrant worker found himself face to face with the long established tradition of the aristocratic landowner and the tenant, of "master and man." Most of the profits derived from the spread of wheat cultivation in Argentina went to the landowners; in Brazil this same story was repeated, for the fazendeiros pocketed not only most of the income from the sale of coffee, but also the profits from the increase of land values. The wages paid to the colonos were only for subsistence, not a real share of the profits. Failing to gain a part of the "unearned increment" of land values, the immigrants to South America sent back discouraging reports which must have compared poorly with stories of the quick wealth to be made in North America.

The Fazenda Paulista

Nevertheless, opportunities to become wealthy are now much better on the fazenda paulista than on the fazenda mineira. Although in São Paulo State there are longer hours of work than in Minas, and the laborers are expected to work harder than in the easy-going Southeast, the wages are higher. Those who are diligent, thrifty, and perhaps lucky, have been

[5] See the treatment of this subject in R. F. Foerster, *The Italian Emigration of Our Times* (Harvard Economic Studies, Vol. 20), Cambridge, Mass., 1919.

able to purchase some land of their own or to move to the city and find employment in the factories.

Coffee production requires a considerable amount of labor. As a first step in the development of a new plantation, the landowner draws up a contract with a tenant obligating him to clear a tract of virgin forest and plant coffee. While the young trees are growing to bearing age, which takes from four to six years, the colono family is permitted to grow its own food crops, such as maize, rice, and beans, between the rows of coffee. At the end of that period, however, the colono must turn the plantation over to the owner and move elsewhere.

When the new coffee fazendas come into production, a large number of rural people are settled on the land. Unlike the tenants in most other parts of Brazil, those on the fazenda paulista are not scattered in individual homes, but are grouped together in villages. The owner himself commonly moves to his new estate, together with managers and overseers. The fazendeiros of São Paulo as a group are closely in touch with the business of producing coffee; they are not, like the ranchers of Argentina or even of other parts of Brazil, interested primarily in pastoral life and willing to leave farming to tenants.

The fazenda paulista, however, is by no means a social unit, as was the old sugar estate of the Northeast. It is essentially a business enterprise which brings a group of people together for a brief period for the sake of profit. Contracts with tenants generally run for only one or two years, after which the tenant family usually moves elsewhere. Not only is the tenant loosely attached to the land on which he works, but even the owner fails to develop any sentimental attachment to his property, and is ready at the first sign of decreasing profits to move on to the virgin lands of the frontier. The objective of both fazendeiro and tenant is more wealth; there is no intention of remaining permanently in the rural districts. The dream of every Paulista is a home in the city. This attitude of mind colors the whole relationship between the people and the land.

Layout of the Fazenda Paulista

The layout of the typical fazenda of São Paulo State resembles that of other parts of Brazil in the relation of its boundaries to the terrain. Estates are divided from each other along the ridge tops or drainage divides. The coffee trees are planted almost exclusively on the ridges and slopes, and almost exclusively also in vertical rows. The accompanying map of land use in an area near Taquaritinga (Map 29, Page 139) shows what is typical of the central area of coffee production. The land devoted to coffee occupies the tops and sides of the ridges, less than half of the total area. The valleys are used for pasture or for food crops or they are left in brush. Standing on the ridge tops one can see little but coffee—long straight rows of coffee as far as the eye can reach. The people, the estate headquarters, and buildings and drying platforms of the fazendas are all grouped in the valleys, especially near the valley heads.

The fazenda paulista usually contains certain standard buildings and other equipment needed for the harvesting, drying, and shipment of coffee. The harvest, which begins sometime in May and lasts till August, consists in stripping the "cherries" from the branches of the trees and transporting them to a central part of the fazenda where the coffee seeds are to be extracted. First the cherries are dumped into large tanks of water in which the ripe and green ones are separated and the sticks and stones eliminated. The cherries are then carried to drying platforms, which are usually made of black tile to absorb the sun's heat. On many fazendas the transportation is by small canals, in which the cherries are floated. On the drying platforms the cherries have to be raked over frequently and in case of rain must be quickly gathered into small piles and covered with tarpaulins. When the cherries are thoroughly dry they are put through a machine which removes the husks and then through other machines which grade the seeds according to shape, weight and size. The coffee is then put in bags (of 60 kilos each) and is ready for shipment or storage. All these processes require not only an abundant supply of cheap labor, but also a special set of structures—tanks, canals, drying platforms,

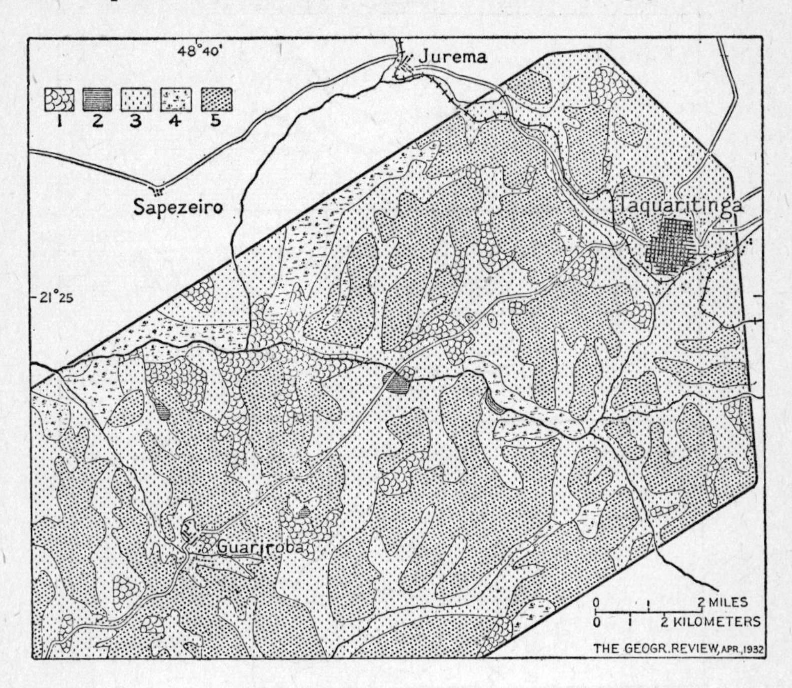

Map 29

1. Woods (7 per cent of area). 2. Truck crops, chiefly maize and vegetables (1 per cent). 3. Pasture (43 per cent). 4. Brush (6 per cent). 5. Coffee (43 per cent).
(Courtesy of the *Geographical Review*, published by the American Geographical Society of New York.)

husking and sorting machines, and storage sheds, as well as a home for the owner and homes for the tenants; all of these are found on the fazenda. A coffee plantation does not require as large an initial investment as a sugar usina, but the investment

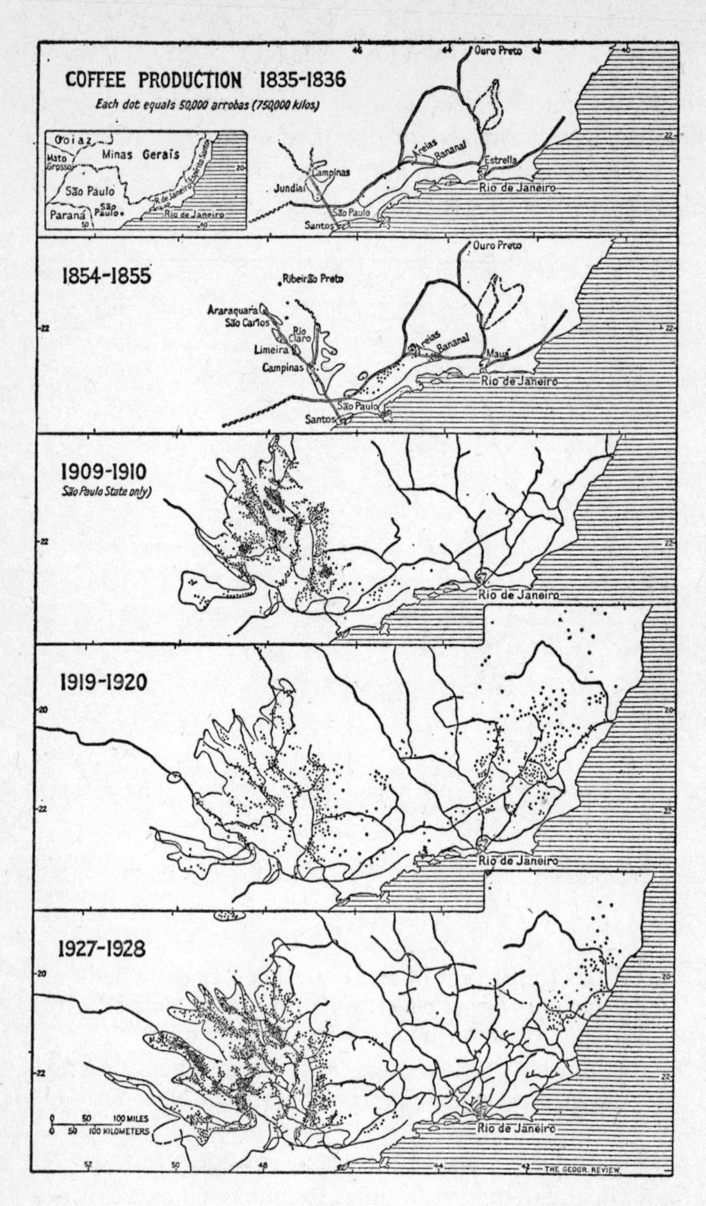

MAP 30

(Courtesy of the *Geographical Review*, published by the American Geographical Society of New York.)

is too large for the small proprietor, and hence there is little hope for the colono who wishes to become a landowner.

Distribution of the Coffee Fazendas

The first advance of the coffee plantations into São Paulo State followed the pre-existing roads, but as the qualities of the soil and surface best adapted to coffee were discovered, a pattern was gradually evolved which came more and more closely to resemble that of the underlying land (Map 30, Page 140). Outside of the Paraíba Valley, the first part of São Paulo State to become a center of coffee planting was the district around Campinas, where, between 1860 and 1885, the new plantations supplanted the older Paraíba fazendas as the chief sources of coffee. From Campinas two roads led into the interior, and along these roads coffee made its advances. One extended northward along the edge of the crystallines through Mogi-Mirím to Uberaba in Minas Gerais; the other went toward the northwest, through Piracicaba (Map 4, Page 8). For a time Campinas, at the focus of these two routes through the coffee plantations, grew more rapidly than São Paulo city.

Certain parts of the region soon appeared to be better suited to coffee than others. The open savannas were avoided in favor of the heavily wooded ridges. Already in the neighborhood of Campinas the planters had discovered the advantages of the terra roxa which had developed on the narrow dike of diabase that cuts through the basement crystallines near that town. It is on this dike, in fact, that the *Instituto Agronómico de São Paulo* with its big experimental plantations is now located. The fazendeiros soon discovered the terra roxa around Ribeirão Preto to the north and São Carlos to the northwest, and they concentrated their attention on these districts.

The great wave of coffee planting in the period between 1885 and 1900 followed not only the routes out of Campinas, but also moved westward from Sorocaba, encountering the

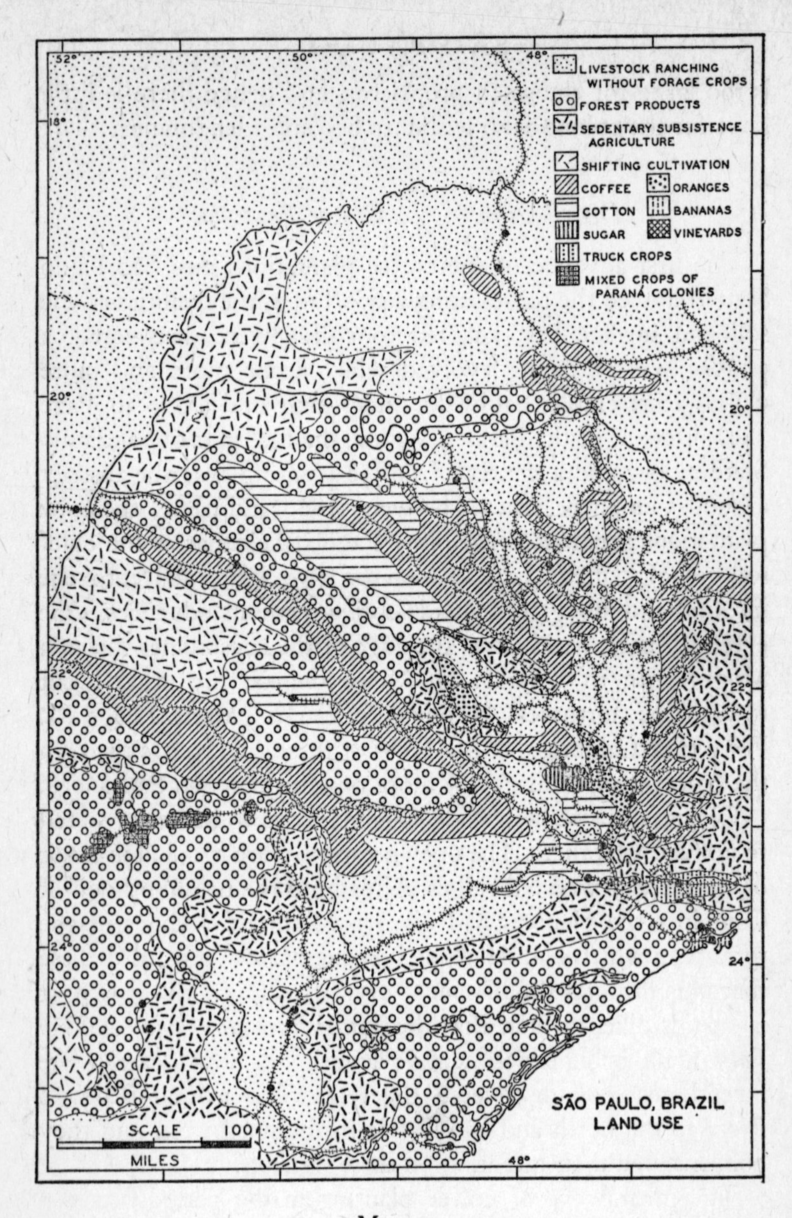
LIVESTOCK RANCHING WITHOUT FORAGE CROPS
FOREST PRODUCTS
SEDENTARY SUBSISTENCE AGRICULTURE
SHIFTING CULTIVATION
COFFEE
ORANGES
COTTON
BANANAS
SUGAR
VINEYARDS
TRUCK CROPS
MIXED CROPS OF PARANÁ COLONIES
52°
50°
48°
18°
20°
20°
22°
22°
24°
24°
48°
SÃO PAULO, BRAZIL
LAND USE
0
SCALE
100
MILES

MAP 31

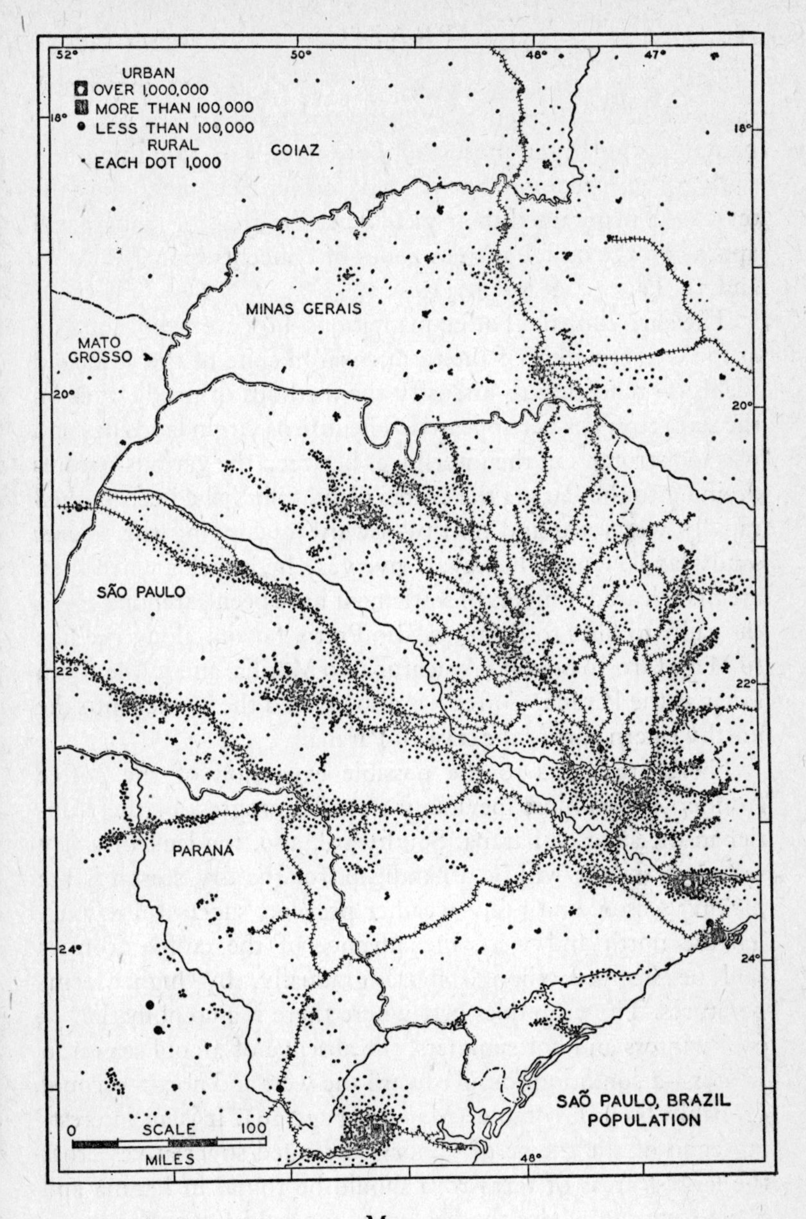
URBAN
OVER 1,000,000
MORE THAN 100,000
LESS THAN 100,000
RURAL
EACH DOT 1,000
GOIAZ
MINAS GERAIS
MATO GROSSO
SÃO PAULO
PARANÁ
SÃO PAULO, BRAZIL
POPULATION
0 SCALE 100
MILES
52°
50°
48°
47°
18°
20°
22°
24°

MAP 32

diabase cuesta near Botucatú. Where the map of the forests once vaguely reflected the distribution of the terra roxa, the map of coffee began more and more to do the same thing, but with greater precision. So well have coffee trees planted on the terra roxa maintained their yields that the areas of diabase still appear on the coffee map as zones of concentration (Maps 31 and 32, Pages 142 and 143).

The spread of the coffee plantations, however, did not stop at the western edge of the terra roxa. In spite of the sustained yields no tendency to intensify the methods of production on the terra roxa has yet appeared. The lure of virgin lands beyond was too strong. On the interfluves between the various streams draining to the Paraná the coffee plantations have been pushed rapidly westward and northwestward, occupying the poorer sandy lands, which, however, give very high yields when they are first cleared. Fingers of settlement have been extended along the railroad lines to Barretos, Rio Preto, far out along the line to Mato Grosso beyond Araçatuba, to Marilia, and in the south as far as the Paraná. Coffee has also crossed the border into the northwestern part of the state of Paraná.

There are limits to the possible expansion of the coffee frontier. Frosts must inevitably stop the progress of the frontier in the state of Paraná. Southward, also, the lack of a dry season in winter will be a handicap, for the dry season is the picking season, and rainy weather prevents successful drying. To the north and west, the advance of the coffee frontier will be stopped, though more gradually, by higher temperatures. The crop does best where there is a combination of cool winters and hot summers; the absence of a cool season in winter—a condition found toward the west and north—would probably be unfavorable (Map 11, Page 20). It is an interesting echo of the theme of "poorly arranged superlatives" that the largest areas of terra roxa should be found in Paraná and Santa Catarina where the climate is too cold for coffee, or in the valleys of northern São Paulo where it is too hot.

Other Uses of Land in the Coffee Region

Within the coffee region itself a relatively small proportion of the land has been used for the chief crop. Before 1875 most of the fazendas grew coffee on only a part of the cultivated land and used the rest for the traditional Brazilian combination of food crops—maize, rice, and beans—and sometimes for a little sugar cane and cotton. During the period of coffee speculation new plantations had almost all their cultivated lands in coffee; but the cultivated lands were only on the ridges, and on every fazenda a large proportion of the land was in valleys. The valley land was used only incidentally for pasture or small temporary gardens cultivated by the tenants for their own needs. Certain districts in the state specialized in other crops (Map 31, Page 142). In the lowland around Sorocaba, for instance, a small area was devoted to cotton. Fruit orchards of various kinds appeared around Limeira and on the railroad between Sorocaba and São Paulo. Around the outskirts of the city of São Paulo there was a considerable development of truck gardening. Throughout the state the area devoted to pasture has regularly exceeded that used for all crops. In the year 1933–34 of the total area in land holdings, only 16.1 per cent was cultivated; and on this cultivated land coffee occupied 49.1 per cent, maize 21.7 per cent, rice 8.6 per cent, cotton 7.6 per cent, and other crops 13 per cent.

Lines of Transportation

During the settlement of São Paulo State certain dominant lines of circulation were established, first by the old colonial cattle and mule roads and later by the railroads. Today the zones of the several railroads are the divisions of the state which are known to the average citizen—rather than the natural divisions suggested by the geographers.

The first stem of the railroad system appeared when a British company built a line from Santos to São Paulo in 1867. The trains are lifted or lowered over the Serra do Mar by means of cables and stationary steam engines, burning British coal. To-day the broad-gauge tracks of the São Paulo Railway pass through the city of São Paulo, and across the mountains which separate the capital from the interior, to the terminus of the line at Jundiaí. The contract under which the company operates prohibits the construction of any competing line between Santos and São Paulo until 1946. The São Paulo Railway is the bottleneck through which the products of the whole region must pass.

The interior of São Paulo, however, has three chief railroad zones (Maps 4, 27, and 31, Pages 8, 92, and 142). The first is the zone where the Paulista, which is owned and operated by Brazilians, extends with the same broad gauge from the end of the São Paulo Railway at the Jundiaí through Campinas, Limeira, and São Carlos to the northern border of the state. A branch line reaches the town of Marilia. Aided by the revenue from the richest part of the state, the Paulista is one of the better railroads in Brazil, in fact, in all South America, and compares well with the best North American lines.

The second railroad zone of São Paulo covers the northeastern part of the state which includes the rich coffee district around Ribeirão Preto. This zone is served by the narrow-gauge Mogyana which connects with the Paulista at Campinas. The Mogyana extends to Araguari, in the Triangulo of Minas Gerais, whence another company has built a line almost to Goiânia in southern Goiaz.

The whole southern part of São Paulo and most of the western part is covered by the zone of the Sorocabana. A narrow-gauge line goes westward from the city of São Paulo through Sorocaba. The main line continues westward to the Rio Paraná, but two important branches lead to the north and the south of it. The first branch connects at Baurú with the Noroeste, a railroad which has been built across the Rio Paraná

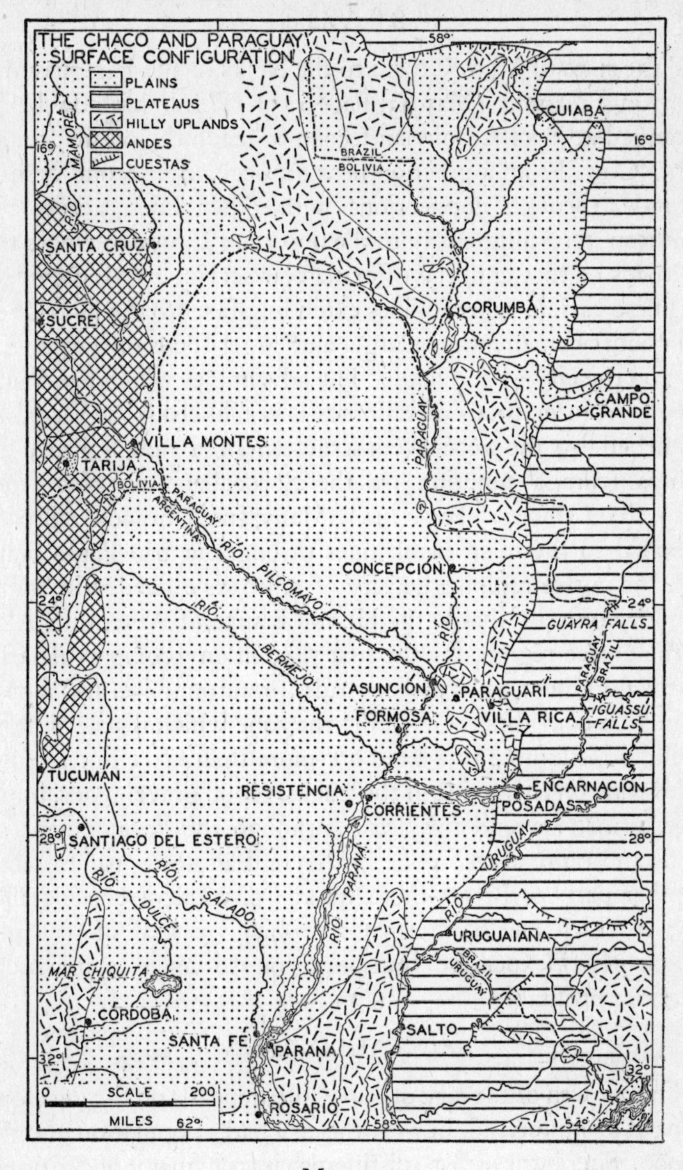

THE CHACO AND PARAGUAY
SURFACE CONFIGURATION
PLAINS
PLATEAUS
HILLY UPLANDS
ANDES
CUESTAS
58°
16°
RIO MAMORE
BRAZIL
BOLIVIA
CUIABA
SANTA CRUZ
SUCRE
CORUMBA
CAMPO GRANDE
PARAGUAY
VILLA MONTES
TARIJA
BOLIVIA
PARAGUAY
ARGENTINA
RIO PILCOMAYO
CONCEPCION
RIO BERMEJO
24°
GUAYRA FALLS
RIO
PARAGUAY
BRAZIL
ASUNCION
PARAGUARI
FORMOSA
VILLA RICA
IGUASSU FALLS
TUCUMAN
RESISTENCIA
CORRIENTES
ENCARNACION
POSADAS
28°
SANTIAGO DEL ESTERO
RIO DULCE
RIO SALADO
RIO PARANA
RIO URUGUAY
URUGUAIANA
BRAZIL
URUGUAY
MAR CHIQUITA
CORDOBA
SANTA FE
PARANA
SALTO
32°
0 SCALE 200
MILES
62°
ROSARIO
58°
54°

Map 33

and the state of Mato Grosso to the banks of the Paraguay not far from Corumbá (Map 33, Page 147). This line is now being extended across the Bolivian Chaco to reach the oil fields near Santa Cruz. From a junction near Sorocaba the second branch extends, through connections with other lines, across the southern states all the way to the border of Uruguay where the railroads of that country offer regular service to Montevideo.

These various railroad lines extending far into the interior of the country are creating a larger and larger focus of transportation on the city of São Paulo. The advantages which São Paulo enjoys from its focus of railroads is not likely to be seriously disturbed by the recent construction of a new railroad to Santos from a junction on the Sorocabana not far from Sorocaba (Map 31, Page 142). Many small branch railroads attached to the main trunk lines throughout São Paulo State give the coffee region a density of railroads exceeded in South America only by that in the Humid Pampa of Argentina. Also in the coffee region, for the first time in any comparable area on the continent, all-weather roads for automobiles and motor trucks are being built. Generally the zone which is accessible to a railroad is limited to a band not more than fifteen or twenty miles wide on either side of the tracks. Good gravel roads, however, greatly extend this area. Although the development of roads and railroads has gone far beyond anything to be found in other parts of Brazil, there are still districts of considerable size in which one of the major problems is that of securing sufficiently inexpensive transportation to make commercial activities profitable.

SÃO PAULO CITY

The growth of the city of São Paulo depends on the development of its hinterland. In 1883 the city had a population of only 35,000. There was little to distinguish it from many of the other small towns in the vicinity which had also been founded in the colonial period; its streets were narrow, irregular, and mostly unpaved; little had been done to modify the natural conditions of its site. In fact, Campinas had been growing more rapidly in the period before 1883 because it, rather than São Paulo, was the focus of the two chief routes of early coffee expansion.

Two important factors seem to have led to the sudden rise of São Paulo. In the first place, the spread of coffee cultivation between 1885 and 1900 opened up for the first time the zone of the Sorocabana, and the major focus of routes was shifted from Campinas to São Paulo. In the second place, São Paulo, being a little higher and cooler, was not subject to such serious epidemics of fever as Campinas. At any rate, it was in this period that modern São Paulo made its beginning. Several new manufacturing industries were started, including textile plants, shoe factories and other industries utilizing local raw materials. In 1905 Brazil was reported to have 110 cotton textile plants, employing 39,000 workers, and most of these were located in São Paulo and Sorocaba.

The population of São Paulo, from the 35,000 of 1883, increased to 239,000 by 1900; it was 340,000 in 1907; and in 1920 it had reached a total of 579,000. At present the population in the metropolitan area is not far from 1,500,000. These figures remind one of the rapid growth of industrial metropolises like Chicago and Detroit. São Paulo was transformed in a little more than fifty years from a small Brazilian town to a city which, to a greater and greater degree, has taken on all the characteristics, good and bad, of its North American prototypes. The enormous increase of population in São Paulo since 1920 is a result in no small part of the migration of workers from the rural districts.

Manufacturing Industries in São Paulo

Although industries are by no means new to this part of Brazil, the big period of industrial expansion, as in Buenos Aires, took place after the beginning of the First World War.

The new industries of São Paulo were given many advantages by the federal government because of the strong political influence of the Paulistas. One of these advantages was a high protective tariff. Another was a tax of two per cent on the value of all goods handled at all the ports of Brazil except Manaus on the Amazon, and Santos, the port of São Paulo. In those industries for which the raw materials as well as the finished products have to be sent to and from other parts of the country by boat, this tax had the effect of compensating the cost of hauling goods over the steep escarpment. The result was the development during the last twenty years of the chief industrial center not only in Brazil but in all of Latin America.

The industries of São Paulo are varied. About 29 per cent of the investment and 38 per cent of the workers are in textile factories. The spinning and weaving of cotton, wool, and jute, and the making of hosiery and silk and rayon goods are the chief textile industries. Next come metallurgy and the construction of machinery, followed by clothing, foods and beverages, chemical products, cement and other building materials, and paper and rubber goods. Industries making use of local raw materials are responsible for 86 per cent of the value of the industrial products of São Paulo. Most of the automobiles and motor trucks now widely used in Brazil are assembled near São Paulo. In many cases the bodies are built of local materials. In 1937 São Paulo, together with its industrial suburbs and Sorocaba, had 9,051 factories, and gave employment to 245,715 workers.

One of the factors contributing in an important way to the industrial growth of São Paulo and the neighboring towns is the development of the near-by water power. The power has been developed by a Canadian company, which has also built the power system of Rio de Janeiro. On the very crest of the Serra do Mar, overlooking Santos, a reservoir has been located, supplied in part by the heavy rainfall, and in part by water pumped from the swampy Tietê Valley. From the reservoir, water is dropped 2,378 feet to a power plant at Cubatão at the base of the "Serra." [6] This is said to be the finest water-power site in South America, with a potential capacity of 750,000 horse power. An abundance of electric energy is available to supply all the needs of the city that can be predicted. In addition, there are smaller hydroelectric plants along the Tieté.

Even so great an industrial center as São Paulo, however, reveals the same curious weakness in rail connections previously noted in the cities of the Southeast. Not only are there several major railroad junctions in its hinterland which are entirely lacking in any urban development, but the city itself is served by only four lines, two of which are single-track and one of which is narrow-gauge. The fact is that the hinterland of São Paulo is able to absorb only a small part of the industrial products of the capital, most of which are sold to urban people either in São Paulo city itself or in other cities of Brazil. In the interior of São Paulo State most of the many small towns have their own equipment of local industries, making furniture, clothing, beer, and many other items for the small local markets.

Urban Pattern of São Paulo

São Paulo city itself is a very different sort of place from Rio de Janeiro. In it we find a pattern similar to that of most big cities in the United States. The highly concentrated commercial district is the famous Triangulo where there are many tall buildings. The Triangulo is surrounded by a "blighted area" of old residences, and the new superior residence districts occupy the ridge tops or the outskirts of the city where real-estate operators have undertaken the necessary planning and advertising. The compact industrial districts are strung along the chief railroads. Surrounding the suburbs there are miles

[6] A North American engineer, Mr. A. W. K. Billings, is responsible for this development. To him the people of São Paulo owe a very considerable debt of gratitude for the works which made possible the rise of their city to its present position.

and miles of unoccupied residential subdivisions, laid out optimistically in the boom years before 1930.

THE DECLINE OF COFFEE

The development of the city of São Paulo and of its immediate hinterland was dependent upon the spread of coffee production over the state and the growth of the speculative fever which accompanied the spread. Now we must go back and watch the spread of coffee from another point of view, for speculation inevitably leads to crisis and collapse, just as it did elsewhere in the Americas. Early in the twentieth century the signs of unhealthy growth appeared and led, step by step, to serious financial difficulties.

The Coffee Crises

The fazendeiros were well off in the period from 1885 to 1896. Land was cheap, the market for coffee was active, and profits were fabulous. Apparently the only problem was to secure enough labor. Coffee production crept ominously upward. In 1899 Brazil produced 9,000,000 bags, but in the next year the big plantings of the early 90's brought the production up to 11,000,000 bags. In 1901 it went up to 16,000,000. In 1902 the state of São Paulo had about 530,000,000 trees of bearing age, and 135,000,000 more trees which had been planted since 1899 were about to come into production. The stage was set for disaster.

The first major crisis was postponed by two things. In 1902 the government prohibited new plantings for a period of five years, and there were severe frosts in the zone of the Sorocabana. But the relief was only temporary; in 1906, at a time when the whole world was consuming 12,000,000 bags of coffee a year, the Brazilian crop was 20,000,000 bags.

This same year the government adopted a system of *valoriza-*

tion providing that a quantity of coffee should be purchased by the state or federal government and stored till the market was ready to absorb it. Since the coffee market is a relatively inelastic one, and coffee itself can be stored for many years without deterioration, there probably would have been no good effect from the government's policy were it not for the fact that years of big coffee harvests are almost always followed by years of small ones. Moreover, the government extended the prohibition of planting to 1912. As a result of small harvests between 1909 and 1912, and the prohibition of planting, the government was able to sell the stored coffee and thus to liquidate its investment.

In 1917, however, another huge harvest made a second valorization scheme necessary. In 1918 severe cold greatly reduced the coffee harvest—and even killed banana plants as far north as Limeira. The government again was able to sell the coffee it had bought, and succeeding years of low yields even made it possible for the government to realize a profit.

In 1924, however, a policy of permanent coffee defense was adopted, but it was not accompanied by any real effort to control the rate of new coffee planting. Merrily the planters pushed forward, aided by the big immigration of the decade after 1918. In 1928 Brazil had a crop of 26,000,000 bags, and in 1930 of 28,200,000 bags. The resources of the government were at an end and the world had already plunged into depression. In March, 1929, the price of coffee was 24.8 cents a pound, but in October, 1931, it had dropped to 7.6 cents. The collapse of the financial structure brought with it political revolution. In October, 1930, a successful revolution brought President Getulio Vargas into power, and the era of the first Brazilian republic (1889–1930), which was associated with the rise of coffee in São Paulo State, came to an end.

The coffee problem since 1930 has not been a simple one. The huge plantings of the '20's little by little came to bearing age. The average annual harvest between 1922 and 1926 was a little under 14,000,000 bags; the average of the period from 1932 to 1936 was nearly 22,000,000 bags. Meanwhile Colombia and Venezuela benefited from the price controls instituted by Brazil and were able to sell larger quantities of their coffee than formerly. Between 1931 and 1937 Brazil destroyed nearly 48,000,000 bags of coffee by dumping them into the ocean or burning them. The year 1930 may well prove to have marked the end of an era.

Changes in Land Tenure

One result of the change that has taken place in São Paulo State is the rapid increase in the number of small properties, that is, of farms of less than 150 acres. Units of this size were not lacking before, and many Brazilians recognized the desirability, for the good of the workers, of establishing peasant colonies on small farms; but as long as a sufficient number of the landowning class were deriving large incomes from the speculative system no change could be made.

Even as early as 1882 the government of São Paulo adopted a policy of helping immigrants establish themselves permanently on the land, and of breaking up the large estates. Colonies of immigrants were settled here and there on small properties sold to them either by the government or by private land companies with the blessing of the government. In some cases the large landowners formed colonies of their own, dividing portions of their estates into small lots which they would sell to immigrants. Their purpose was to keep a source of day laborers near by to be used when pressure of work demanded. Unfortunately, in spite of these attempts, about 48 per cent of the immigrants to the state later returned to their own countries and of those who did not leave few remained permanently in farming. Only about half the Portuguese and Italian immigrants remained as farmers; the others went as soon as possible into the cities. Only the Japanese and some of the peoples from Eastern Europe have remained in the rural areas.

The number of peasant colonies has increased rapidly in the last decade. For the first time it was definitely more profitable for the large landowners to sell their estates in small pieces. No small part of the investment in buildings and industries in São Paulo city came from landowners who had removed their capital from the production of coffee. But the former coffee estates were not turned over to pasture, as was so common in the Southeast; they were subdivided and quickly occupied by former tenants to whom a somewhat greater measure of prosperity had belatedly come.

Several parts of São Paulo State today show marked concentrations of land occupied by small holders. Perhaps the largest concentration is in the inner lowland, which has long been avoided by coffee growers. The zone of largest concentration extends well into the northwest along the line of the Paulista, but the density of population is greatest in the triangle bordered by Campinas, Sorocaba, and Piracicaba. The people are engaged in "mixed farming"—which is not a characteristic of Brazil as a whole—for in addition to some coffee they raise sugar cane, cotton, and oranges. The phrase "mixed farming" is not wholly an accurate one, for sugar cane is grown more around Piracicaba than elsewhere, as are cotton around Sorocaba and oranges along the Paulista (Maps 4, 27, and 31, Pages 8, 92, and 142). Along the alluvial lowland of the coast, near Santos, recent years have witnessed the rapid spread of banana cultivation. In 1925 this district was producing some three to four million bunches a year; but in 1937 the production reached eleven million bunches.

From 1918 to 1935 many Japanese came to Brazil, and some of the Japanese colonies today offer striking examples of effective settlement by small farmers. The land company known as the *Kaigai Kogyo Kabushiki Kaisha*, under the direction of the São Paulo government, has established many thousands of Japanese immigrants on their own little sixty-acre farms. Today, of the 193,000 Japanese estimated to be in Brazil,

130,000 are in São Paulo State, forming about 2 per cent of the population. There are many Japanese settlements in the truck-farming area around the outskirts of São Paulo. A pure Japanese colony has been established in the warm, rainy valley of the Iguapé, in the Zone of the Escarpment. But the greater proportion of Japanese immigrants, wherever they may have gone originally, are now concentrated in certain parts of the western frontier.

The Zone of the Frontier

The pioneer movement which started when the coffee planters began clearing the forest around Campinas and which swept like a wave over São Paulo State did not come to an end with the collapse of the coffee boom in 1930. Since that date the frontier of agricultural settlement has advanced still farther toward the west, only the pioneers are now small farmers, not tenants working for large landowners. The majority of the pioneers come from the older zones of settlement in São Paulo State. Many different kinds of people are involved. As we have said, there are considerable numbers of Japanese, some of whom are new immigrants settled by the K. K. K. K. There are a few people from Bahia and other parts of the Northeast who come to the frontier intending to return home soon with their gains. There are very few new European immigrants. The great majority of the pioneers come from other parts of São Paulo with the result that there is a rapid depopulation and decadence of areas back of the frontier. So many tenants have left that even the coffee fazendas on the terra roxa lands have been obliged to omit certain of the cultivation practices, and to leave parts of the crop unharvested for want of workers. Not only have the tenants departed from the coffee estates; there has even been a considerable migration of peasant proprietors from the small farms on which they were supposedly fixed. Even the hard-working Japanese are caught in the scramble for quick profits. As the new frontier rolls westward through the wreckage of the forest it leaves behind it a land rapidly depopulated and abandoned. Today decadence is apparent in most parts of the old coffee zone, the result more of scarcity of workers than of low market prices.

Cotton and Coffee

Cotton rather than coffee is the crop which, since 1934, has brought about the great rush of pioneer settlement. The Paulista cotton is a short-staple variety which enters into direct competition with the product of the Cotton Belt of the United States. In 1932 there were only about 30,000 people in São Paulo State engaged in producing cotton, and fewer than 200,000 acres devoted to it. By 1935 the area used for cotton had jumped to more than 1,500,000 acres and 250,000 people were reported as cotton farmers. Around Marilia, coffee trees not yet of bearing age were pulled up to make room for the new boom crop. The whole procedure was strictly in the Brazilian tradition, but it was the Japanese pioneers who produced 46 per cent of the cotton of that year.

Cotton is not a new crop in São Paulo State. For many decades cotton and coffee have reacted to variations in price in much the same way as maize and wheat in the Argentine Humid Pampa. When the boll weevil invaded the Cotton Belt of the United States, or when acreages there were reduced by the government, the result was increased plantings in Brazil, especially in São Paulo. In years when frosts reduce the coffee crop, the losses are in part offset by large cotton yields. Each time the cotton crop tends to increase, some of the people in São Paulo speak of new diversification of crops in this one-crop region and of the coming stability of agriculture. Then cotton production declines and the planting of coffee goes forward again unchecked.

Unfortunately, however, cotton is not a crop which can be combined with coffee in a stable and harmonious agricultural economy. Both crops require a large labor supply and for both of them the harvest season, with its peak of labor demand, comes at the same time of the year. The cotton farmers of São Paulo who sell to foreign markets are what the economist calls "marginal producers"; that is, their product comes on the market only to make up a deficiency of supply and they quickly drop out when the supply from other less expensive sources is ample. Because of the relatively small investment and the temporary nature of Paulista agriculture, this shift in and out of production is accompanied by little disaster and little dislocation.

Since 1933 São Paulo State has grown from a third to nearly a half of all the cotton produced in Brazil, and since 1936 cotton has occupied second place in the crop acreages of the state. From 50 to 75 per cent of the plantings in São Paulo were located on the western frontier; but in the older parts of the state there was also considerable cotton planting. On many of the small farms maize, rice, and beans were replaced by cotton. In the midst of the coffee fazendas, even of the rich Ribeirão Preto district, cotton was planted in the valleys.

Whether the cotton boom has come to an end or not cannot be said yet, but a new boom has already started in São Paulo as it has in the Southeast. There has been a marked falling off in demand for Brazilian cotton since Japanese purchases began to decline in 1938 and especially since the outbreak of the Second World War. However, by 1938 another speculative wave had begun to move over São Paulo. The planting of oranges came to occupy more and more the attention of Paulista farmers, whose interest in cotton was waning. Orange cultivation was concentrated in the Paraíba Valley, and along the line of the Paulista Railway between Campinas and Limeira (Map 31, Page 142). The trees were set out in vertical rows, crowded as close together as possible in order to bring the maximum profit per acre. Little attention was paid to soil conservation in the planting. It is still too early to say that oranges will replace cotton permanently and to specify what their relations to coffee will be.

The Paraná Colonies

The Rio Paranapanema marks the southern boundary of São Paulo State (Map 4, Page 8). Just south of this river, in northwestern Paraná, is Brazil's latest zone of pioneer settlement, the Paraná colonies (Map 31, Page 142). Northwestern Paraná possesses advantages for pioneer settlement which may make possible a much more stable form of land use than is to be found on the frontiers of São Paulo State. The advantages are inherent in the land itself. The surface is made up of broad, gently rounded interfluves and valleys with slopes gentle enough to be used for crops. The Rio Paranapanema has cut a deep gorge far eastward into the plateau. Its southern tributaries have also taken deep bites out of the plateau as they have cut headward into Paraná, but the upper parts of these tributary valleys still have rather gentle slopes. Between the tributary valleys on the southern side of the Paranapanema, the broad interfluves extend fingerlike toward the northwest. Except for a few patches where sandy soils are found, most of the area is covered with terra roxa (Map 1, Page 4). The whole district lies within the zone of transition between land with frost every year and land with no frost. In the deep valley of the Paranapanema there is malaria, but the district of the colonies is high enough to be free from it. The original forest consisted mostly of broadleaf, semideciduous woods, with a mixture of Araucaria pine in areas subject to frosts. The physical characteristics of the land proved to be remarkably favorable for the kind of settlement which was attempted.

Shortly before 1930 the coffee frontier was just beginning to cross the Paranapanema into northern Paraná (Map 30, Page 140). The uncleared woodland in advance of the zone of settlement, as in São Paulo State, was divided in large properties, although the only inhabitants of the land were scattered groups of Indians and half breeds, chiefly near the Rio Paraná. A British land company combined several large properties by purchase, and proceeded to make a survey of the land. The *Companhia de Terras Norte do Paraná* planned the settlement of this area in 1931, before the first clearing was made in the virgin forest. The railroad and the main and secondary roads were laid out along the ridges and the towns were located at intervals suitable to the proposed economy. Rural lots were given narrow frontages along the ridge-top roads, and were extended in strips down to the streams on both sides. When the settlers purchased their lots, they agreed, according to the law of Paraná, to leave at least 10 per cent of their land in forest—a very important regulation both for conserving valuable timber and for protecting the steeper slopes from soil erosion. Instead of the haphazard and irregular pattern of settlement characteristic of the frontier in São Paulo State, the Paraná colonies show all the effects of careful planning.

The movement of settlers into the Paraná colonies was rapid. In 1937 there were 29,000 people in the area, of whom 19,000 were farmers. Already Londrina, the chief town of the district and only about five years old, had a population of nearly 10,000.

In spite of the differences which set off the Paraná colonies from the pioneer zone of São Paulo State, the district is essentially a part of the São Paulo region. The main source of its colonists is São Paulo; its chief connections are with the city of São Paulo by way of the Sorocabana; its closest contacts, as indicated by business offices and newspaper circulation, are with São Paulo rather than Curitiba, the capital of Paraná.

The northwestern part of Paraná probably would have proved unsuited to the traditional fazenda paulista, with its vast acreages of one crop. Where the land is so irregularly spotted with places subject every winter to frosts it would have been impossible to plant coffee exclusively, even on the ridges. Yet the small proprietor in this district has the advantage over the colonists farther south in Paraná—in that many small frost-free areas give him an opportunity to share in the big profits to be derived from tropical crops. If all the land could be used for such crops, speculation in coffee and cotton might have predominated, as it has north of the Paranapanema. In the Paraná colonies stability is gained through a most unusual mixture of crops. On the warmer north-facing slopes, the farmers grow coffee, cotton, oranges, pineapples, and even sugar cane. On the south-facing slopes or in the valley bottoms where frost accumulates each winter—spots which are marked by the presence of the pines—the farmers raise wheat, barley, maize, potatoes, and other typically midlatitude crops. A considerable part of the production of the colonies consists in the fattening of hogs on maize—that familiar, stable, but unspectacular agricultural system known in the United States as the "corn-hog economy."

THE SERTÕES

The frontiers of close settlement on the west and north of the São Paulo region are very irregular. In the west of São Paulo State and Paraná clearings are being advanced along the railroad lines toward the Rio Paraná, but only along the line of the Sorocabana have they actually reached that river. Elsewhere unoccupied virgin forest lies between the river and the first outposts of the coffee or cotton planters. The more accessible forests are being utilized for their valuable cabinet woods, which, when shipped to São Paulo, provide the raw material for an important furniture business. In the more remote forests, only a very small population of Indians and people of mixed ancestry practice a kind of shifting cultivation which makes little permanent impression on the land. In the north, the frontier of close settlement has reached the southern bank of the Rio Grande on the border between São Paulo and Minas Gerais. Beyond these frontiers are the sertões (Map 32, Page 143).

The sertões beyond the São Paulo frontier were first penetrated more than three centuries ago by bandeirantes. Restlessly searching for sources of wealth, the explorers pushed far to the north and west. They followed the Tieté Valley through the belt of forest in western São Paulo and crossed the highlands of southern Mato Grosso to the Rio Paraguay. In 1719, shortly after the discovery of gold in Minas Gerais, they found gold-bearing gravels in the vicinity of Cuiabá, on one of the head-water tributaries of the Paraguay. In many scattered places between Cuiabá and Goiaz, gold and diamonds were both found in small quantities. To Cuiabá came many gold seekers with Negro slaves whose descendants today form a large portion of the population of the sertões of that district (Map 16, Page 31). The chief use which the bandeirantes and their descendants made of the sertões, however, was for the grazing of cattle. In the course of time the better areas were divided into huge estates with vague boundaries over which cattle ranged, with a minimum of care required.

The roads to the sertão, like all the roads developed by the Portuguese, seldom were turned aside from the most direct routes by steep slopes, but they were turned aside by dense forest. The semideciduous forest along the eastern side of the Rio Paraná proved to be so great a barrier to roads between the sertões of southern Mato Grosso and the town of São Paulo that long detours around the northern end of the forested area were necessary (Map 28, Page 128). Convoys of cattle and mule and oxcart loads of mineral products returned to São Paulo by way of western Minas Gerais. The lines of travel not only from southern Mato Grosso, but also from distant Cuiabá, skirted the northern end of the woods on the way to that part of the state of Minas Gerais which is known as the Triangulo (Map 4, Page 8). Into this part of Minas, too, came the road from Goiaz. The routes from all the sertões of the north and west came to a focus on the town of Uberaba, whence a well-traveled course could

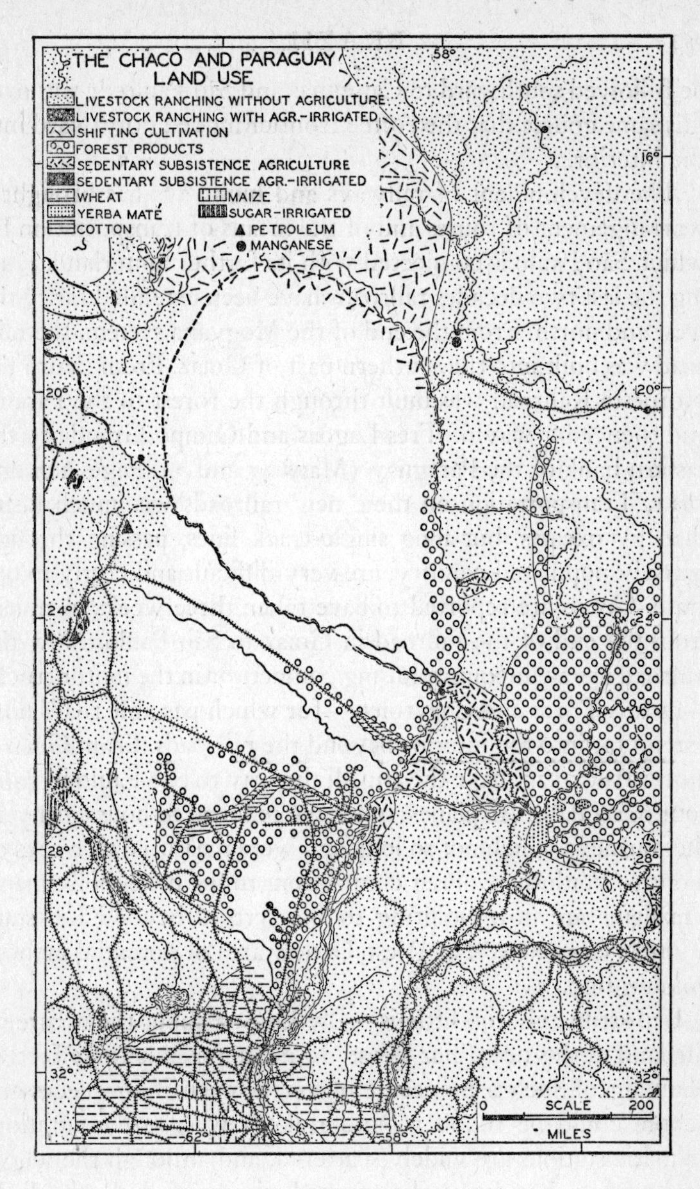
THE CHACO AND PARAGUAY
LAND USE
LIVESTOCK RANCHING WITHOUT AGRICULTURE
LIVESTOCK RANCHING WITH AGR.-IRRIGATED
SHIFTING CULTIVATION
FOREST PRODUCTS
SEDENTARY SUBSISTENCE AGRICULTURE
SEDENTARY SUBSISTENCE AGR.-IRRIGATED
WHEAT
MAIZE
YERBA MATÉ
SUGAR-IRRIGATED
COTTON
PETROLEUM
MANGANESE
58°
16°
20°
20°
24°
28°
28°
32°
32°
62°
58°
SCALE
0
200
MILES

MAP 34

be followed southward to Campinas and São Paulo. It was over this same course that the coffee frontier moved northward into the interior.

The development of railways and highways has brought a rearrangement of routes and of the means of transportation by which São Paulo is connected with its farther hinterland. During the last two decades railroads have been extended far to the west and north. From the end of the Mogyana system, the railroad was built into the southern part of Goiaz. From Baurú the Noroeste Railroad was built through the forest to the Paraná, and thence by way of Tres Lagôas and Campo Grande to the eastern bank of the Paraguay (Maps 33 and 34, Pages 147 and 163). Transportation on these new railroads was much faster than by oxcarts, but long single-track lines, passing through sparsely populated country, are very difficult and costly to operate. Goods are reported to have taken three weeks in transit from the end of the railroad in Goiaz to São Paulo. Now the railroad has an uncompromising competitor in the motor trucks —mostly Fords and Chevrolets—for which passable roads now extend far into the interior beyond the railroads. From Goiaz a motor truck can make the trip all the way to São Paulo in from four to six days. Airplanes, too, have reduced to hours many of the journeys which not so long ago were measured in weeks or months. With these closer connections to the metropolis, many Brazilians are now pointing to the sertões beyond the state boundary as a new "Far West," a new area of potential pioneer colonization.

Unfortunately too little is really known about the nature of the land in this new "Far West" to make possible the effective planning of such a pioneer movement, even if the necessary people could be found to undertake a westward migration. Climatic stations are widely scattered, and although the whole area seems to be adequately supplied with rainfall, there is little information regarding seasonal irregularities, nor is there sufficient information concerning the soils and the availability of water underground. Nevertheless the region can be described in general terms.

The Sertão of Southern Mato Grosso

A remarkably sharp contrast in vegetation is found along the Rio Paraná (Maps 12 and 28, Pages 21 and 128). On the São Paulo side the dense forests cover all the west-facing slopes of the tableland; but on the other bank the scrub forests and the grasslands appear, a sharp vegetation change which has yet to be explained.

Three kinds of vegetation are found in crossing Mato Grosso between the Paraná and the Paraguay. In the east and extending as far west as Campo Grande (Maps 33 and 35, Pages 147 and 166) is a type of vegetation which the Brazilians call *campo cerrado,*—a savanna with scattered thickets of deciduous scrub forest (Map 12, Page 21). Further investigation of the region may show that the various kinds of grass-forest mixture have an important bearing on the physical quality of the land and its potential value for agricultural settlement. The designation of the vegetation as campo cerrado has the unfortunate effect of masking under a cloak of seeming uniformity a pattern of distribution which is, in reality, quite varied. For example, the terra roxa occurs in many places under this cover of vegetation, being especially prominent around Campo Grande, where its distinctive red coloring stains not only roads and buildings, but also even the animals and the people.

Immediately west of Campo Grande one encounters the second vegetation type of Mato Grosso—the pure grasslands, or *campo limpo* (Map 35, Page 166). The treeless country runs in a narrow band southward from the Noroeste Railroad to the border of Paraguay; it follows the high country of the drainage divide between the tributaries of the Paraná and those of the Paraguay. Only in the ravines which have been cut back into the divide can surface water be found, and here there are little patches of forest.

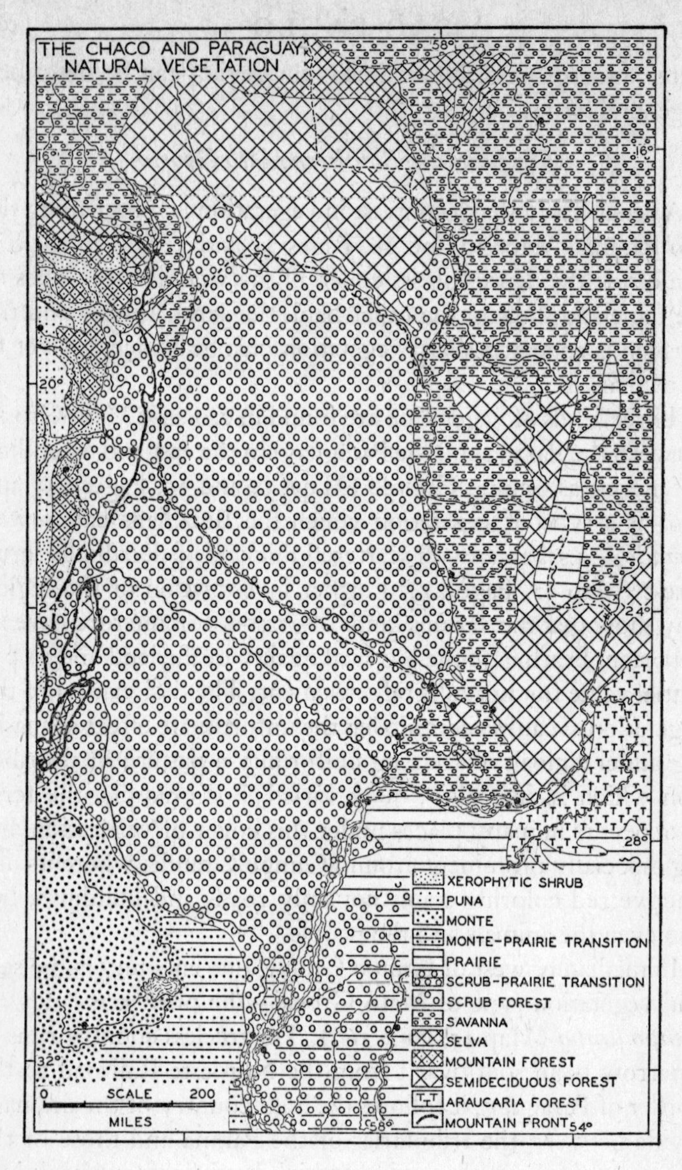
THE CHACO AND PARAGUAY
NATURAL VEGETATION
58°
16°
16°
20°
20°
24°
24°
28°
32°
0 SCALE 200
MILES
58°
54°
XEROPHYTIC SHRUB
PUNA
MONTE
MONTE-PRAIRIE TRANSITION
PRAIRIE
SCRUB-PRAIRIE TRANSITION
SCRUB FOREST
SAVANNA
SELVA
MOUNTAIN FOREST
SEMIDECIDUOUS FOREST
ARAUCARIA FOREST
MOUNTAIN FRONT

MAP 35

© Charles Perry Weimer

Avenida das Nações in Rio de Janeiro. Here a new business and government center been built where once there was a hill; the hill was used to fill in the bay for the new airfield.

Contrasts in living exist in all countries. A slum district on one of the hills of
Above: the residence of a wealthy Brazilian near the same city.

erest in sports and out-door life is illustrated here by the spacious soccer field of the afogo Club and (*above*) the beautiful Copacabana Beach, both in Rio de Janeiro.

View of the *pantanal*, on the upper Paraguay River in Mato Grosso. *Above:* a remark
air view of the Great Escarpment at Santos. The intake for the great water-power p
at Cubatão is at the end of the reservoir.

Both the campo limpo and the campo cerrado are utilized for the grazing of cattle. The pure grasslands offer especially good pasturage except for the difficulty of finding surface water. Only in the rainy season (summer) can the herds remain on the high country; in the dry season (winter) they are driven farther to the east. On the large cattle ranches, which average as much as 5,000 acres each, the animals receive little attention from the small seminomadic population of herders. The permanent rural settlements are found only at ranch headquarters. For the whole district Campo Grande has become the leading commercial town, a position achieved first when the Noroeste gave it rail connection to the east.

The campo limpo is terminated sharply on the west by a west-facing line of cliffs (Map 33, Page 147). The top and the steep front of this cuesta, as well as the valleys which have been cut back into it, are heavily forested (Map 35, Page 166). Between the base of the cuesta and the Rio Paraguay the vegetation is again savanna. The country, however, is a floodplain. Areas which are flooded seasonally are either grassy or are covered with tall evergreen trees; only on the hills which stand above flood-level is the deciduous scrub forest to be found. The wet lands are called *pantanal* by Brazilians.

On the higher ground at the base of the cuesta above the floods a string of old cattle estates, established during the eighteenth century, have their headquarters. The animals graze on the wet savannas during the dry season and seek refuge on the higher ground when the floods come. Except for its isolation, this district is reputed to be among the best of Brazil's tropical grazing lands.

Only recently has the Paraguay Lowland been made directly accessible to the rest of Brazil. During the first three quarters of the nineteenth century the use of the Paraguay for navigation was discouraged by the unfriendly policies of the dictators of Paraguay. After the Paraguayan War, however, the river was opened to international commerce, and small river boats began to make regular trips to this remote western part of Brazil. Corumbá was established originally as a defense post where a line of crystalline hills cross the lowland and offer a site for strong fortifications. When the river was opened to international traffic, Corumbá's importance was increased because it was the head of navigation for the river boats which ascended from Buenos Aires and Asunción. Rubber, gold, ipecac, hides, and skins, from farther up the Paraguay or from the lowlands near by, were gathered on the waterfront of Corumbá for shipment downstream.

The Noroeste has not yet reached Corumbá; a ten-hour boat trip connects the town with the end of the railroad. But plans have been laid for the extension of the Noroeste across the Chaco to the Bolivian oil fields around Santa Cruz; if these plans are carried out, Corumbá's future as the strategic center of the Brazilian Chaco would seem to be assured. Already it has become the junction of air routes; regular passenger service connects it not only with São Paulo city, but also with La Paz in Bolivia, and a weekly service is maintained to Cuiabá.

The Sertão of the Triangulo and Goiaz

São Paulo has also extended its connections by rail and motor road northward into the Triangulo of Minas Gerais, and beyond into Goiaz. All of this region is covered with campo cerrado. In part because of its position at the focus of the routes from the more distant regions, the Triangulo has the largest herds of cattle, the densest population, and the largest number of small settlements of any section of the pastoral sertões in the hinterland of São Paulo (Map 32, Page 143). The herds have been greatly benefited by the introduction of zebu stock and the crossing of these hardy animals with the native cattle. Around the larger towns, like Uberaba and Uberlandia, there are scattered areas devoted to maize, manioc, rice, beans, and sugar cane. In recent years, too, there has been in southeastern

Goiaz a significant increase in the planting of tobacco for export.

The distribution of people in the sertão of the Triangulo and Goiaz is being changed with the construction of the railroad in much the same way that population changes accompanied the extension of the Central to Pirapora. At each new railhead a town springs up, and people are attracted from the many scattered settlements near by. The growth of each railhead town is thus accompanied by the depopulation of the surrounding country. At present the railhead is at Anápolis, near the drainage divide between the Paraná and the Amazon.

On a high plateau forty miles west of Anápolis is Goiânia, the new state capital of Goiaz. In the midst of the sertão one comes upon a modern well-planned city, for Goiânia, like Belo Horizonte, was created in the wilderness. The old fever-ridden town of Goiaz, on low ground not far away, has now been virtually abandoned in favor of the new capital, which embodies some of the most up-to-date ideas of city-planners.

The vast depopulated areas and the surprising modern cities of the sertão deep in the heart of Brazil have come about with the extension of the railroad into the wilderness. Cattle are still, as they always have been, the chief source of wealth, but in the sertão they cannot be fattened. They are grazed far and wide there and then driven south to Barretos in São Paulo, near the end of the Paulista, or to Uberaba in the Triangulo (Maps 4 and 31, Pages 8 and 142). There the animals are fattened on the native grasses, which are especially nourishing in the northern part of São Paulo. Later they are shipped to São Paulo city for slaughter.

São Paulo city is the focus of all the varied activities of the sertão. Even more than Rio de Janeiro, this other city of over a million inhabitants is in a position to act as the hub of a great inland tributary area. Not only because of its energetic and economically advanced people, but also because of the ease with which the lines of communication can be brought to a focus on this state and this city, São Paulo is bringing the distant sertões more and more firmly into its sphere of influence. The more varied the activities which are carried on both in the immediate hinterland and farther out, the more stable will be the urban center. The development of a real westward movement, not a new wave of speculative exploitation leading to a further advance of the hollow frontier, should be of major interest to the urban people of the nucleus.

Nevertheless, speculative gain continues to be the ruling force in the economic life of this most progressive region. Lack of permanence remains a fundamental characteristic of the relation of the people to the land. Still the lure of big profits from virgin soils tears people away from lands already occupied, even from those areas which are physically capable of much more intensive development. In the absence of more abundant capital in a land of generally insufficient population, and in the face of an abundance of unused resources, no approach toward stability seems to be possible. Now even the city itself is seized upon for speculative gain, just as other people in other lands have sought big profits from growing urban communities; the newest device imported from abroad to wring still greater profit from the land is the skyscraper.

Chapter VI

THE SOUTH

THE PART OF BRAZIL which we shall call the South possesses certain characteristics which set it off sharply from São Paulo, and from the older regions of settlement in the Southeast and the Northeast. It includes the three states of Paraná, Santa Catarina, and Rio Grande do Sul. Each of these states has a core of concentrated settlement which is separated from the neighboring clusters of people by thinly populated territory (Maps 15 and 36, Pages 30 and 173). The largest of the clusters is that of Rio Grande do Sul, in which there are some three million people; each of the other two clusters has about a million. In contrast to other parts of Brazil the settlement of the South seems to be more closely attached to the land; it is less temporary and shifting; it includes a larger proportion of small owners who work their own farms; and, above all, the rapid increase of population in the older settlements is promoting a pioneer expansion, and is leading to the development of frontiers which are not hollow.

Expanding settlements in all Latin America are few. We have described one in Antioquia in Colombia, and another in Middle Chile. In the three clusters of people in the South of Brazil we find expansion without a hollow frontier again strikingly illustrated. Nor has expansion here resulted from any considerable amount of immigration; it is almost wholly supported by local excess of births over deaths. Only a small fraction of the European immigration into Brazil went to the southern states, yet the rate of population increase in the South is extraordinary. The net growth per thousand per year is 23.9 among the small farmers of this part of Brazil—a rate which in all Latin America, outside of the West Indies, is probably exceeded only in Guatemala and in Antioquia, and equaled only in Costa Rica.

That the colonists in southern Brazil should have developed this kind of settlement and have created frontiers which are not hollow is a matter of great importance not only for the Brazilian nation, but also for students of the distribution of people in Latin America. Why should the South rather than any other part of Brazil have been occupied by people capable of establishing stable patterns of settlement and of supporting frontiers of new settlement without loss of population in the center? Will the answer to this question suggest the reasons for the lack of such expanding settlements elsewhere? It is best not to accept any one simple explanation; we shall find that in this problem as in others the interpretation of social phenomena involves the interplay of many complex factors, racial, social, economic, and political, and all these factors must be examined historically and geographically.

THE LAND

To what extent is the character of the land itself responsible for this contrast between the South and the other regions of concentrated settlement in Brazil? In any attempt by mankind to occupy any part of the earth for a long period of time it is a prime necessity that a workable connection be made between the methods of gaining a living and the resources of the land. A connection cannot be said to be permanently workable if it is a destructive one, and if it leads, therefore, to the decline of population or to the impoverishment of the people. Any attempt to interpret the arrangement of people without reference to the character of the land on which they live is incomplete. Let us, therefore, see what significant changes take place in the physical

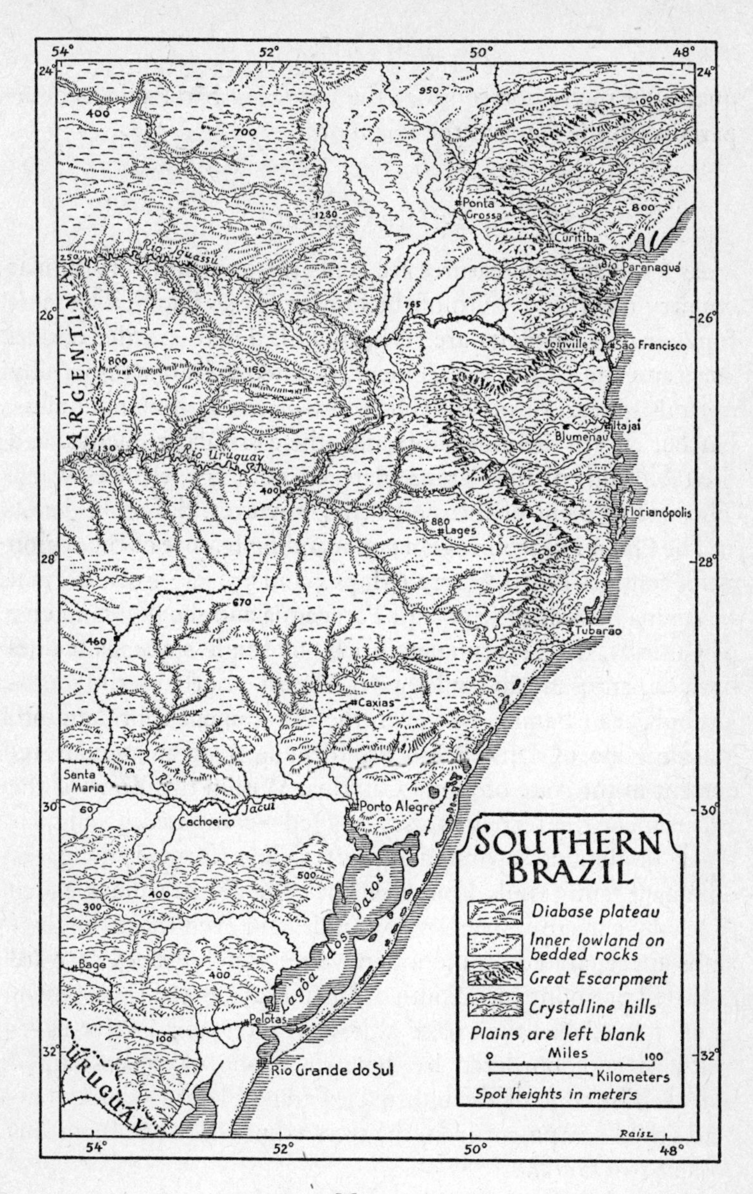
SOUTHERN BRAZIL
Diabase plateau
Inner lowland on bedded rocks
Great Escarpment
Crystalline hills
Plains are left blank
Miles
0
100
Kilometers
Spot heights in meters
ARGENTINA
URUGUAY
Ponta Grossa
Curitiba
Paranaguá
Joinville
São Francisco
Itajaí
Blumenau
Florianópolis
Lages
Tubarão
Caxias
Santa Maria
Cachoeiro
Porto Alegre
Bagé
Pelotas
Rio Grande do Sul
Rio Iguassu
Rio Uruguay
Rio Jacuí
Lagôa dos Patos
Raisz

MAP 36

quality of the region south of the border of São Paulo as compared with the lands to the north of it.

Surface Features

As far as surface features are concerned we find very similar country north and south of the border of São Paulo. The same fundamental elements are to be found. There are the coastal zone and the Great Escarpment. Inland, the crystalline hilly uplands appear, surmounted in a few places by low mountains. Farther on are the inner lowlands, the east-facing cuestas, and the tablelands of the Paraná Plateau sloping gently westward. The arrangement of these elements, however, differs in detail.

The Great Escarpment is a commanding feature of the region as far south as Porto Alegre (Maps 5 and 37, Pages 9 and 175). In Paraná between the port of Paranaguá and the highland city of Curitiba, the Escarpment forms one single slope, as it does back of Santos in São Paulo State. Almost exactly on the southern border of Paraná, however, the Escarpment is broken into a wide zone of faulted blocks, forming a great angular reëntrant in the state of Santa Catarina. Within this Zone of the Escarpment the terrain is very rugged—composed of angular block mountains separated by rift valleys formed along the dominant fault trends. Only near the coast do the valleys widen to produce narrow swampy lowlands; and even there the lowlands are separated by mountain ridges which extend seaward as cliffed promontories. South of latitude 28° S. the Escarpment again approaches the coast, although it remains, as far as its southern end, bordered by a narrow zone of down-faulted blocks. The edge of the unbroken Paraná Plateau which dominates the Escarpment from the west is known to the Brazilians as the *Serra Geral*.

Above the Great Escarpment the various surface elements described in São Paulo continue into Paraná (Maps 1, 4, 5, and 37, Pages 4, 8, 9, and 175). The crystalline hilly upland has the same general character, although south of the Paulista border it is surmounted by only two small ranges of mountains. One important difference appears in the inner lowland: in Pa-

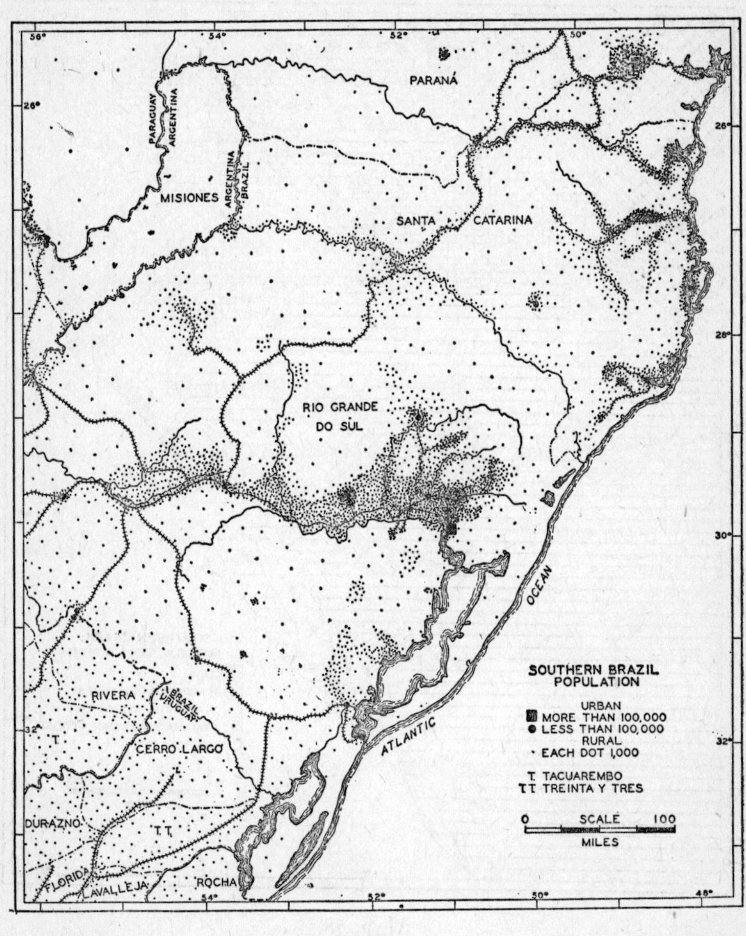

Map 37

raná and the neighboring portions of São Paulo and Santa Catarina, the rock stratum which rests immediately on the crystallines is a sandstone of Devonian age. Unlike the formations which border the crystallines in most of the São Paulo region, this sandstone is very resistant, and so forms another cuesta which stands abruptly above the general level of the granites

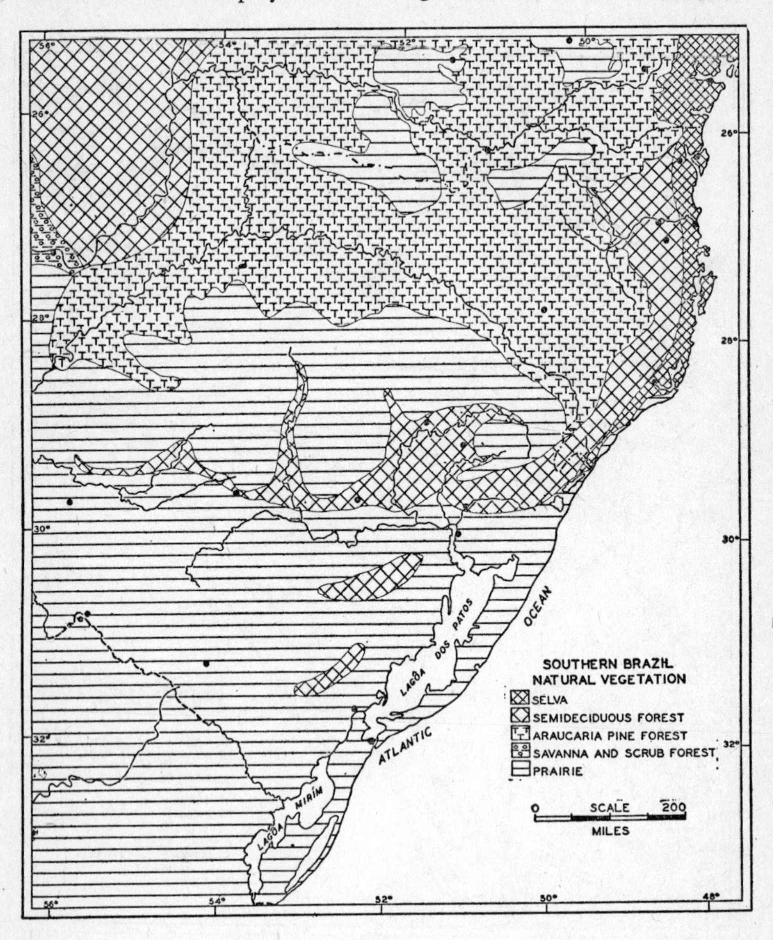

MAP 38

and gneisses, and slopes gently westward into the inner lowland. This we shall call the *Devonian cuesta*. The western margin of the inner lowland is drawn along the front of the diabase cuesta.

All these various features—crystalline upland, inner lowland, and east-facing cuestas—trend in a great semicircle far to the west as they cross Paraná. This westward bend extends from

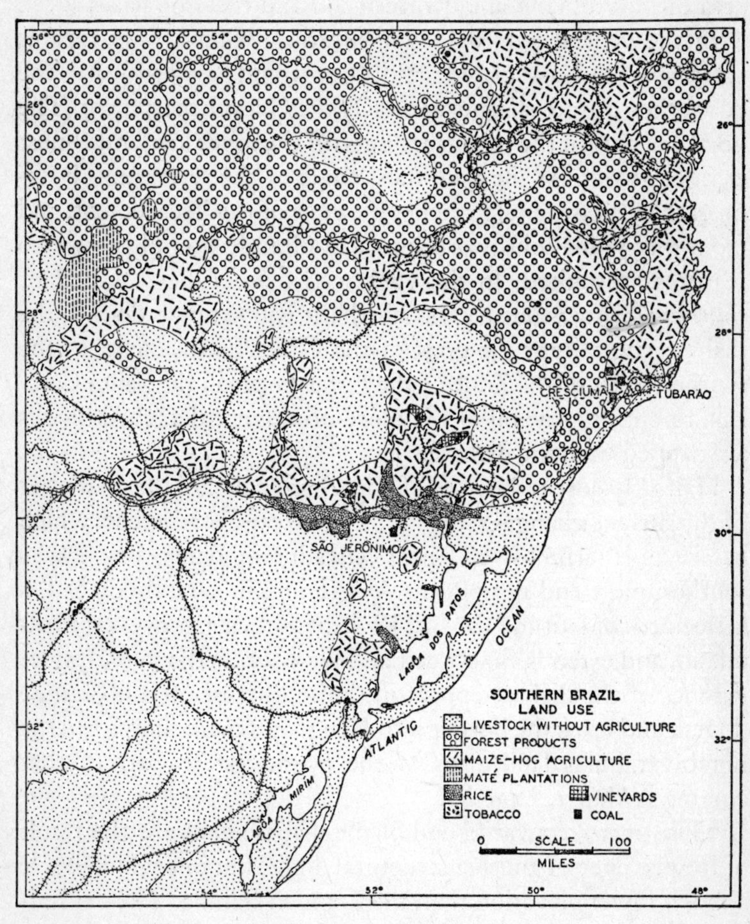

Map 39

the latitude of Sorocaba in São Paulo to the central part of Santa Catarina. Persons familiar with geological maps will recognize evidence here of a structural dome, from which the cover of younger strata has been stripped back leaving the ancient crystalline rocks exposed in the center. The city of Curitiba is situated roughly at the apex of the dome, in the midst of a wide area of hilly upland about three thousand feet above sea level.

In the central part of Santa Catarina, where these various structures and associated landforms trend back toward the coast, they are cut sharply across by the Great Escarpment. The northern part of the re-entrant cuts off the inner lowland almost at right angles. At the innermost angle of the re-entrant, however, the diabase cuesta reaches the edge of the Escarpment, and from that point southward into Rio Grande do Sul these two features are united. In the very well defined Serra Geral of southern Santa Catarina and northern Rio Grande do Sul, the diabase cuesta caps the crest of the Great Escarpment. In the southern part of the Zone of the Escarpment in the Santa Catarina re-entrant several of the more prominent detached blocks are capped with the diabase.

Half way across the state of Rio Grande do Sul the character of the surface changes radically. The Great Escarpment, which has its northernmost end near Salvador in Bahia, reaches its southernmost end near Porto Alegre in Rio Grande do Sul, a little north of latitude 30° S. The diabase cuesta, however, turns inland, and extends almost east and west across the state. Lower patches of the diabase appear in the southwest of Rio Grande do Sul, and cross the border into Uruguay where they form the notably tabular landforms of the northwestern part of that country (Map 1, Page 4).

This great westward bend of the diabase cuesta is the result of the presence of another structural dome, but one which lies at a much lower elevation than the dome in Paraná. The crystallines appear in the center, forming a wide area of hilly upland in southern Rio Grande do Sul, but at a general elevation of only about a thousand to fifteen hundred feet. The formations which produce the inner lowland in Paraná also form a lowland in Rio Grande do Sul. This is the Jacuí Basin, a belt of low east-west ridges and terraces lying between the crystallines on the south, and the front of the diabase cuesta to the north. The cuesta itself is sharply cliffed at its crest where the layers of diabase appear; but its lower slopes, which are gentler and more rounded than the crest, are formed on layers of red sandstone. The whole cuesta is cut by tributaries of the Rio Jacuí which drains the lowland between the cuesta and the crystalline upland.

The coast of this southern part of Brazil is rocky and precipitous only in the middle part between São Francisco and Tubarão (Map 5, Page 9). The alluvial lowland of southwestern São Paulo continues southward to form the swampy, flat country around Paranaguá and São Francisco. Itajaí and Florianópolis, on the contrary, are located in the midst of hilly country —Florianópolis on the western side of a block mountain which is essentially a part of the Zone of the Escarpment but which has been separated from the mainland by the sinking of the coast. South of Tubarão, and extending into Uruguay almost to Montevideo, the hilly land of the interior is fringed by a wide coastal zone of alternating sand bars and lagoons, with many sand dunes. The largest of the lagoons are the Lagôa dos Patos into which drains the Rio Jacuí and the Lagôa Mirím.

The most important difference in the surface features of the South as compared with those of São Paulo is the much greater area of diabase and of the resulting terra roxa (Map 1, Page 4). The diabase underlies much of western São Paulo, but only along the crest of the cuesta or in the deeper valleys is it not covered by layers of sandstone. In Paraná, Santa Catarina, and northern Rio Grande do Sul the diabase is exposed at the surface over all the territory west of the cuesta, even extending across the border into Argentina and Paraguay. This is one of the world's largest lava plateaus. The Rio Paraná and its tributaries have cut deep canyons back into the resistant diabase, and at the heads of these canyons are some of the world's most spectacular waterfalls. The Guayra Falls on the Paraná, known in Brazil as the Falls of *Sete Quedas*, are located at the northeast corner of

Paraguay (Map 33, Page 147). Better known are the Iguassú Falls, produced where the Rio Iguassú, on the border of Brazil and Argentina, tumbles over the edge of the diabase into the Paraná Canyon. The falls on the Rio Uruguay are smaller, and are scattered along the course of the river downstream to the Uruguayan town of Salto.

The varied geological structure of the South of Brazil permits the existence of many different kinds of mineral resources. In the crystalline area of Rio Grande do Sul, for instance, there is copper; in Santa Catarina and Paraná there are small sources of high quality iron ores; and among the sedimentary strata which lie between the crystallines and the diabase there are seams of coal. The coal is thick enough to be mined at two places—at São Jerônimo in Rio Grande do Sul, and inland from Tubarão in southern Santa Catarina (Map 39, Page 177).

Climate and Vegetation

Some of the climatic and vegetation contrasts along the southern border of São Paulo on the highlands have already been described. The northern limit of frosts, revealed by the arrangement of the pine forests, is a line of great significance. Frosts, however, are limited to the highlands and are never experienced either in the deep valley of the Paraná or along the coast. Frosts occur rarely in the valley of the Jacuí in Rio Grande do Sul. Of similar importance is the change in southern São Paulo from the tropical rainfall regimen marked by dry winters to the regimen of abundant rains in all months, characteristic of the South.

From Sorocaba southward on the highlands, the vegetation cover undergoes a gradual change from tropical semideciduous forest to pure grass prairie. The semideciduous forest extends far southward in the deep valley of the Paraná, but is replaced at higher elevations by the frost-resistant pine forests. The prairies which occur in patches throughout southern São Paulo, Paraná, and Santa Catarina become more extensive than the forests in Rio Grande do Sul south of the Uruguay Valley. This is a region of plentiful rainfall, in which the prevalence of grass instead of forest has never been adequately explained.

The details of forest-grassland distribution in this broad zone of transition are closely related to the underlying rock formations. The Devonian cuesta, for instance, presents a landscape which is almost completely devoid of trees except for the little forest patches at the ravine heads where springs occur. Much of the inner lowland is grass-covered. The diabase and the crystallines become less and less forested as one proceeds southward. "Predominant grasslands with ravine-head forest patches" describes the vegetation of the diabase plateau in northern Rio Grande do Sul.

Contrasts of climate and vegetation along the coast are not so abrupt as on the highlands. The climatic conditions in summer show only minor differences between Santos and Rio Grande do Sul. There are the same gray skies, the same heavy rainfall, the same high temperatures. The average temperature of the warmest month at Santos is 77.9°, at Blumenau, 75.9°, at Porto Alegre, 76.5°, and at Santa Maria, near the head of the Jacuí Valley, 76.8°. But the winters are definitely cooler in the South. The coldest month at Santos averages 66.0°, at Blumenau, 58.3°; and at Porto Alegre, 56.3°.

The cooler winters are reflected in the vegetation cover by the gradual elimination of the tropical rain forest, and by the descent of the semideciduous forest from the higher part of the Escarpment almost to sea level. The rain forest, which forms a continuous screen of dense growth all the way southward from Bahia, reaches its southern end a little north of latitude 30° S. It is replaced by the lighter semideciduous forest; and this forest also extends in a band along the south-facing slope of the highland far across Rio Grande do Sul.

Relation of the Population Clusters to the Physical Features

The relation of the clusters of people to these features of the surface, the climate, and the natural cover vegetation needs to be observed carefully (Map 36, Page 173). In Paraná, as in São Paulo, the chief area of settlement is on the upland, in an area of crystalline hills; in each the coastal zone is well settled only in the vicinity of the port; and in each the chief urban center, the nucleus of the highland population cluster, is located above a place where the Great Escarpment forms a single slope. Farther south, in Santa Catarina and Rio Grande do Sul, the population clusters occupy the lowlands and valleys, and the highlands are sparsely settled. It should be noted that the winters of the South are cooler, although the possible effect of this on the activities of the inhabitants must be balanced by the fact that most of the agricultural work is done in summer under conditions of temperature and humidity which are scarcely to be distinguished from those of the coastal region farther north. The cooler winters reduce the activity of disease-carrying insects, although no part of Brazil is far enough south to extend beyond the limits of these insects. Frosts prohibit the planting of coffee except in northern Paraná, as previously described, but on the lowlands sugar cane can be raised, even in the Jacuí Valley of Rio Grande do Sul. These are the chief contrasts between São Paulo and the South which are inherent in the land itself.

SETTLEMENT OF THE SOUTH BEFORE 1822

Not until a historical study of settlement shows an actual causal connection between the facts concerning the land and the distribution of people can such a connection be asserted. To point out the relation between the lowland settlements and the cooler winters, or between the highland settlements and the places where the Great Escarpment forms one slope rather than a zone is not to establish any proof that this relationship was actually a motivating force in the minds of the settlers. For involved in this question are also the physical qualities, the psychological attitudes, the inherited traditions and taboos of the people, and all the countless accidents which play such an important part in the irrational course of human events.

Currents of Penetration

During the colonial period two groups of people entered the southern part of Brazil. One of these came southward along the highlands from São Paulo. The bandeirantes, ill at ease in the heavily forested country, soon discovered the grassy prairies in the inner lowland south of Sorocaba, and followed them southward into Paraná. As early as 1680 an expedition had followed the grassland belt to the Banda Oriental and had founded, on the shores of the Plata opposite Buenos Aires, the town of Colonia, which the Portuguese called Sacramento. Before the middle of the seventeenth century the grasslands of Paraná had been divided into large cattle estates and animals from this sertão were being sent back to the markets of the Southeast. By the middle of the eighteenth century the open campos of Santa Catarina had been similarly occupied.

Meanwhile the bandeirantes had also been successful in the discovery of gold in this southern sertão. In 1654 a small source of precious metal was discovered in the stream gravels of the crystalline upland of Paraná and the little town of Curitiba was founded in the midst of the mining country by people who came overland from São Paulo.

The second group of people entering the south came from São Vicente near Santos and pushed southward along the coast. There were two chief objectives: the discovery of gold, and the protection of this southern part of Brazil from the Spaniards and the French. Small quantities of gold were found in the stream gravels of the coastal zone between Iguapé and Paranaguá; and to connect the new mining centers with São Vicente

—a connection which was maintained by boat—the little ports of Iguapé and Paranaguá were established, the latter in 1654.

Both Paranaguá and Curitiba, therefore, were originally founded to serve small mining communities. One had its connections with São Paulo, the other with São Vicente; for more than a decade there was no connection between them. Contact was finally made in 1668, when the Portuguese crown granted a capitanía of all the lands "around Paranaguá." The new governor promptly extended his control over the highland mining community of Curitiba, and thereafter the two places were closely united. Not until railroads were built late in the nineteenth century did people discover that, from the point of view of easy grades, by far the best route from the coast to the plateau was from São Francisco and Joinville to Rio Negro in southern Paraná (Maps 5 and 39, Pages 9 and 177).

Meanwhile, southward penetration along the coast continued. Wherever the nature of the terrain seemed to offer special advantages for defense, forts and garrison towns were established, such as São Francisco and Florianópolis. Island sites were especially advantageous owing to the danger of attacks by the Indians who lurked in the dense forests of the mainland. Porto Alegre, on a ridge of high ground near the head of the Lagôa dos Patos, faced the unobstructed prairie lands of the south for which Spaniard and Portuguese were already competing.

Colonial Cattle Road

For the most part the two currents of settlement remained separate and distinct. The forest of the Zone of the Escarpment proved to be as much of a barrier to the people of the South as it had to those of the north. The coastal fortresses made few connections with the land back of them; but the grasslands of the interior and of the south were quickly occupied by the cattlemen.

The chief connection of the southern sertões with the centers of Brazilian colonial life was an overland trail. The annual fair at Sorocaba attracted convoys of mules and cattle that traveled all the way from the Banda Oriental. Towns were established as supply stations along the way. The concentration of grazing animals in the grasslands of Paraná and southern São Paulo must have rivaled that in the Triangulo of Minas Gerais around Uberaba.

Parts of this old colonial cattle road are still visible in the region. Over most of the route no evidences remain of the exact course of the road, if indeed there ever was a well-defined road through the grassy prairies. But wherever the cattle had to pass through heavily wooded valleys to cross a stream, they were forced to follow a narrow way. Over the centuries that this route was followed, the feet of countless animals have cut paths on the valley slopes which have led to the formation of gullies. Where the old road crosses each valley today the slopes are carved into miniature "badlands" with narrow ravines and knife-edge ridges. The present automobile road and the railroad follow approximately the line of this old trail, and from them the signs of the cattle days can still be seen.

On the whole the great southland remained a sertão, occupied at a few points by military garrisons, and oriented economically toward Sorocaba. The people of São Paulo were much too poor to become sugar planters, even where climatic conditions permitted. Furthermore, although gold formed the basis of the original settlements in the crystalline area of Paraná and along the coast next to it, no such rich gold-bearing gravels were found here as in Minas Gerais. It was not a very valuable country in the colonial period, and the Portuguese hold on it was not very strong.

Principally with the idea of establishing a firmer grip on the southern border where wars with the Spaniards were very troublesome, the government of Portugal decided to populate the area with people who could be depended on to hold their lands, if necessary, by force of arms. A number of settlers from the Azores were introduced into the grasslands south of Porto Alegre. They were primarily soldiers and pastoral people, not agricultural colonists; they were selected for their ability to fight, not for any ability to labor. In the course of time most of the grassland area of Rio Grande do Sul was thinly occupied by a mixture of Portuguese of this type and of Spaniards.

POPULATION CLUSTER OF RIO GRANDE DO SUL

The creation of the present three distinct clusters of population in the South has been largely accomplished since the independence of Brazil. Of the three, as has been said, Rio Grande do Sul is the largest. It is therefore appropriate to discuss this state first and then to proceed in order northward to São Paulo with discussions of Santa Catarina and Paraná.

In 1822 the new Brazilian emperor Dom Pedro I recognized the necessity of getting a stronger hold on the South to guard against the threatened northward expansion of the Spaniards. Consequently in 1824 a group of German peasants, laborers, and craftsmen were brought over and settled in the new colony of São Leopoldo, located in the previously neglected forest lands a little north of Porto Alegre (Map 5, Page 9). Between 1824 and 1859 more than 20,000 Germans were brought to Brazil with government aid, and placed on small farms in this region. Most of the German colonies were arranged in a kind of festoon along the terraces of the northern side of the Jacuí Valley and on the lower slopes of the cuesta where red sandstones form the underlying rock. They all began as clearings in the semideciduous forest, where such typical German crops as rye and potatoes were planted. Somewhat later maize was planted to be fed to hogs.

At first the conditions in the new colonies were bad. Only recently in Brazilian history has the construction of good all-weather roads to connect a zone of settlement with a market been widely recognized as a necessity, and even today in too many instances this necessity is overlooked. The establishment of colonies which are promptly lost in the sertão without a chance to sell surplus products and to buy such things as salt, oil, or clothing has seldom led to stability in settlement, whether in Brazil or in the United States or elsewhere. In the South of Brazil those colonies which were able to solve the problem of transportation were successful. The sad plight of the isolated pioneers of Rio Grande do Sul was reported in Germany in 1859, and for a time further emigration to that region was prohibited. Little by little, however, the problem was solved, in part by connections with river ports along the Rio Taquarí or other tributaries of the Jacuí which gave access to Porto Alegre, and in part by the construction of the railroad westward from that city (Map 39, Page 177). Land values were, and still are, determined more by the proximity of a piece of land to a line of transportation than by the quality of the land itself. Fortunately, Porto Alegre stands at the focus of what is perhaps the finest system of inland waterways in Brazil outside the Amazon.

Between 1870 and 1890, a new group of pioneers arrived in Rio Grande do Sul. These were the Italians, who came chiefly from the provinces of northern Italy. They settled on lands along the crest of the diabase cuesta, above the German settlements, but still in the belt of semideciduous forest. Alfredo Chaves and Caxias are the centers of the Italian colonization as São Leopoldo is the German center. Like the Germans, the Italians occupied small farms and built substantial homes, creating a landscape strikingly different from that of the Northeast, the Southeast, or São Paulo, where the habitations of the rural workers are only temporary, camplike structures. The houses of the European colonists are built of wood, and made in the architectural styles familiar in the homeland. As the Germans concentrated their attention on rye, maize, and hogs, so the Italian settlements could always be distinguished by the presence of vineyards.

Expansion of the Colonies

The most extraordinary feature of this zone of pioneer colonization, however, is its continued expansion. By 1859 a census indicated the presence in Rio Grande do Sul of 20,493 Germans. Two generations later, about 1909, there were no fewer than 200,000 people of German descent. During the whole period from 1824 to 1934, somewhat fewer than 85,000 immigrants from Germany came to Rio Grande do Sul; yet the population of German descent in that state numbers at present about 520,000 out of a total population of 3,100,000.

The process of expansion reminds one of Antioquia in Colombia. Here was no hollow frontier; yet the very individuals who were found clearing the forests at the edge of settlement were again and again the same. As in the United States the people with the pioneer spirit, the unquenchable optimism of the frontier, could not endure the civilization they worked so hard to establish. They sold their properties, often with an increase of forty or fifty times the original value, and moved on, leaving the settlements to their less adventuresome sons and daughters. From São Leopoldo settlers advanced westward along the lower slopes of the diabase cuesta and on the terraces above the northern bank of the Jacuí, founding one after another the string of German settlements which reach now beyond Santa Maria. After the belt of woodland along the cuesta had been occupied, the German pioneers, together with other Europeans, entered the forests along the Rio Uruguay in the northwestern part of the state.

Although the forested parts of Rio Grande do Sul had originally been partitioned among a few landowners the landowners were only too glad to sell their land in small lots at reasonable prices, for they had been unable themselves to get such wealth from this region as the fazendeiros of São Paulo were getting from their properties. By 1909 there was scarcely a large estate left in the zone of the European settlements. As a result, the small farmers of the South, unlike those elsewhere in Brazil, were not forced to adapt themselves to a society already established; they were free to create their own society, which was essentially a rural democracy.

The Italian pioneers shared with the Germans an extraordinary biological vitality. Among the people who live today on the large pastoral estates of the South, the net growth of population is 6.9 per thousand; but among the colonists living on their own small properties, the net growth is 23.9 per thousand. This applies not only to the Germans but also to the Italians, and, in the regions farther north, to the Poles. The Italians, however, did not expand over as much territory as the Germans. There is a spirit of attachment to the family among these people that keeps several generations together, if not in the same home, at least near by. The young men have provided an important source of temporary laborers on the job of railroad construction and in the maté forests, but they always return home to add their wages to the family income. The result is an increasing density of population around the original colonial nucleuses.

Present Region of Settlement

The European colonists are credited in this part of Brazil with the creation of the vital spark of energy which, in the course of time, has produced a civilization out of the wilderness. The influence of these people in the whole life of this zone of settlement can scarcely be measured, for it goes far beyond mere numbers of citizens of European descent. Although the dominant theme of the region is Brazilian, it is a new kind of Brazil set off from the rest of the country by the presence of a considerable number of people who know how to engage in the hard physical work of pioneering in the forests and who are content with the relatively modest profits of an economy which is not speculative.

In the rural area back of Porto Alegre, four chief zones of

settlements can now be discerned—zones which are highly contrasted in their populations and their forms of economic life, but zones which have now been brought to a distinct focus on Porto Alegre. The first of these zones is the oldest—the pastoral zone—which lies south of the Rio Jacuí and extends almost unbroken to the borders of both Uruguay and Argentina. In a few scattered spots in the forest just west of the Lagôa dos Patos there are a few districts of European agricultural settlement; but the vast area of prairie lands has never been seriously considered a farming country. It is used today as it was in the colonial period, although perhaps by a larger number of people. This is the domain of the gauchos, the herdsmen whose cattle and sheep roam the pastures of the large estates with a minimum of care. The herds are not of the new European breeds, such as those which have transformed the Humid Pampa of Argentina; they are descended from the scrub cattle of the colonial period, and they are marketed chiefly for hides, tallow, and for the production of *xarque* or salt beef which is bought by the poorer people throughout the cities of Brazil.

There has never been much development in Rio Grande do Sul, of that most productive mixture of stock raising and agriculture known as "mixed farming." The pastoral people and the farmers, here as in Argentina, are two different groups, whose attitude on life can scarcely be translated from one to the other. Whether these southern prairies can be utilized for the production of Brazil's supply of wheat depends more on the success of a campaign to transform the way of living of the gaucho than on the physical quality of the land. In the absence of detailed studies of soil and moisture, it would seem probable that, with an entirely different agricultural system, which probably means different people, the prairies of the South could be made to support a much denser population on the basis of a farm system not unlike that of parts of the North American Corn Belt.

The second zone in the rural background of Porto Alegre is the flood-plain of the Rio Jacuí—especially of its northern tributary, the Rio Taquarí. Of the four zones, this is the most recent in origin, and is occupied almost entirely by the so-called Luso-Brazilians, that is, Brazilians of Portuguese origin. Its one big product is rice, and the system of production is characteristically Brazilian. There are no public works controlling the water—no reservoirs, canals, drains, or other works built and maintained at public expense. Each owner must develop these things for himself. Unfortunately, unlike the rice district of the Paraíba Valley, the natural floods of the Jacuí system come at the wrong time of the year for rice, for the heaviest rains in this part of the South come in winter. Some of the estates have small reservoirs for storing the flood water until summer; others have small pumps to provide the necessary water for irrigation. Most of them depend on such moisture as is left over from winter floods. The system of land tenure, too, is the large estate with tenant workers. Yet this rice-growing district contributes an important part of the food supply for the people of Porto Alegre.

No contrast of settlement could be sharper than that drawn between the Luso-Brazilian rice area, and the German settlements on the terraces and cuesta slopes to the north which constitute the third zone. Not only are the villages strikingly different in their architecture, and the rural habitations obviously intended to be permanent homes, but also the care taken in the cultivation of the land, and in the embellishment of the natural landscape, informs one that here, at last, is a district in which the people intend to live permanently. Maize and hogs predominate among the farm products, but there are also rye and potatoes. Around Santa Cruz, too, has appeared one of Brazil's chief tobacco-growing districts. Rio Grande do Sul as a whole now produces about the same amount of tobacco as Bahia, and the two together account for about 66 per cent of the Brazilian supply.

Still higher above the valley of the Jacuí is the fourth zone—the zone of the Italian colonies. Here again the character of the rural homes and of the villages is different, but if there is perhaps less of the German neatness, there is none the less an air of stability. From the many vineyards draped over the rounded hills of the front of the cuesta come more than 90 per cent of the grapes produced in Brazil, and a large part of the wines. These products do not enter into foreign markets, but they are able to compete with imported wines throughout Brazil especially for the use of the poorer people.

Porto Alegre

Industrial development during the last twenty years has made big advances throughout Rio Grande do Sul, especially in the city of Porto Alegre. After São Paulo and Rio de Janeiro, Porto Alegre now has the largest industrial equipment. Its industries make use of the products of the agricultural and pastoral hinterland. Leather tanning is one of the oldest of the industries, for the German settlers long ago made a home occupation of the preparation of the hides they purchased from their neighbors, the gauchos. There are many textile factories manufacturing woolen yarn, and woolen cloth and garments. The sheep of the southwestern part of the state provide the raw material. In addition there are many breweries, and wineries, and other food-processing establishments scattered throughout the small towns of the farming area, or concentrated in larger units in Porto Alegre and Pelotas. Electric power is furnished by a North American company which makes use of the local supplies of coal.

Today Porto Alegre, which is the capital of Rio Grande do Sul, has a population of some 368,000. Built on a ridge of hills which reaches the left bank of the river, it is situated near the junction of five waterways,—the Lagôa dos Patos and four tributaries of the Jacuí which converge on the site from the northeast, north, and northwest. Many of the connections between Porto Alegre and its hinterland are by water. In addition, railroads now connect Porto Alegre with the Argentine lines at Uruguaiana (Map 33, Page 147) and with the Uruguayan lines at Sant' Anna do Livramento (Map 39, Page 177). The railroad center where these lines cross, and where the long overland connection northward to São Paulo begins its ascent of the diabase cuesta, is the growing town of Santa Maria.

The city of Porto Alegre is an inland center. It cannot be reached by ocean steamers, for the Lagôa dos Patos is too shallow to be navigated by any but shallow-draught boats. Two ports compete for the transshipment of the goods brought in and out of Rio Grande do Sul. One is the port of Rio Grande do Sul, located at the outlet of the river which drains the Lagõa dos Patos, and the other is Pelotas.

Coal

The industrial establishments of Porto Alegre, and to a certain extent those of the smaller communities of Rio Grande do Sul, derive most of their power from local supplies of coal. The smaller plants use coal to supplement wood, which is the prevailing fuel. But the coal mines are chiefly supported by the demand for coal in the capital city, both for power and for the production of gas.

There are two chief coal-mining districts in the South. The one which is of chief importance in the supply of Porto Alegre is the district around São Jerônimo (Map 39, Page 177), located in the open campos a short distance south of the Rio Jacuí. About a thousand people are clustered in this district, in which there are three mines. The mine workers are settled in a model community which would put to shame some of the mining villages of North America. The cost of transportation is low, for the haul by rail from São Jerônimo to the banks of the river is a short one, and the rest of the haul to the wharves of Porto Alegre is by river barge—one of the cheapest means of transportation.

The coal itself, however, is of distinctly low grade. It occurs in seams which vary greatly in thickness and contain narrow lenses of clay and much pyrite. As it comes from the mines, this coal contains as much as 40 per cent ash. When it is put through a washing process at the mine, the ash content can be lowered to between 20 and 30 per cent. Nevertheless, the impurities are so great that special types of equipment are required when the coal is used for heat or gas. Only in an inland city like Porto Alegre could such coal compete, without government aid, with imported coals; but the high cost of transshipment of foreign coals from ocean steamers to lake boats has the same effect as a protective tariff in insuring a market for the product of the local mines.

The second coal-mining district is in Santa Catarina, inland from Tubarão not far from the southern border of the state. There are several mines in this district, all requiring a forty-mile rail haul to the nearest port, near Tubarão. The coal of Santa Catarina, however, is of somewhat better quality than that of Rio Grande do Sul. Although the ash content is still very high, certain of the coals from Tubarão can actually be made into coke; and it is coal from this source which is to be utilized in the proposed new Brazilian steel industry in the Paraíba Valley.

POPULATION CLUSTER OF SANTA CATARINA

The next population cluster north of Rio Grande do Sul is that of Santa Catarina, which contains only about a third as many people as its neighbor on the south. Both in its origin and its present condition it differs greatly from the district just described.

European Colonies

When Dom Pedro I decided to establish Colonies of Europeans in the South, his attention was focused chiefly on Rio

Grande do Sul. Only one such attempt seems to have been made farther north. A group of German mercenaries who had revolted from the Brazilian army in Rio de Janeiro, were placed in a colony not far from Lages, above the crest of the Serra Geral. This was not long after 1822. But almost at once this locality was found to be impossible for the colonists owing to the attacks of the Indians who lived in the forests of the Zone of the Escarpment. The new settlers abandoned their homes on the upland, and fled to the coastal settlements around Florianópolis. As the Indian menace was gradually eliminated, the forested country between the pastoral sertões of the highlands and the not very prosperous Luso-Brazilian towns clinging to the coast was left virtually unoccupied.

In 1848 a German surgeon named Dr. Herman Blumenau recognized the possibilities of settlement in this district. He saw in the valleys of the Zone of the Escarpment similarities to the Rhine, and pictured a day when these valleys might form important highways to the interior. His immediate concern was the settlement of a number of Germans from Pomerania who came "seeking liberty, happiness, and eternal tranquillity, through close attachment to this new land." The seventeen original colonists who arrived in 1850 were supplemented by more than six thousand before 1870. They cleared the land and established their farms and towns in the valleys inland from the port of Itajaí, especially around Blumenau and Brusque. Among these people were representatives of many different parts of Germany, although the Pomeranian group was the largest. Today the Pomeranian style of house, made of brick with outside beams, is a characteristic feature of the landscape, as is also the presence of good all-weather roads.

This new pioneer zone did not remain purely German. A number of Austrians and Swiss joined the group, and also a large contingent of Italians. In 1882 the German-speaking people made up 71 per cent of the total, the Italians 18 per cent, and the Portuguese only about 10 per cent.

A rapid increase of population took place also in this region, and expansion from it has been notable. Unfortunately, however, the nature of the terrain does not permit such compact settlement as was possible in the belt of forest along the cuesta front in Rio Grande do Sul. New pioneer colonies in Santa Catarina, at least in the first years of expansion, spread to new areas over the intervening ridges and mountains. Joinville, in back of the port of São Francisco, budded off from Blumenau. Then as the route from Joinville inland was found to be in reality the easiest one along this whole stretch of coast, the German frontiersmen advanced up and over the crest of the Serra Geral and began to expand over the highlands. Rio Negro was settled in 1887. Today, Germans from Santa Catarina, who can trace their origin back to the settlements at Blumenau, are found all over the interior of Paraná, and, as merchants and business men, in the city of Curitiba.

The loss of population pressure by scattered expansion, however, did not produce a depopulation of the original nucleus. With the final elimination of the Indians, new clearings have pushed far inland up to the very headwaters of the Rio Itajaí and the other short streams of the Zone of the Escarpment. At present the pioneers of this district are cutting the last remnants of the forest in the valley heads near the crest of the Escarpment.

Present Region of Settlement

The last available census, taken in 1927, counted 98,663 people in the nuclear area of European settlement around Blumenau. The population density in a few places along the valley bottom is as high as 60 per square mile. Around certain centers the proportion of people of European origin is very high. Of the people of the town of Blumenau, for example, 63 per cent claim German as their mother tongue, and 33 per cent claim Portuguese. In the rural district around Blumenau the proportions are 75 per cent and 22 per cent. But there are also included in the same zone of dense population certain places which are predominantly Italian. Around one of these Italian towns, only 5 per cent are Portuguese, 7 per cent German, and 88 per cent Italian. In the region as a whole the proportion of nationalities as determined by the mother tongue is 40 per cent Portuguese, 40 per cent German, and 20 per cent Italian. Almost all of these people speak Portuguese, but use the mother tongue in the homes. Until recently the German colonists established and maintained many of their own schools, where the instruction was in German. Since 1938, however, it has been illegal to give instruction in any language except Portuguese. German cannot be taught until the fifth grade, and then only as a foreign language. Dr. Reinhard Maack estimates the people of German origin in Santa Catarina, whether or not they still speak German, at about 275,000 out of the total population of a million.

The agriculture which the German and Italian colonists now practice is, like that of Rio Grande do Sul, characterized by good farm techniques and a stabilized use of the land. The farming of this region is essentially a maize-hog combination, with hogs as the marketable product. The German farmers grow maize and manioc, and feed hogs and milk-cattle. Today, butter from Blumenau, exported through Itajaí, finds a ready market in Rio de Janeiro. To this combination the Italians add rice, tobacco, and vineyards.

Many industrial establishments are to be found in the small towns of the region, especially along the coast in Florianópolis, Itajaí, Joinville, and São Francisco. Many different products are manufactured, ranging from paper to beer—of excellent quality. The factories are mostly small, but their products enter to a certain extent into the domestic commerce of the Brazilian coast, contributing, like those of Rio Grande do Sul, to the increasing commercial importance of the central city, Rio de Janeiro.

Although the majority of the European immigrants in Santa

Catarina have not intermarried with the Luso-Brazilians, there are some mixtures to be found on the border zone between the older colonies of the coast and the later European settlements of the Zone of the Escarpment. The Germans, especially, are proud of their German heritage, of their techniques of agriculture, and of their low percentage of illiteracy. Although most of them would insist that Brazil was their homeland, they would also insist on the importance of the German contributions to the Brazilian nationality. Isolated as they are from the best aspects of Brazilian civilization, the persistence of the German tradition in this region is not at all surprising. There can be no doubt of the justice of the German pride in the accomplishments of this group of pioneers. It must be recognized, however, that this society of stabilized peasant proprietors was not exposed to the lure to quick wealth offered by the planting of coffee—a lure which proved irresistible to the German settlers in Espírito Santo.

POPULATION CLUSTER AND COLONIES OF PARANÁ

The settlement of Paraná is different, again, in its origin and its composition from that of the other southern states. Paraná includes fewer Germans, for one thing; and most of the Germans who are widely scattered over the state came originally from the expanding colonies of Santa Catarina. Among the European pioneers the first to be established in Paraná were the Italians. Today, however, most of the people there are of Slavic origin—Poles, Russians, Ruthenians, and Ukranians. The characteristic covered wagons of these people represent a peculiar importation from Europe into this part of the Latin-American landscape.

European Colonies

Colonization by European immigrants has taken place much more recently in Paraná than farther south. Between 1876 and

the frontier of new settlement in northwestern Paraná: cotton in a newly cleared field, and (*above*) a young coffee plantation.

A new clearing in the pine forest of northwestern Paraná; and (*above*) the railr
between Curitiba and Paranaguá crossing the Great Escarpment.

w of a clearing in the tropical selva on the banks of the Rio Negro, a little upstream n Manaus. *Above:* This picture shows seed beds for young rubber trees at one of the Ford plantations.

A small coasting steamer stops at Santarém on the Amazon, while laundering goes o
the foreground. The five-gallon oil tin, lower right, is standard equipment for all s
of uses in Brazil.

1879 the state government conceived and carried through a plan to colonize the rural territory around Curitiba with small farmers whose products would help supply the needs of the city. The land available for settlement of this kind was limited on the east by the increasing rainfall near the crest of the Great Escarpment, and on the west by the bold front of the Devonian cuesta. The elevation of about 3,000 feet restricted the crops to those which could be produced in areas subject to annual frosts. All the land had long before been included in the large estates of the Brazilians; but since these estates had never brought their owners much wealth there was no objection when the state government offered to purchase them from the fazendeiros. After securing title to the land, the government proceeded to mark off small lots, and, displaying most unusual foresight, to build good roads radiating from Curitiba throughout the new pioneer area. Italians and Poles, brought to Brazil with the aid of the state government, were settled on the land; and since the area was readily accessible to a large and growing urban market where these colonists could sell their eggs, milk, vegetables, and meat the whole scheme was successful and profitable. By 1885 there was no room for new colonists in this area; the Germans who began to come into Paraná from Joinville in Santa Catarina about this time, after establishing a group of farms around Rio Negro, had either to proceed into the inner lowland to the west or to remain in Curitiba, as merchants.

The establishment of pioneer colonies, however, did not stop after the completion of the Curitiba scheme. Since 1890 many new colonies have been planned and settled, some by private land companies, and others under government auspices—for the state government has maintained its intelligent interest in pioneering. Some of these colonies have prospered; others have failed. In almost every case the determining factor has been the degree of accessibility to a market.

One of the earlier colonial ventures was a marked failure because of isolation. Between 1889 and 1896 about 51,000 Poles entered Paraná, and were sent to a new pioneer zone then being established on the northern slopes of the Iguassú Valley, west of União da Vitória (Map 5, Page 9). The rich terra roxa of this region gave the new settlers amazingly good crops, but only those colonists who had been established within ten miles of the railroad could get their products to a market easily enough to make a profit. Those who went, hopefully, to more distant regions were literally lost in the sertão. After a few years of trial they found that the only product they could get to a market was hogs driven over trails impassable for wheeled vehicles. Soon these remote settlers followed the example of the mixed breeds of the western forests (known in this part of Brazil as *caboclos*); they became migratory farmers, making clearings in the forests, planting maize, permitting the hogs to do their own harvesting, and then abandoning the openings for new land. A considerable area of the forests of western Paraná has thus been destroyed by a very small number of people.

Other colonial settlements, however, were more fortunate. The Polish colonies, within reach of transportation facilities, became stabilized. Around Ponta Grossa a settlement of Russians, Poles and Germans was established about 1898, and proved to be as successful as the earlier colonies around Curitiba; Ponta Grossa, a supply town on the old colonial cattle road, has had a new lease of life in recent years, since it has become an important rail junction (Map 39, Page 177) and a focus of the new state automobile roads now being built into the western sertão. A little north of Ponta Grossa, along the railroad line, a Dutch colony has been successful; and during the last decade a new German colony was established, partly on the open grasslands, partly in the forest, but within easy reach of the town of Castro (Map 4, Page 8).

The newest frontier in Paraná lies to the west of the diabase cuesta, on the good terra roxa of western Paraná. We have already described the remarkable Paraná colonies of the northwestern part of the state—colonies which belong geographically to the São Paulo region. Farther south there are other new pioneer areas, occupied by Poles and Germans, such as Mundo Novo, Terezina (Map 4, Page 8), and Guarapuava (Map 5, Page 9). New automobile highways are being built to these places, and even before they are surfaced with gravel, motor trucks are at work bringing the products of the frontier farms back to the thriving cities. The lesson has been well learned in Paraná, that pioneering involves both colonists placed on the land and urban markets in which they can sell their produce.

Forests of Western Paraná and Santa Catarina

The forests of western Paraná and Santa Catarina offer today Brazil's chief area for new colonization. This is the part of Brazil where there is the largest area of good land, free from tropical insects, and not so remote as to make the costs of road building excessive. Perhaps this is the largest area with these qualities left in the world, where European colonization can still be carried on and where land can still be made available to settlers at low cost.

The forests of western Paraná are themselves of considerable value. They are an important source not only of lumber for building construction, giving rise to such thriving lumber centers as Piraí, north of Castro (Map 4, Page 8), but also of charcoal, which is Brazil's most widely used fuel. The problem of charcoal and firewood is becoming more pressing as the more accessible forests are cut for these purposes, but in 1936, when the danger of increasing scarcity was being widely discussed, fully half of the freight carried by the railroads of Paraná still consisted of these forest products.

Maté

The forests of western Paraná also include important stands of *Ilex paraguayensis*, the tree whose leaves are used for maté.

Between March and September each year a small army of maté collectors goes into the forests—collectors recruited now from many of the pioneer colonies, especially from among Italians and Poles. The leaves are stripped from the trees and dried over small fires before being shipped by mule to the nearest railroad. Curitiba has become Brazil's chief maté center, where the leaves are further dried and pulverized before being packed for shipment.

Maté is widely used throughout southern Brazil, Uruguay, and Argentina, but outside of this part of South America, it is little known. Because no very large market has ever been built up, it has never brought such speculative prosperity to Curitiba as other wild products have brought to other Brazilian cities. Brazil produces about half of the total world supply of maté, and Argentina accounts for about half of the world consumption. Yet, in the Brazilian manner, planting the trees has been left to other people: the Argentine maté plantations of Misiones (Map 39, Page 177) are increasing their productivity and may soon greatly reduce the market for Brazil's wild crop. Nevertheless, even if western Paraná has not experienced such a boom as shook the rubber forests of the Amazon, maté has provided welcome supplementary income to the people of the southern states.

Present-day Paraná

The population of Paraná, supported, thus, by varied economic activities, is estimated today at about 1,000,000. Of these, about 180,000 are Slavs, about 126,000 are Germans, and about 35,000 are Italians. The city of Curitiba is the focus of much of the colonial activity, and reflects the prosperity and relative stability of its hinterland by a steady if not spectacular growth. In 1938 its population was about 125,800. Although Paraná possesses, along with Santa Catarina, some of Brazil's best colonial land, and although the government of Paraná has been a leader in the enlightened administration of pioneer areas, there is still much room for improvement. Especially needed are careful surveys of the land in advance of settlement, and widespread education in the methods of soil conservation. For, good as the soils of western Paraná undoubtedly are, it must not be forgotten that, in terms of physical characteristics, they are most like those of the southern Appalachian Highlands in the United States—a region where unguided settlement has led to widespread soil destruction and to the development of a large area of rural poverty.

What do we learn from all this about the problem of Brazil's population? What differences can be observed between the parts of Brazil north of the border of São Paulo and the parts south of it? And of what importance are the differences?

Many writers point to the more invigorating climate of the South. Whether or not the somewhat lower winter temperatures result in producing an important increase of energy among the inhabitants of this country might be open to question for two reasons. In the first place no studies of the effect of temperature on energy have been made in this part of Brazil; and in the second place, even if the climate of the South were found to be less enervating than the coastal climates farther north, there are other factors which may be of much greater importance. The population of the South, especially of Rio Grande do Sul, was carefully selected, first, in the days of the early Portuguese settlers, for military capacity, and later, when the Germans were brought in, for capacity to do the hard work of woodland pioneering. We must not disregard the fact that in no other part of Brazil do the people enjoy such a satisfactory diet—the result of a greater variety of food crops, of cheaper meat, and of a different dietary tradition. That climatic conditions do, both directly and indirectly through the reduction of insect pests, have an effect on human energy need not be doubted; it is open to question, however, whether this effect may not be offset by human ingenuity, or whether other factors, such as diet, may not prove more important in producing health and energy.

In addition there are certain other differences between the South and the rest of Brazil. An outstanding peculiarity of the country south of the Paulista border is the absence of any source of speculative wealth. To be sure, certain parts of the South can and do grow sugar cane; but in the sugar period of the sixteenth and seventeenth centuries, the people of São Paulo who were settling the southern sertão were not wealthy enough to pay the heavy cost of setting up engenhos and buying slaves, and in those days sugar cane was excluded from the South for reasons of tradition and economic background. Later, although gold was discovered, and even led to the foundation of some of the chief towns, no such wealth of precious metals and gems was ever gained from any part of the South as led to the boom settlements of Minas Gerais. Because of frosts, coffee can only penetrate the northern fringe of Paraná, and so, during the last half century, the South could not share in this great speculative product. Finally, the collection of maté failed to bring in such wealth as rubber brought to the Amazon.

As a result of all these things, the system of the large rural estate, with its feudal society and its many tenant workers, could never become well established in the South except on the grazing lands of the campos. The forests, although partitioned like most Brazilian lands among a few owners, were never effectively occupied by the Luso-Brazilians. When colonists arrived in Brazil who were familiar with the techniques of forest living, these lands were mostly empty and ready for settlement. The pioneers who established themselves in the South were able to create their own society of small farmers, unhampered by the presence of any other social organization. There can be no doubt of the great contribution made by the German pioneers, who, as in southern Chile, led the way into the forests; but one may doubt whether the settlers of

Blumenau would have been able to preserve their "eternal tranquillity" any more effectively than did the German settlers in Espírito Santo if big speculative profits from the planting of coffee had been within their reach.

Chapter VII

THE NORTH

FROM THE POINT of view of a geography of man, the North of Brazil constitutes a problem area, not because people are present there in great numbers, but because it is "one of the world's great deserts." The North,[1] or that part of Brazil covered by great expanses of tropical rain forest, makes up more than 40 per cent of the national territory, but it is inhabited by less than 10 per cent of the population. Furthermore, this 10 per cent is mostly concentrated around São Luiz in Maranhão and Belém in Pará, both near the ocean; the great basin of the Amazon is one of the world's larger areas of very sparse population, with a density of less than .5 per square mile over the region as a whole (Map 15, Page 30).

Much too simple is the answer commonly given to the problem of sparse population in the Amazon—that the climate is unsuited to settlement by Europeans. Contained in the thick forests of the area there is a wealth of resources, some already exploited, some awaiting use. Many well-informed persons, who have traveled in this region, have been impressed with its possibilities. Why, indeed, should this part of Brazil be occupied by so few people, when the value of the exports, measured on a per capita basis, places the Amazon among the world's richest regions?

[1] The North includes chiefly Maranhão, Pará, Amazonas, and the Territory of Acre.

In 1853 Alfred Russell Wallace wrote the following estimate of the possibilities of settlement:

There is no country in the world where people can produce for themselves so many of the necessaries and luxuries of life. Indian corn, rice, mandioca, sugar, coffee, cotton, beef, poultry, and pork, with oranges, bananas, and abundance of other fruits and vegetables, thrive with care. With these articles in abundance, a house of wood, calabashes, cups, and pottery of the country, they may live in plenty without a single exotic production. And then what advantages there are in a country where there is no stoppage of agricultural operations during the winter, but where crops may be had, and poultry be reared, all the year round; where the least possible clothing is the most comfortable and where a hundred little necessaries of a cold region are altogether superfluous. With regard to the climate I have said enough already; and I repeat, that a man can work as well here as in the hot summer months in England, and that if he will only work three hours in the morning and three in the evening, he will produce more of the necessaries and comforts of life than by twelve hours daily labor at home.[2]

These assertions have yet to be tested. For whatever reason, the history of man in the North of Brazil can almost be described as a caricature of the Brazilian economy. In this region the temporary, exploitive character of Brazilian economic life is carried to an extreme; here we find again and again illustrations of the disaster which follows the attempt to collect the fruit without planting the tree; here is a land abundantly endowed with resources only waiting to be collected. The planting of the tree, however, requires so much labor and so much capital that the establishment of the more permanent and intensive forms of land use seems to be impossible. Once more we find difficulty in determining whether destructive exploitation is a cause or a result of sparse population. In recent years, however, the whole traditional system of exploitation meets a challenge in the Ford plantations: at last Wallace's enthusiastic evaluation of the possibilities of life in the Amazon Region is

[2] *Travels on the Amazon and the Rio Negro*, London, 1853, pp. 55–56.

being put to the test. Setting aside, as far as possible, all preconceptions and prejudices regarding life in the rainy tropics, let us examine the facts objectively.

THE LAND

Popular misinformation seems to be more widespread regarding the North of Brazil than it is regarding any other region of South America. This is the result in part of the deep-seated preconceptions concerning the effect of tropical rainy climates on people of European origin, in part of the exaggerated stories of the rubber days, and in part, no doubt, of the well-known Hollywood version of life in the tropical forests. The Amazon Region is, actually, the world's largest area of tropical rain forest; it does lie almost exactly along the equator; it is true, as Roy Nash puts it, that the problem here is "whether man can be happy in the rain"; yet we may not assume that the mechanical ingenuity of European people cannot lead to a solution of tropical living as it has led to the solution of living in the severe winter climates of the higher middle latitudes, long relegated to barbarians by the writers of the past.

Surface Features

Only a small proportion of the Amazon Region can be described as a plain. Above the junction with the Rio Negro and the Rio Madeira (Map 40, Page 211), the plain widens out like a spatula, until a distance of some eight hundred miles separates the highlands to the north and to the south (Map 1, Page 4). This is the part of the basin lying east of the Andes, drained by the Purús, the Juruá, the Javary, and the main stream.[3] Most of the surface of this large area is underlain by

[3] The main course of the Amazon is given different names in different sections: The Peruvians call it the Río Marañón; from the Brazilian border eastward as far as the junction of the Rio Negro, the Brazilians call the main stream the Solimões; and from the Rio Negro to the sea they call it the

unconsolidated gravels, sands, clays, and silt. About 90 per cent of this surface is above the level of the highest floods. The floodplain of the main stream is mostly less than fifty miles wide.

East of the junction of the Amazon with the Rio Negro and with the Rio Madeira the bordering highlands come closer and closer together, until only the immediate floodplain of the river is left as a band of lowland between them. East of the junction of the Xingú, however, the plain again widens out, leaving a broad area of low country on either side of the mouth. This lowland extends along the coast northward into the European colonies of Guiana, and southeastward to Maranhão. Because of the gradual submergence of the land where the Amazon empties into the sea its mouth is embayed; there is no delta, although the yellow, silt-laden waters discolor the ocean for as much as two hundred miles offshore.

The floodplain of the Amazon is similar in its pattern and its dimensions to the lowlands bordering other great rivers, such as the lower Mississippi. The area covered by water in time of flood is only twenty miles wide at Obidos and Santarém, but for most of the course below the Rio Negro it is fifty or sixty miles wide. The floodplain is bordered by sharp valley bluffs which stand at least 150 to 200 feet above the swamps along the river. The river meanders across this lowland between the valley bluffs, swinging at intervals against the margins of the floodplain; frequently its channel is shifted, leaving oxbow lakes and swamps; along its banks, and also along the sides of the abandoned channels, there are natural levees which stand a little higher than the rest of the floodplain; and all these features between the bluffs are arranged in the characteristic crescentic patterns of all river-built plains.

The Guiana and Brazilian highlands, which all but join near

Amazonas. We use the English name, Amazon, to refer to the whole course of the main stream as far as the Pongo de Manseriche in Peru where the Río Marañón emerges from the Andes.

mouth of the Amazon, are built of the same fundamental elements. There are the crystalline hilly uplands, surmounted by a few massive mountain ranges, or by conical-shaped mountain remnants, and surmounted also by the sandstone-capped tabular uplands or plateaus. The Amazon itself follows the axis of a huge structural basin, a portion of the earth's crust which is in the process of sinking very slowly. Immediately bordering the river in its lower course are the tabular remnants of relatively young sedimentary rocks which cover the deeply buried crystallines, as along the coast of the Northeast. On the northern edge of the floodplain northeast of Santarém, the edge of these younger strata forms a taboleiro the top of which stands as much as 1,150 feet above sea level, forming a major landmark along the river.

The main stream has a remarkably low gradient all the way from the front of the Andes to the sea. Although careful measurements of altitude have yet to be made, it is approximately correct to give its elevation at Manaus as only about a hundred feet above the sea. The Amazon is deep enough to permit ocean boats of less than fourteen-foot draught to sail all the way to Iquitos in eastern Peru.

The Amazon tributaries, however, are all interrupted by falls and rapids where they cross areas of crystalline rock. The falls of the Madeira, above Porto Velho, which may be reached by shallow-draught ocean vessels, are situated where the river cuts through the westernmost projection of the Brazilian Highland. The tributaries west of the Madeira are all navigable for river boats far upstream into Acre Territory (Map 14, Page 23). East of the Madeira, on the other hand, the Amazon tributaries are all interrupted by rapids within 200 miles of the main stream. The Tapajóz is navigable for 175 miles, the Xingú for 120 miles, and the Tocantins for about the same distance. In the highlands these streams are so frequently interrupted by falls and rapids that they are quite useless for navigation except by canoe. On the northern side, the Rio Negro is navigable for

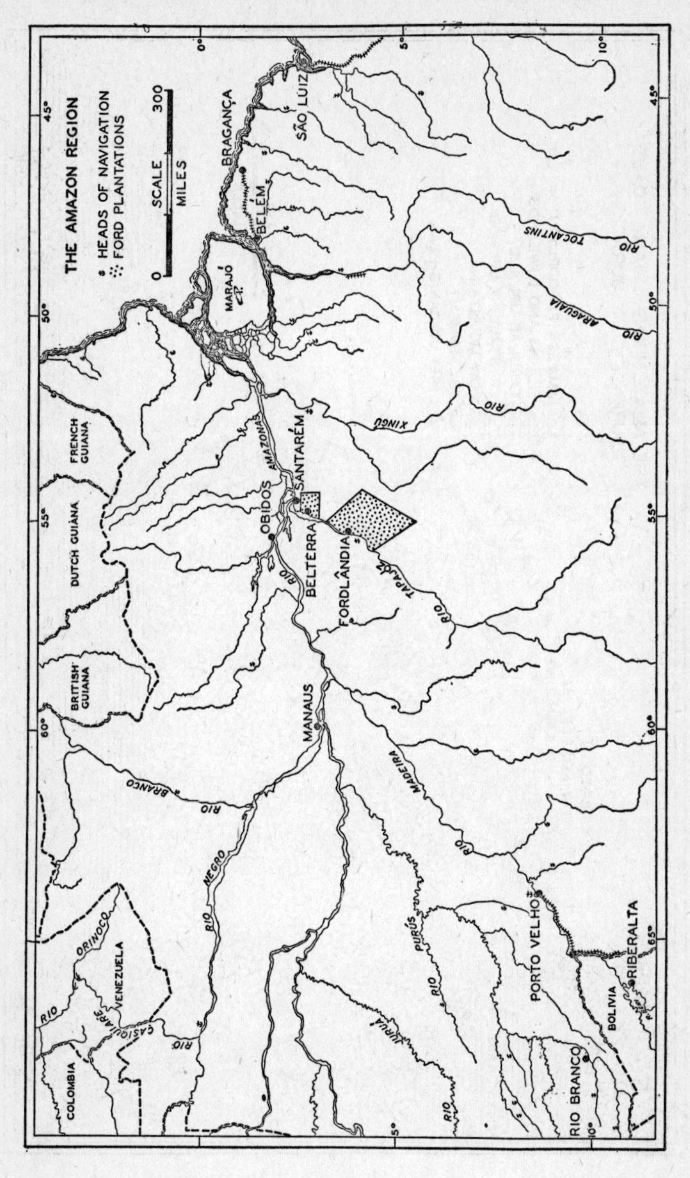
THE AMAZON REGION
HEADS OF NAVIGATION
FORD PLANTATIONS
SCALE
0
300
MILES
BRAGANÇA
SÃO LUIZ
BELÉM
MARAJÓ
FRENCH GUIANA
DUTCH GUIANA
BRITISH GUIANA
OBIDOS
SANTARÉM
AMAZONAS
BELTERRA
FORDLÂNDIA
RIO TAPAJÓZ
RIO XINGU
RIO TOCANTINS
RIO ARAGUAIA
MANAUS
RIO MADEIRA
RIO BRANCO
RIO NEGRO
RIO ORINOCO
VENEZUELA
COLOMBIA
RIO PURUS
RIO JURUÁ
PORTO VELHO
RIBERALTA
BOLIVIA
RIO BRANCO

MAP 40

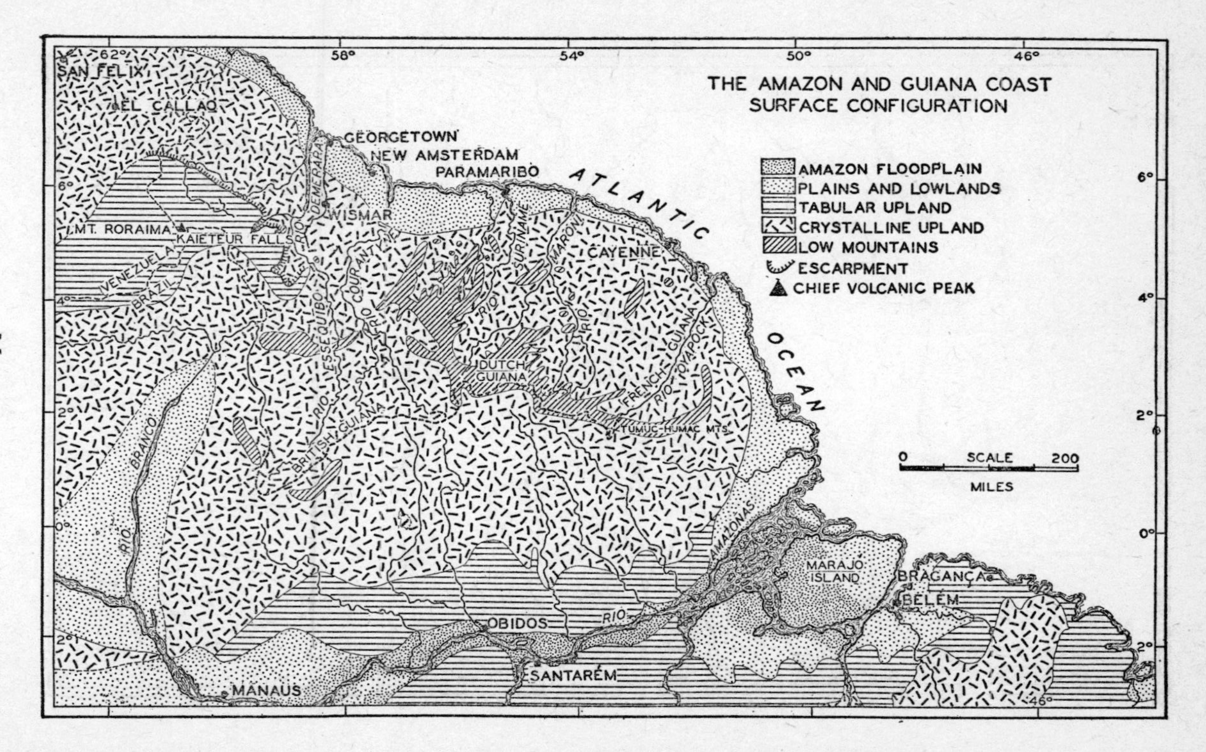
THE AMAZON AND GUIANA COAST
SURFACE CONFIGURATION
AMAZON FLOODPLAIN
PLAINS AND LOWLANDS
TABULAR UPLAND
CRYSTALLINE UPLAND
LOW MOUNTAINS
ESCARPMENT
CHIEF VOLCANIC PEAK
0
SCALE
200
MILES
ATLANTIC
OCEAN
SAN FELIX
EL CALLAO
GEORGETOWN
NEW AMSTERDAM
PARAMARIBO
WISMAR
DEMERARA
MT. RORAIMA
KAIETEUR FALLS
VENEZUELA
BRAZIL
RIO ESSEQUIBO
RIO COURANTYNE
SURINAME
MARONI
CAYENNE
DUTCH GUIANA
BRITISH GUIANA
FRENCH GUIANA
RIO OYAPOCK
TUMUC-HUMAC MTS.
RIO BRANCO
AMAZONAS
MARAJÓ ISLAND
BRAGANÇA
BELÉM
OBIDOS
SANTARÉM
MANAUS
62°
58°
54°
50°
46°
6°
4°
2°
0°

MAP 41

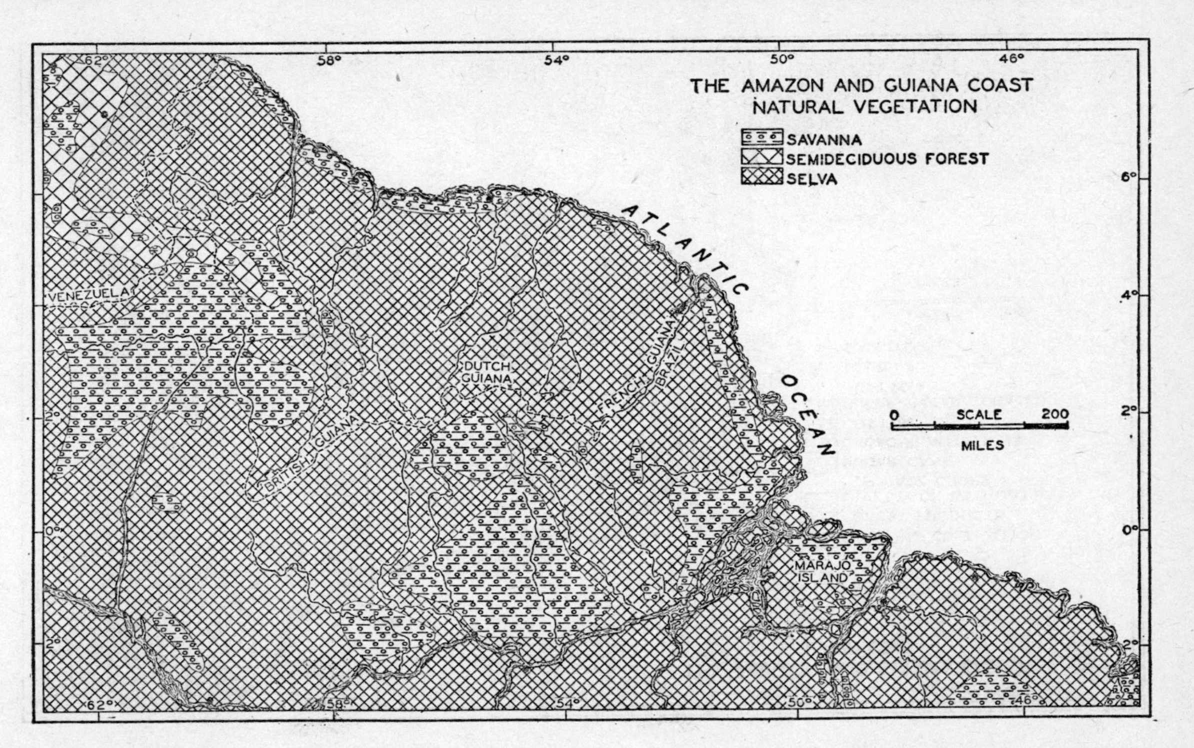
THE AMAZON AND GUIANA COAST
NATURAL VEGETATION
SAVANNA
SEMIDECIDUOUS FOREST
SELVA
ATLANTIC
OCEAN
0
SCALE
200
MILES
VENEZUELA
BRITISH GUIANA
DUTCH GUIANA
FRENCH GUIANA
BRAZIL
MARAJO ISLAND

MAP 42

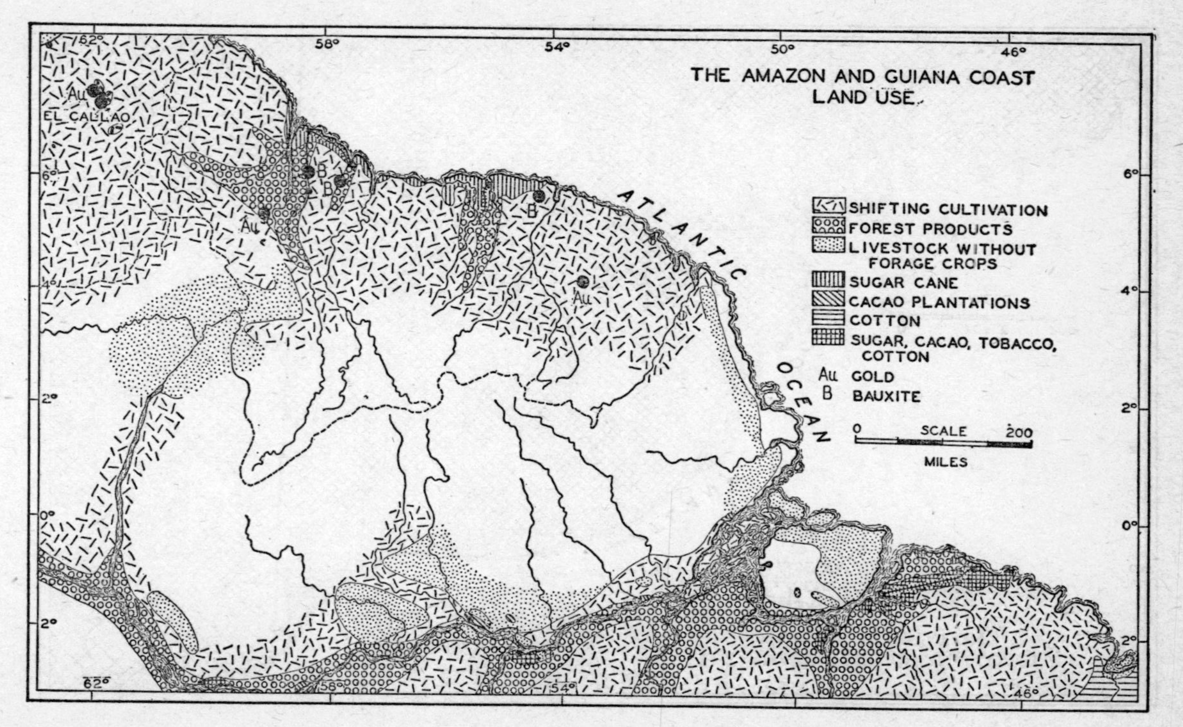
THE AMAZON AND GUIANA COAST
LAND USE
SHIFTING CULTIVATION
FOREST PRODUCTS
LIVESTOCK WITHOUT FORAGE CROPS
SUGAR CANE
CACAO PLANTATIONS
COTTON
SUGAR, CACAO, TOBACCO, COTTON
Au GOLD
B BAUXITE
0
SCALE
200
MILES
ATLANTIC
OCEAN
EL CALLAO
Au
B
62°
58°
54°
50°
46°
6°
4°
2°
0°
2°

MAP 43

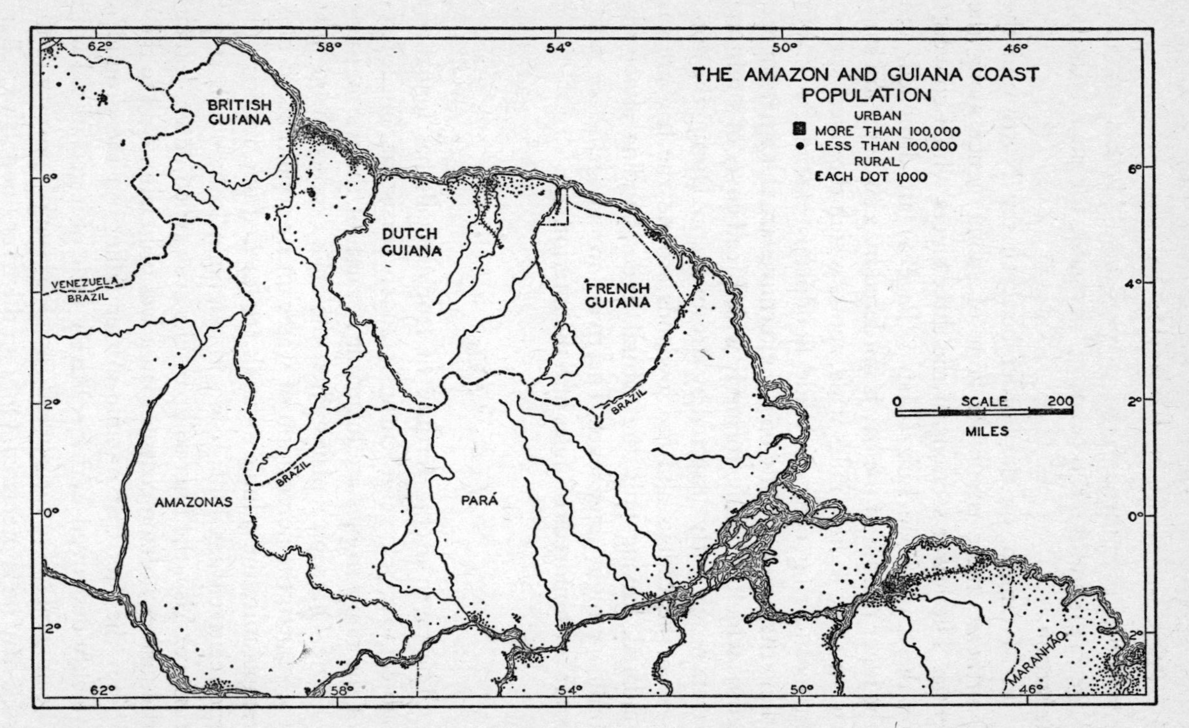

THE AMAZON AND GUIANA COAST
POPULATION
URBAN
MORE THAN 100,000
LESS THAN 100,000
RURAL
EACH DOT 1,000
0
SCALE
200
MILES
BRITISH GUIANA
DUTCH GUIANA
FRENCH GUIANA
VENEZUELA
BRAZIL
BRAZIL
BRAZIL
AMAZONAS
PARÁ
MARANHÃO
62°
58°
54°
50°
46°
6°
4°
2°
0°
2°

MAP 44

river boats even through the narrows above Manaus (Map 41, Page 212); and the Rio Branco is navigable for small boats far upstream.

In Maranhão, on the border between the North and the Northeast, there is another zone of submergence along the coast. The lower sections of the three rivers which converge on the bay of São Luiz (Map 2, Page 6) are drowned, and the inner margin of the bay is bordered by a swampy lowland, twenty-five to fifty miles wide, across which the rivers sprawl in meandering courses. Wide floodplains extend far inland along these rivers. Only on the interfluves are there flat-topped mesas which tell of the formerly widespread cover of sandstone strata now greatly dissected by stream action. During the flood season the valleys and the lowlands around the bay are inundated, leaving only the natural levees standing above the ordinary high-water level. The rivers are navigable for small craft for hundreds of miles into the interior.

Soils

The myth of the fertility of tropical soils has long been subject to attack, yet it remains strangely persistent. The forests of the rainy tropics are luxuriant because of the warm, moist climate. On tropical plains where the soil is exposed throughout the year to the percolation of water under conditions of high temperature the soluble minerals are leached out, leaving only the relatively insoluble iron and aluminum compounds at the surface. Also, the finer soil particles are carried down, leaving the surface horizon coarser than it was originally. Add to these things the fact that organic matter falling on the ground is quickly destroyed so that relatively little of it gets mixed with the mineral soil to form humus, and the essential poverty of the soils may be appreciated. Only on the river floodplains, where new layers of silt are deposited with each flood, are the soils fertile.

Fertility, however, is not a quality inherent in soil alone: it can only be measured in terms of specific soil uses. The tropical lowland soils, outside of the floodplains, are infertile for shallow-rooted crops; ordinary food crops growing in soils which are so deficient in mineral properties do not provide the mineral salts necessary for good diet. Tree crops adapted to the climatic conditions, on the other hand, are more dependent on favorable ground-water conditions than they are on the quality of the surface soil.

Climate

One of the commonest items of misinformation concerning the Amazon Region is the belief that its temperatures are unbearably high. As a matter of fact, they are not so high as those of a summer heat wave in central North America. The highest temperatures in South America occur along the Caribbean Coast and in the Gran Chaco of Argentina. Temperatures in the Amazon Region are high, but not excessive; the most disagreeable effect of the temperature is its monotony—disagreeable, that is, to people accustomed to the nervous strain of the rapid and extreme temperature changes characteristic of mid-latitude cyclonic climates. At Santarém, for example, during the period from 1914 to 1919 the highest temperature recorded was 96.3° and the lowest was 65.3°. The average for the year is 78.1,° and the range between the average of the warmest and coldest months is only about 4°.

The humidity, on the other hand, may be high enough to be very uncomfortable, especially in places protected from the wind. In the rainy tropics the steady movement of the easterly trade wind over the oceans brings great quantities of moisture onto the land, but it also makes living quite comfortable in spite of the humidity. As one proceeds inland the relative humidity decreases—at Manaus it averages 78 per cent—but the wind also decreases in strength and becomes variable. Day and night throughout the year, the winds blow strongly on the eastern coasts; but inland there are times when the wind dies down. The difference between daytime temperature and night temperature may be as much as 15°; such a drop of temperature results, in some protected places, in the formation of low banks of fog.

The rainfall of the whole Amazon area is abundant. Only in the upper part of the basin, and along the coast, are the averages more than 80 inches a year (Map 8, Page 15); but no part of the area can be considered dry. The rains come during the period from January to June when the warm, moisture-laden equatorial air masses from the North Atlantic sweep far southwestward into the interior of South America (Map 9, Page 16). The drier part of the year, from July to December, is in reality only a season of less rain. In both rainy and dry seasons precipitation comes in the form of violent showers, followed by sudden clearing. Great rolls of cumulus cloud, the swish of rain on the leaves of the forest, and the smell of the warm earth suddenly moistened are common experiences in this region. The nights are almost always brilliantly clear.

The Forest

With the forest, more than with any other feature of this region, must man contend. In the forest are the riches of the region; on the control of the forest the settlers must expend the greater part of their energies, and when this work is relaxed the deep, mysterious cover of growing things creeps back again to hide from view all traces of man's destructive presence.

The forest looks monotonous, but in reality it is as diversified as the land itself. It is composed of many different species of trees and shrubs, thousands of species in a square mile; and there are few places where many of one kind are concentrated. In the absence of a rhythm of life, imposed by cold or drought, each species of tree burgeons forth with flowers, ripens its fruits, and drops its leaves, each in its own period. Birds of the most extraordinary variety, drawn to feed on the ripened fruit of a forest giant, will move to a new locality as other trees are ready to tempt their appetites. But all this life, this exuberant vitality of growth, is concentrated high overhead in the foliage of interlaced branches. Underneath, on the floor of the forest, where man must move about, all is dark, silent, deathlike. Only where light can penetrate to the ground, as along the banks of a stream, or in a clearing which has been abandoned, does that thicket of underbrush appear which is popularly termed jungle.

On the higher surfaces of the crystalline uplands there are numerous interruptions to the thick cover of forest (Map 42, Page 213). Grassy savannas, with scattered trees, even come to the edge of the valley bluff north of Obidos. In many places the forest is patchy with grassy openings. On stretches of the floodplain, too, there are swampy areas filled only with coarse grasses—little areas of wet savanna on which scrawny cattle graze, knee deep in water.

The Amazon forests differ remarkably from those of Africa in that they do not harbor a population of large animals. Monkeys, snakes, insects, and birds live in the treetops; sometimes tapirs can be found coming to the water to drink; and in the rivers are many kinds of fish and turtles. But on the whole, the Amazon Region is notably deficient in large land animals.

SETTLEMENT BEFORE THE RUBBER PERIOD

The two centers of Portuguese wealth in Brazil during the first part of the colonial period were Salvador and Recife. Although the mouth of the Amazon was included in Portuguese territory by the Treaty of Tordesillas, neither Pará nor Maranhão appeared so satisfactory for sugar planting to the early settlers as did the country in Bahia and Pernambuco because of the extensive annual inundations characteristic of the drowned river mouths of the North. The wealthy planters established themselves around Salvador and Recife, and to these places came the cargoes of Negro slaves from Africa, for the great prosperity of the sugar business in the Northeast was based on the labor of the Negroes.

Meanwhile sugar cane was also planted around the two primary settlement centers of the North—São Luiz and Belém. São Luiz, founded during the sixteenth century on its protected island, became an important sugar port, with numerous plantations strung along the natural levees of the bordering lowland. During the seventeenth century the state of Maranhão shared with the Northeast a considerable amount of prosperity, and São Luiz was surpassed in importance only by Salvador and Recife. But there was one great difference between the sugar industry of Maranhão and that of the Northeast. In the North the labor was furnished chiefly by Indian slaves: the costs of production proved to be so much higher where the relatively inefficient Indians were used that by the end of the seventeenth century the sugar plantations of Maranhão had been definitely excluded from the market.

Penetration of the Amazon

One of the chief sources of Indian slaves during the colonial period was the Amazon Region. In 1616 a Jesuit mission was founded at Belém, and from this place missionaries moved inland along the rivers, establishing mission stations on the valley bluffs where the river, swinging against the margin of its floodplain, made these bluffs accessible. Although most of the interior was originally assigned to Spain by the Treaty of Tordesillas, the Spaniards were too much involved with the occupation of the West Coast and the Andes to pay much attention to this vast domain so difficult to reach from their side of the continent. Meanwhile Portuguese slave raiders followed quickly in the footsteps of the missionaries; for a time Manaus was important as a concentration point for slaves captured at many scattered places farther upstream.

The arrival of the Europeans brought disaster to the native peoples. Epidemics decimated the crowded populations of the mission stations and slave raiders carried into captivity those who survived the ravages of disease. Today scarcely ten thousand Indians inhabit the great empty forests. Small tribes are found chiefly in remote places, for the surviving natives have learned to fear and avoid white men. The Indians still practice a shifting cultivation of manioc and maize, supplementing their starchy diet with fish and eggs, rarely with a little meat, but sometimes with the fruits and nuts they find in the forest. They make little permanent impression on the forest, for their abandoned clearings are soon obliterated by new growth—visible only from the air by the variations in the coloring of the unbroken sea of foliage.

Agricultural and pastoral activities in the North were concentrated in only a few spots. The territory in the vicinity of São Luiz and of Belém, after the decline of the early sugar plantations, was utilized for the grazing of cattle, which is even today the chief economic activity of both these districts—cattle pastured on the wet savannas of the swampy areas, cattle forced sometimes to swim for their lives during the floods, cattle hardy enough to survive the insect pests of these lowland areas. Both Belém and São Luiz prospered for a time during the eighteenth century on the production of coffee, cotton, and rice, until other parts of Brazil produced these things more cheaply. Settlements appeared around Santarém, Obidos, and Manaus. Around each of these places there were small areas devoted to cacao, sugar cane, and other tropical specialties, but remarkably little area was devoted to subsistence food crops. Back of Obidos, and in places along the floodplain, the savannas were used for cattle. Far up the Rio Branco, north of Manaus, cattle were, and still are, pastured on the dry savannas (Map 43, Page 214).

Nevertheless, further attempts to establish agricultural colonies in the region were actually made. Shortly after the end of the North American Civil War a group of people from the Southern States of the United States, desiring to continue under a regime of slavery, established a settlement not far from Santarém, bringing their slaves and tools with them. In the 1870's this group was visited by a North American traveler and found to be filled with pioneer zeal, enthusiastically engaged in clearing the forest and planting cotton and sugar cane. But the place selected for the colony was too remote. Although steamboats sailed the Amazon after 1866, making Santarém a regular port of call, the cost of transporting the small volume of cotton or sugar to distant markets, and of importing essential articles, was so great that the American colony near Santarém was almost entirely cut off from the outside world. No Occidental pioneer colony which remains in isolation has been successful in the modern period, whether in the Amazon or elsewhere. Today only a few impoverished families remain, and these have thoroughly lost the optimism which is the chief source of strength for the successful pioneer.

THE RUBBER PERIOD

When the world was ready for rubber, the Amazon Region began the spectacular period of forest exploitation which resulted in scattered settlement in widely separated places. In the tropical rain forest south of the main stream, and in the headwater areas of eastern Bolivia, Peru, Ecuador, and Colombia, there are two chief species of tree from which rubber can be produced. The better of these species is *Hevea brasiliensis*, from which latex, a milklike substance, can be extracted from cuts in the bark. The other is the *Castilla ulei*, from which rubber can be extracted only by cutting down the tree. Like all the other species in the tropical rain forest, both Hevea and Castilla trees are widely scattered, seldom with many individuals standing close together. No source of rubber comparable to the Hevea tree has been found in any other part of the world, although most of the world's rubber now comes from a variety of Hevea which is much more productive than the native wild trees of the Amazon.

Exploitation of Rubber

Rubber was not a product of major importance until two things happened. The first was the discovery of the vulcanizing process in 1839 by Charles Goodyear—a process which makes it possible to keep rubber from becoming sticky in hot weather or brittle in cold weather. The second was the manufacture of various mechanical and electrical devices in which rubber is an essential element, such as automobile tires and electric insulation. In 1827 Belém exported 69,174 pounds of rubber; in 1853 the exports jumped suddenly to 5,214,560 pounds.

Here was a situation characteristically Brazilian. A new world market of unlimited possibilities suddenly makes its appearance; Brazil finds itself in possession of a monopoly of the raw material needed to supply this market; the chief factor limiting the increase of production is the scarcity of labor. The immediate result—a frantic rush to the rubber forests and a mad scramble to share in this new source of speculative wealth. Land was purchased in Belém or Manaus without any preliminary survey, much as one would draw a hand in a poker game. Later, the purchaser would find out whether he was wealthy beyond his dreams or had completely lost the purchase price—all depending on the number of rubber trees that could be found in his forest. Who in that region and in that atmosphere of speculative profit could have thought of undertaking the hard work of clearing the forest, preparing the land, planting young rubber trees, and caring for them during their period of early growth.

The chief problem was finding laborers to do the work. The story of the recruiting of the rubber gatherers is not a pretty one—especially in the eastern parts of Bolivia, Peru, Ecuador, and Colombia, where the arm of the law could scarcely reach across the Andes. The virtual slavery and the almost universal mistreatment of the Indians, many of them recruited from the highland communities of the Andes, makes a sad chapter of human brutality, now long since closed. In the Brazilian Amazon conditions were scarcely better. Most of the workers who came into the region during the '70's and '80's were from the drought-stricken regions of Ceará. People from Ceará poured into the Amazon during part of the rubber period in numbers averaging 20,000 a year; but few of them returned. Today a very large proportion of the Brazilians scattered over this vast extent of territory came originally from the sertão of the Brazilian Northeast.

The rubber was gathered by workers who were almost literally buried in the forest. The owner of a tract of land recruited his workers in Belém or Manaus, loaned them the funds with which to buy not only essential items of equipment but also tinned foods. Each family of workers was then transported to a spot on the river bank accessible to the launch of the owner, and there deposited and left to build a rude shelter for a home. From each isolated camp the gatherer cut for himself a path or *estrada* through the forest, leading perhaps to as many as two hundred rubber trees. The latex tapped from these trees was brought to the camp and there formed into solid rubber balls by smoking over a slow fire. There could be no supervision of the tapping methods and no care of the trees to insure their continued productivity. At intervals the owner's launch would make its appearance to pick up the product, and to leave supplies, for which the worker was never quite able to pay—and thus always remained in debt.

Pattern of Settlement

Since the only means of transportation were the river boats, and since the rubber was brought down the smaller rivers to the larger ones and finally to the main stream, the chief centers of settlement appeared at such strategic spots as the river junctions or the heads of river navigation. The owner could establish his base at the outlet of the rivers which gave access to his lands and from that spot control all that passed up or down. The chief concentration of both people and wealth was in the two major cities of Manaus and Belém. In these places money was squandered as it is in a gold-rush town. The Brazilians, lovers of music and the artistic life, built in Manaus that great monument to the Brazilian system—the opera house, whose vast dome with its orange diamonds on a green background (the colors and design of the Brazilian flag) still dominates the city and is visible even over the forest as one approaches from downstream.

There were rich rubber forests beyond the limits of navigation along the southern tributaries of the Amazon. Towns were founded at the heads of navigation, and roads, passable only for oxcarts, were built through the forests to the stretches of water above the rapids which were navigable by canoe. Railroads were projected with unlimited optimism, but only one is still in operation. In 1878 the construction of a railroad around the great falls of the Madeira was started; but the terrible toll of malaria forced the abandonment of the project. When Brazil succeeded in getting the rich Acre Territory from Bolivia in 1903, part of the agreement included the construction by Brazil of a railroad to give the remainder of eastern Bolivia access to navigable water. The line was to start at Porto Velho to which ocean steamers could come and was to extend to Riberalta on the Río Beni, above the uppermost rapids (Map 40, Page 211). In 1913 the line was completed from Porto Velho to the Bolivian border, but a bridge across the Madeira and a short extension beyond to Riberalta remained unbuilt. By 1913 the rubber period was over.

Collapse of the Rubber Business

Brazil's system of destructive exploitation of rubber collapsed because someone else planted the trees. In 1876 an Englishman named Henry Wickham collected some Hevea seeds in the Tapajoz Valley. These were sprouted in the Kew Gardens at London, and then transplanted in the Botanical Gardens in Colombo, Ceylon. "Wickham's Baby" they call the big rubber tree at Colombo from which came the seeds to start the first rubber plantations of Malaya and Sumatra in 1896. The plantation rubber comes from the same kind of tree as did the wild rubber of the Amazon; but for a number of reasons the costs are only a fraction of the costs of collecting the wild product. The yield of rubber per tree per year in the Amazon forest is only about three pounds; the Malayan varieties of Hevea yield from 10 to 17 pounds. One man in the Amazon could scarcely attend to more than two hundred trees; in a rubber plantation one worker takes care of more than five hundred trees. In the Amazon there could be no supervision of the tapping methods and no care of the trees; in a plantation the trees can be given the attention of experts to guarantee maximum yields. In the Amazon the workers were exposed to all the dangers and hardships of life in the forest; on a plantation the workers are carefully housed, given medical attention, and a carefully regulated diet. Close to the rubber-growing region of Malaya and Sumatra are such densely populated lands as Java, Indo-China, Siam, and India, where large numbers of efficient workers could easily be recruited. No such source of labor is available, under existing world conditions, in the Amazon Region.

There could have been but one result. In 1905 the plantations of British Malaya and Dutch Sumatra produced only a small fraction of the world's supply of rubber. In 1910 they produced 9 per cent; in 1914 they produced 60 per cent; and by 1924 the plantations accounted for about 93 per cent. Early in 1909 the increasing demand for rubber for use in the manufacture of automobile tires caused a frenzied boom in the Amazon, even in the face of the growing competition of the plantations. Credits were extended; new laborers were hastily recruited and sent into the forests. But in April, 1910, the whole crazy financial structure of credits collapsed, ruining large numbers of the speculators. Rubber production continued to increase until 1912, and even longer in places where Castilla trees could be cut down. But since 1912 Brazil has had only a very minor share of the world's production of rubber.

Decadence

The collapse of the rubber business left many of the rubber workers stranded. Many of them drifted into Manaus, Obidos, Santarém, or Belém, to swell the population of those places. For most of the time, however, there was little economic activity by which these people could gain a living. Many parts of the cities were virtually abandoned in favor of temporary homes scattered in the outskirts. Yet, strange to relate, there was little increase in the amount of land devoted to the production of food crops. It was estimated during the '20's that in the whole Amazon Region there was scarcely a hundred square miles devoted to any kind of agriculture, let alone the production of local supplies of food. In the interior many of the smaller towns whose names still appear on standard maps are entirely abandoned, engulfed in the rapidly advancing jungle.

It is said in Brazil that if money is to be made from the most poverty-stricken of areas, the Syrian traders will make it. In the Amazon the Syrians have taken over most of the retail trading. By advancing loans to the isolated groups of people outside of the larger urban centers, they have established their control over them. Just as the rubber owners used to do, the traders now control the passage of goods up and down the streams by placing their posts at strategic river junctions. So powerful are some of the larger traders that permission to travel in these remote spots depends on their word. From the pitifully small volume of an enormous variety of forest products contributed by individuals scattered over this vast area, the traders are able to take the very considerable profits. The forest products include gums, nuts, roots, cabinet woods, and the skins of rare animals.

The most valuable single items coming from the Amazon today are the edible nuts. The Brazil nut, collected from the forest giant known as *Bertholletia excelsa*, is brought to Belém for shipment. Workers are sent out into the forest, especially along the Rio Tocantins, at the time of the year when the nuts ripen. Again no cultivation is attempted—only the collection of a product which has fallen from the tree. Today Brazil produces the greater part of the world's supply of Brazil nuts; yet already even this supremacy is threatened by plantations of this tree now set out on an experimental basis in British Malaya.

São Luiz is the shipping point for the Babassu nut, a source of vegetable oil. The Babassu palm grows wild in the zone of transition between the rain forest and the savannas and scrub forests of the Northeast; there are large areas covered by this valuable tree throughout Maranhão and Piauí. Again, the product is collected by workers temporarily recruited for the job, and there are no plantations. Yet the Babassu nut brings to São Luiz at least a temporary increase of activity, and attracts to it a new stream of migrants.

Agricultural Settlement in Pará

Agricultural settlement was actually attempted in Pará. Along the railroad line which extends from Belém to Bragança there were, in addition to groups of small farmers raising food crops for the supply of Belém, Japanese colonists. A Japanese land company owns more than 2,500,000 acres in Pará, although the company has been able to settle no more than 2,000 Japanese at the most. Many of the original settlers have in recent years moved to São Paulo to swell the current of migration to the western frontier of that state, yet Pará remains the most important agricultural area in the whole Amazon Region—the most important, that is, outside of the Ford Plantations.

THE FORD PLANTATIONS

In 1927 an event of great importance took place in the North of Brazil. The *Companhia Ford Industrial do Brasil* purchased a tract of land, including some 2,500,000 acres, along the right bank of the Rio Tapajóz about 135 miles upstream from the Amazon. The area was known as Fordlandia. At the nucleus of the settlement a modern town was built. About 8,400 acres of rubber trees were planted before a number of unexpected difficulties began to appear. Diseases attacked the plantations of Hevea trees while the same kinds of trees, widely scattered through the rain forest, seemed to be immune. Also Fordlandia was found to be so hilly that soil erosion became critical and the use of machinery was difficult. In 1934 a part of the original concession was exchanged with the state of Pará for a new tract of land, including 600,000 acres, only 30 miles up the Tapajóz from Santarém. This new tract is called Belterra (Map 40, Page 211). Up to April, 1939, about 12,500 acres had been planted with rubber in this area. The more nearly level land at the new site permits the more efficient use of machinery and better agricultural practices. Selection of disease-resistant stock and the grafting of high-yielding Malayan varieties on the hardy roots of indigenous trees are expected to overcome the technical problems of rubber growing in the Amazon.

The Ford project remains essentially an experiment. Rubber has not been produced commercially so far, although some of the plantations have been tapped since 1937. Even at full production, the Ford Plantations could scarcely account for more than a fraction of the world production. The importance of the project is not so much in the effect it may have on the world rubber supply as in the light it throws on the question of the habitability of the Amazon and the possibilities of stabilized economic development.

At present the population of Fordlandia and Belterra is approximately 12,000. The workers and their families are housed in modern dwellings, carefully screened and protected from insects. The whole colony receives free medical attention, and is supplied with food on the basis of carefully determined needs of tropical workers. There are schools, recreation facilities, and other services unknown not only in other parts of the Amazon, but even in the more prosperous parts of rural Brazil. Today the Ford Plantations rank among the most healthful places in Brazil. At last the estimate of the habitability of the Amazon as written nearly ninety years ago by Wallace is being put to the test.

The Lesson of the Ford Plantations

What light does the experiment of the Ford Plantations throw on the problem of the empty Amazon? Plainly the kind of living which has made its appearance in Fordlandia and Belterra could not be supported on the basis of the exploitation of resources in the Brazilian manner. Some persons insist that these new standards of living could not be supported by an ordinary plantation economy even if it were operating at full capacity. On the other hand, other persons claim that the increased productivity of workers who are protected from disease and who are adequately nourished would more than make up for the increased cost of a standard of living such as is being maintained at the Ford Plantations. Perhaps it is true that only an outside organization, amply supplied with funds, could support such an expensive project. Still we may ask whether stabilized settlement is rendered impossible by the nature of the land or by the economic, social, and political system under which the settlement process must go forward. It is not difficult to imagine a changed economic world, in which settlement in the Amazon would be possible. If such a change takes place, the preconception that the climate itself is responsible for the failure of settlement will be clearly tested by actual experience.

Meanwhile one other aspect of the problem must be understood. Even to bring the whole available area of the Ford Plantations into full production would require a much larger number of workers than are at present available. To clear any considerable area of the Amazon country and bring new rubber plantations into production which would seriously rival the plantations of Malaya and Sumatra would require an enormous number of immigrants. Under what conditions such a migration to the North of Brazil might take place is difficult to conceive. Under present conditions the Brazilians would not be likely to permit the entrance of any adequate number of Oriental people, nor of any other single foreign group; yet as long as São Paulo continues to produce one form or another of wealth, the remote Amazon is not likely to prove sufficiently attractive to reverse the present trend of the Brazilian population. The possibilities of development in the North, as in most other parts of Brazil, are fundamentally restricted by lack of people.

The great blank spot on the map of population is not likely soon to be filled. Not that the land, because of its inherent character, prohibits the settlement of white people in this region; not that the technical skill of the Occidental peoples is insufficient to solve the problem of tropical living; but rather that the application of this technical knowledge is rendered impossible at present by the attitudes, traditions, and systems of living of Occidental people. So the Syrian trader, thoroughly adjusted to the situation as it exists, continues to grow rich; flurries of speculative fever from time to time stir the cities and send people scurrying over the grass-grown streets. Still, from the midst of the encircling woods, the great orange and green dome of the Manaus opera house stands as a supreme monument to the poetic aspirations of a people intoxicated by a moment of easy wealth.

Chapter VIII

BRAZIL AS A POLITICAL UNIT

NEARLY HALF of the continent of South America belongs to the United States of Brazil. But most of this enormous territory, whatever may be its possibilities, remains empty. Although more than half of the people of South America are Brazilians, the land they occupy is so vast that in only a few isolated areas have they been able to build up a population density greater than ten persons per square mile. Most of Brazil, even after four centuries, remains a frontier land in the sense that a sparse population exerts a minimum of control over it. The spirit of the speculator and the methods of the miner have produced shifting and unstable patterns of people. Yet the urge to obey the slogan *fique rico*,[1] comes more naturally to the imaginative mind of the Brazilian than does the desire for permanence and stability to be won only by less spectacular forms of toil.

A speculative economy is not the peculiar possession of Brazil. In a sense this type of economy characterizes the whole Occidental world. The desire for loot and quick profits motivated the settlement not only of Portuguese and Spanish America, but also of Anglo-America. But in North America and in a few parts of Latin America, the increasing number of people in relation to land and resources diminished the opportunities

[1] *Fique rico* means literally "get rich." It is the slogan of the Federal lotteries of Brazil.

for continued speculative profits. In Brazil speculative economy has survived four centuries of settlement in most parts of the national territory. The continued effort to collect the fruit without planting the tree constitutes the Brazilian variation of the fundamental Latin-American theme in the story of El Dorado.

The definition of the effective national territory is more difficult to make in Brazil than it is in most other countries of Latin America. Between the relatively small areas of the interior from which Brazilian citizens have never derived a profit and in which not even a subsistence economy has ever been established, and the regions of concentrated settlement on or near the Atlantic coast, there is a wide intermediate zone of transition—the lands known as the sertões. In this intermediate zone a very few people, widely scattered, contrive to make a permanent living from a large amount of land. Only intermittently, perhaps, is any one section put to use; only to a very minor degree do these regions contribute to the Brazilian economy as a whole; yet they cannot be entirely excluded from the effective national territory. Nor can the importance of the sertões in the evolution of the Brazilian way of living be measured in terms of the convoys of cattle which emerge from them. The typical Brazilian attitude toward the land, the feeling of futility that frustrates all attempts to advance to a more intensive form of land use and relegates the concepts of the conservation of resources to the realm of academic theory—these attitudes have developed in the presence of the sertões, and these attitudes condition the relation of people to the land even in the centers of Brazilian civilization, even in the great cities.

These generalizations do not constitute a criticism of Brazil or of Brazilians. In fact, the achievement of the Portuguese Americans in building a civilization of their own when considered against this background of vast area is recognized as a major accomplishment, and one which justifies the belief that among all the nations of Latin America Brazil possesses the greatest possibilities of future development. During the past four hundred years Brazil has struggled with an unbroken circle of cause and effect relations: a sparse population in the midst of vast area leads to a continuation of the speculative economy, to destructive exploitation, and to lack of stability; and exploitation and lack of stability lead to a continuation of the condition of sparse population. Brazil is one of the few parts of the world which, in terms of the present world economy, needs more people. A great flood of immigration, furnishing the man power necessary to develop a "westward movement" might break the circle and support the kind of chaotic development which led to the settlement of most of the United States between 1870 and 1914. In recent years such a flood of immigrants could not have been welcomed to Brazil without serious danger; and the Brazilian leaders are inclined to favor a slower and perhaps, in the long run, sounder spread of settlement over the interior. In the meantime, the Brazilian economy remains speculative, exploitive, and unstable.

THE BRAZILIAN ECONOMY

Sugar, gold, and coffee have, in turn, ruled Brazil. To a lesser degree several other products—rubber, for example—have gained places of prominence, but these other products either have not been important enough, or have not remained important long enough, to enable their producers to exert a powerful influence on the affairs of the nation as a whole. Each of these three ruling products has, one after the other, dominated a period of economic history, and each has supported the settlement of a different region.

Exports

Since the last days of the Empire, coffee has been Brazil's leading export product; and during this period Brazil has maintained her position as the world's leading coffee producer. In

1938, of all the coffee exported from Latin America, 57 per cent, in value, was produced in Brazil. The relation, however, of coffee shipment from Brazil to the shipment of other Brazilian products has been changing: in 1928 coffee made up 71 per cent of the total value of Brazilian exports, but since 1936 it has accounted for less than 50 per cent, being only 45 per cent in 1938. This decrease in the proportion of coffee exports is the result not of a decline in the volume of shipments, but rather of a decline in coffee prices and also of a marked increase in the value of other exports. In 1938 Brazil exported over 17,000,000 bags, which was the largest amount in more than a century. The actual volume of production, then, has not declined and, in spite of the program of coffee destruction, huge stocks still fill the warehouses of São Paulo State. Nevertheless to a greater and greater degree other products are increasing in relative importance.

Cotton, which has been the second export product of Brazil in terms of value since the end of the rubber period, has never been one of the country's economic "rulers." Cotton, unlike sugar, coffee, and rubber, did not enter the world market as a new product of which Brazil held a virtual monopoly. Cotton growing in Brazil has brought prosperity only in those years when other sources of supply in the world have failed. Brazil has played the role of a marginal producer, whose participation in the world market becomes possible only when areas of cheaper production cannot meet the demand. During the last half of the eighteenth century, Brazilian cotton, coming almost entirely from the Northeast, held a place of importance on the European market, but a decline of cotton prices during the early part of the nineteenth century, resulting from the increasing shipments from regions where the costs of production were lower, forced the Northeast out of the market. Brazilian cotton was again in demand when the Civil War in the United States curtailed production from the "Cotton Belt." The peak of production at this time came in 1871–72, when 362,130 bales were exported from Brazil, with the Northeast accounting for over 350,000 bales, or about 96 per cent. This figure was not reached again until 1934. During the First World War high prices resulted once more in an increase of cotton growing in Brazil, this time in São Paulo State. In one of the war years São Paulo's share of the Brazilian production was over 50 per cent. Since 1930 the share of the total accounted for by São Paulo has varied from about 30 per cent to nearly 50 per cent. In the periods when Brazil's cotton could not penetrate the international markets, it did find a slowly increasing market in the textile factories of São Paulo. When the United States adopted a policy of cotton restriction in the 1930's Brazil again entered the world markets; in 1938 cotton made up 18 per cent of the value of all exports, and in that year Brazil accounted for 70 per cent of the cotton exported from Latin America. Only in a country of easily shifted agricultural patterns, a country in which agriculture is carried on principally by tenants on large estates, could such great movements in and out of production take place without severe financial dislocations.

The remainder of Brazil's list of exports is a long one, and each of the items accounts for only a small proportion of the whole export trade. Third in terms of value is cacao, with 4.2 per cent in 1938. After cacao, come, in turn, hides and skins (4.1 per cent), oranges (2.2 per cent), Carnauba wax (2 per cent) and many small items making up some 24 per cent.

In the purchase of Brazilian products the United States has long been in the lead. More than half of Brazil's coffee finds its market there (54.7 per cent in 1938). After the United States, but with much smaller purchases, come France, Germany, and other European nations. None of Brazil's cotton, however, goes to the United States. As a result of the increase of cotton exports from Brazil, the proportion of her exports going to the United States has dropped. In 1938 the United States took 34.3 per cent of Brazil's exports, Germany 19.1 per cent, and Great Britain

8.8 per cent. Germany made big gains in that year because of the barter arrangements by which machinery was exchanged for cotton.

Imports

Before the First World War Brazil's imports consisted of coal and a great variety of manufactured articles. The great expansion of the industries of Brazil during the last two decades has resulted, however, in certain major changes in the list of imports. Machinery now stands first on the list, for Brazil possesses neither the equipment nor the skill to compete in machine tooling. In 1938, machinery made up more than 50 per cent of the value of imports. Wheat is now the second item, though for a time it was first. After these two items come iron and steel in the form of rods, bars, sheets, tubes, and rails. Coal and gasoline are still high on the list in spite of heavily subsidized national industries in coal mining and oil refining. There is a long list of lesser items.

The period just before the outbreak of the Second World War witnessed competition between Germany and the United States for first place among the countries sending these commodities to Brazil. While exchange difficulties were handicapping the payments for goods from North America, Germany was ready to barter locomotives for cotton. In both 1937 and 1938 Germany ranked first by a fraction of a per cent, as well as can be judged by computations and estimates of the values involved in the barter arrangements. Nevertheless, the total trade of the United States with Brazil was increased during those years. Germany, in 1938, was credited with 25 per cent of Brazil's imports, the United States with 24.2 per cent. Third on the list, with 11.8 per cent, was Argentina, which was the chief source of Brazil's wheat imports. Fourth was Great Britain, with 10.4 per cent.

Relation of Exports and Imports to Population Centers

Brazil's foreign trade is to a large extent concentrated in a few regions. Of all exports in terms of value in the period 1936–37, 48 per cent came from São Paulo State. Most of the exporting was through the port of Santos. Only 11 per cent was exported through Rio de Janeiro, and 7 per cent (mostly cacao) through Salvador. The import trade, on the other hand, is mainly concentrated in Rio de Janeiro (41 per cent) and Santos (38 per cent); the third port is Rio Grande do Sul with only 5 per cent.

There are two main reasons for this concentration of the imports at Rio de Janeiro and Santos. In the first place, in the federal capital and in São Paulo and its hinterland live the majority of the Brazilians who can buy things from abroad. Here are the chief markets for locomotives, for industrial machinery, and for automobiles; in these cities are most of the people who eat white bread; in Rio de Janeiro and São Paulo are most of the new buildings which require such construction materials as re-enforcing rods and beams—though some are also found in Porto Alegre. In the second place, Rio de Janeiro has become the chief distributing point from which imported goods are shipped by coasting steamer to the other parts of the country, from Rio Grande do Sul to Manaus.

Domestic Trade

Rio de Janeiro is the hub of internal trade. Of the goods exported by coasting steamers for Brazilian destinations in 1937, Rio de Janeiro accounted for 30 per cent; and of the goods imported from other Brazilian ports, Rio de Janeiro received 19 per cent. As long as Brazil's areas of concentrated settlement remain near the coast, the continued supremacy of Rio de Janeiro in terms of domestic trade would seem to be assured.

No other Latin-American country can look forward to such a continued development of domestic commerce as Brazil. This estimate is justified not only because of the relatively large number of people within the limits of one political unit, but also because of the great variety of resources and products which exist within Brazil's vast area. Potential products range from those of the tropics to those of the middle latitudes; and from those of the farm and ranch to those of the mine and the factory. The adoption of protective tariffs has increased the internal exchange of goods, and the abolition of the state export duties in 1930 has still further aided the free flow of commodities from one part of the country to another. Nearly half of the coastwise trade in 1936 consisted of manufactured articles; about a third was made up of foodstuffs; and the remainder comprised various raw materials and livestock. Any movement leading to an increase of the purchasing power of the rural Brazilians would have enormous repercussions on the growth of domestic trade and domestic industries.

Probably Brazil must be listed among the very few countries in the world still possessing opportunities for the expansion of industries based on the exploitation of still essentially untouched resources. The extraordinary material growth of the United States was produced by the simultaneous expansion of urban industries and the growth of the farm frontier. In the United States the frontier has practically disappeared but in Brazil there is still an opportunity for pioneer expansion on the margins of settlement, and for the simultaneous growth of manufacturing industries in the cities.

MANUFACTURING INDUSTRIES

Manufacturing industries have been growing in Brazil since 1889. To a notable degree they are concentrated in the two great cities of São Paulo and Rio de Janeiro and in the smaller towns around these cities. At the present time São Paulo is the largest center of manufacturing industries in all of Latin America. In São Paulo and the towns around it there was concentrated in 1938 as much as 43 per cent of all the industrial investment in Brazil. Of the total of this investment, 73 per cent was located in and near Rio de Janeiro and São Paulo, and 10 per cent was in and near Porto Alegre. Furthermore, this concentration in the Southeast and in São Paulo was increasing, for in 1907 the proportion of the total investment located in these regions was only 61 per cent.

The specific reasons for this localization of manufacturing are somewhat different for each industry. There are six facts concerning São Paulo, however, which seem to be directly or indirectly involved in each case. These are: (1) São Paulo is the urban center of the region which has recently passed through one of Brazil's major economic cycles of speculative profit, and as a result this city enjoys a concentration of wealth and a spirit of economic optimism; (2) São Paulo and Rio de Janeiro, as explained previously, are located at the center of Brazil's domestic market and are closely connected with that market by coasting steamer; (3) these advantages have led to a concentration in these two cities of both domestic and foreign investment in new enterprises; (4) the first-class hydro-electric systems which have been built to serve both São Paulo and Rio de Janeiro provide an abundance of low-cost power; (5) in these cities there is gradually being built up a reservoir of trained industrial workers; and (6) because of all these advantages the tempo of the economic life is quicker in these cities than it is elsewhere in Brazil.

Modern industries first appeared in Brazil after 1889—after the abolition of slavery and the beginning of the republican era. Small scale industries serving restricted localities existed long before this, and still survive, even close to São Paulo. The process of transition from the "feudal" type of local industry—preserved because of high cost of transportation—to modern large-scale establishments can be studied from the historical records of the Industrial Revolution in Western Europe: this same process can be observed in the field today in Brazil.

The rate of industrial progress was slow at first. Even in 1913 Brazil was largely dependent on foreign sources for most of its manufactured goods. In that year Brazil imported about 30 per cent of the cotton textiles and 60 per cent of the woolen textiles that were consumed. Brazil even imported as much as 30 per cent of its jerked beef. But the First World War cut off the sources of these supplies and greatly accelerated the rate of domestic industrial growth. The total industrial investment in 1907 was only 669,000 contos; by 1920 investment had increased to 3,200,000 contos. Investment continued to increase at a more and more rapid rate, reaching 20,000,000 contos in 1938, and 25,000,000 contos in 1940.

The number of manufacturing establishments and the number of workers also showed an increasing rate of growth. In 1907 there were 2,988 establishments and 136,420 industrial workers in Brazil. By 1920 there were 13,336 establishments and 275,512 workers; and by 1938 there were 70,026 establishments and 1,412,432 workers.

Such a large increase in the number of industrial workers in Brazil could not have taken place without either a large immigration or a movement from the rural districts toward the urban centers. Immigration was greatly reduced during the period following the First World War and became nothing more than a trickle after 1930. Most of the new urban wage workers were former tenants on the coffee estates of São Paulo, or had been engaged in other rural pursuits elsewhere in Brazil. The rise of the great cities of São Paulo and Rio de Janeiro has been accompanied by a decline in the rural population of the hinterlands of these cities.

In Brazil as a whole the processing of foodstuffs is the most important industrial activity; the foodstuff industries made up 34 per cent of the total in 1938. The Second World War has brought increased attention to foodstuffs, especially to the canning of meat. Nevertheless, many other kinds of industry have been established in Brazil. These include textile manufactures of all kinds, iron and steel, clothing, chemicals, and many others. In 1913 Brazil exported 37 different kinds of manufactured or semimanufactured items; in 1941 Brazil exported 457 different manufactured items of which 253 were finished manufactures. All these data reveal in one way or another the extraordinary industrial growth of the country and the increasing variety and complexity of its industrial structure.

Foodstuff Manufactures

The foodstuff industries, which stood first on the list of all Brazilian industries in 1938, include a variety of types. The meat packing industries stand first, and these have advanced most rapidly during the Second World War. Other foodstuff enterprises include the processing of coffee, sugar, and grains, the milling of wheat, and the manufacture of beverages and dairy products. Of all the food industries 27 per cent of the total value of production in 1938 came from São Paulo State, where meat packing was the leading item. Meat was also the leading item in the second and third states—in Rio Grande do Sul, which produced 17 per cent of the total, and in Minas Gerais which produced 16 per cent. The city of Rio de Janeiro was fourth, producing 13 per cent of the total; but here the foodstuff industries consisted largely of the processing of coffee and grains and the milling of imported wheat.

The importance of cattle in the rural economy of Brazil, not only in the sertões but also in the progressive agricultural area of São Paulo State, is reflected in the position of the meat packing industries. Even excluding the production of xarque, which supplies the cheaper domestic trade, Brazil produces more than a million tons of meat per year. Most of it is beef, and only a small proportion is pork and mutton. Since the Brazilian beef cattle come from the open ranges of the interior they are not carefully bred, as are the high-quality animals of the Argentine Humid Pampa; furthermore, the meat is relatively lean since the animals are fattened on grass, not on maize or alfalfa. Before the present war Brazilian beef was favored among the Italians for its lean quality, but it did not find favor on the British market where fat meat is preferred. However, most of the Brazilian meat is used for canning, and in this form it competes in Great Britain and the United States with the Argentine product.

Three Brazilian states are of chief importance in the production of meats. These are Rio Grande do Sul, which in 1938 produced 24 per cent of the Brazilian total, São Paulo, which produced 23 per cent, and Minas Gerais, which produced 22 per cent. A fourth Brazilian state, Rio de Janeiro, produced only 5 per cent of the total.

As stated previously, there are many other kinds of foodstuff manufacturing establishments in Brazil beside those engaged in the processing of meat. In São Paulo and Rio de Janeiro there are industries engaged in the processing of coffee, rice, and maize. In Porto Alegre and the port of Rio Grande do Sul there are plants engaged in the processing of oats and barley. The milling of wheat is largely concentrated in Rio de Janeiro—70 per cent of the total—because most of the wheat consumed in Brazil is imported from Argentina, and most of the people who can afford to eat white bread live in Rio de Janeiro and São Paulo. As a reflection of the large number of people of Italian origin in São Paulo, we may note that 60 per cent of all the establishments for the manufacture of macaroni and spaghetti are in this state. Minas Gerais leads Brazil in dairy products—50 per cent of the butter and 63 per cent of the cheese. Only in the processing of sugar and the manufacture of alcohol does the Northeast appear: Pernambuco produces 32 per cent of the alcohol; but even in the case of this product, the next three states are São Paulo—14 per cent, the state of Rio de Janeiro—13 per cent, and Minas Gerais—13 per cent.

Like the wheat milling industries, the Brazilian breweries are mostly dependent on imported raw materials. Beer of very good quality is produced in both large and small establishments; the small ones, as might be expected, are most numerous in the German areas of the South. Of all the Brazilian beer, 47 per cent is manufactured in Rio de Janeiro, 40 per cent in São Paulo, 8 per cent in Rio Grande do Sul, and 3 per cent in Paraná.

Wine is not so important as beer in the Brazilian market, and, unlike beer, is produced from local resources. Brazil does not possess the type of climate best suited for this kind of industry, but from the vineyards of Rio Grande do Sul cheap wines are produced for the domestic market. Of the Brazilian total, 80 per cent is manufactured in Rio Grande do Sul.

Brazil produces large amounts of mineral water, both natural and artificial. Minas Gerais leads in the natural mineral waters. Such famous mineral springs as those of Lambarí, Caxambú, and São Lorenço produce 40 per cent of the total. São Paulo produces 21 per cent from its mineral springs, such as those of Lindoia and Prata. These waters are sold all over the country. Of the artificial mineral waters, São Paulo produces 44 per cent and Rio de Janeiro 25 per cent.

Textile Manufactures

Second in the chief groups of industries in Brazil are the textile industries. The production of textiles increased 23 per cent between 1938 and 1940 and the growth continues at an accelerated rate. Brazil's domestic market is not yet adequately supplied from these industries; but with the aid of a protective tariff considerable continued growth can be anticipated, and the raw materials can be had within the country.

São Paulo leads in the textile field. This region produces 39 per cent of the cotton textiles, 43 per cent of the wool textiles, and 77 per cent of the silk and rayon textiles. Cotton textile factories are numerous also in Minas Gerais, where 16 per cent of the Brazilian total is produced; in Pernambuco, 11 per cent; in Rio de Janeiro city, 10 per cent; and in the state of Rio de Janeiro, 9 per cent. Woolen textile plants are also found in Rio de Janeiro city, 24 per cent, and in Minas Gerais, 4 per cent; but in this field Rio Grande do Sul occupies a position second only to São Paulo, producing 27 per cent of the total. Most of the raw wool comes from this southernmost state and must be shipped to the factories of São Paulo and Rio de Janeiro. Of the silk and rayon textiles, Pernambuco produces 18 per cent, and the state of Rio de Janeiro produces 3 per cent.

Considering the pool of skilled textile workers being built up in São Paulo city, the continued supremacy of this industrial center can be expected. It is not at all improbable that in the post-war period the São Paulo industries may expand enough to supply exports to other Latin American countries in competition with the ordinary grades of textiles from Great Britain and the United States.

Iron and Steel Manufactures

Brazil has very real opportunities for the development of large-scale iron and steel plants. The great ore deposits and some of the conditions regarding their use have already been described (p. 111 ff). During the period between the First World War and the Second World War, Brazil's domestic market for iron and steel manufactures was between 300,000 and 400,000 tons a year. Of this amount only 35 per cent was supplied in 1938 from domestic industries, and 65 per cent had to be imported. After the present war the need for replacements and new construction in Brazil will result in a large increase in the domestic requirements for iron and steel, and it is estimated that by 1950 the market should be able to absorb some 600,000 tons per year. The new steel plant which is being built at Volta Redonda, located in the Paraíba Valley a little west of Barra Mansa, is planned to produce about 300,000 tons of iron and steel per year. It is estimated that the plants already in operation can expand sufficiently to account for another 300,000 tons. The new plant will be known as the *Companhia*

Siderúrgica Nacional de Volta Redonda. The very difficult problems which must be met both in the expansion of the steel industries already in operation and in the supply of raw materials and fuel to the Volta Redonda plant have already been examined.

At the present time Minas Gerais leads all the rest of Brazil in total production of iron and steel manufactures. In this state were produced, in 1938, 91 per cent of the pig iron, 55 per cent of the rolled iron, and 60 per cent of the steel. Minas Gerais produced in that year 65 per cent of all the iron and steel products, while São Paulo produced 20 per cent and the State of Rio de Janeiro produced 14 per cent. Since Volta Redonda is located in the State of Rio de Janeiro, these proportions will change radically in the years after the war. Eventually Brazil should be ready to enter the export field.

Clothing Manufactures

Next in order of importance in Brazil as a whole are the clothing industries. While the Brazilian industries cannot produce clothing of a quality to equal the best grades of Europe and North America, still a very good grade of clothing is being manufactured. Where style is important, as in the shoe business, Brazilian shoes, styled in the Brazilian manner, can compete with the best imported products.

In the clothing industries São Paulo stands far in the lead. This leadership is based not only on the presence of capital to be invested and on the easy access to the large domestic market, but also on the supply of cheap but increasingly skilled labor available in the city of São Paulo. São Paulo produces 61 per cent of the clothing, while Rio de Janeiro city produces 11 per cent, Rio Grande do Sul 11 per cent, and Minas Gerais 6 per cent. When boots and shoes are considered alone, Rio Grande do Sul stands somewhat higher on the list. São Paulo produces 50 per cent of the footwear manufactured in Brazil, Rio Grande do Sul 20 per cent, Rio de Janeiro city 12 per cent, and Minas Gerais 7 per cent.

Other Manufactures

There are many other kinds of manufacturing industries in Brazil, and the list is growing year by year in length and in variety. To indicate the complexity of the Brazilian industrial structure it may be sufficient to describe briefly only a few other types: leather, chemicals, matches, rubber, paper, wood, and tobacco.

São Paulo occupies first place in the production of tanned leather. Of the total Brazilian production 36 per cent comes from São Paulo, 19 per cent from Minas Gerais, 13 per cent from Rio Grande do Sul, and 10 per cent from Rio de Janeiro. São Paulo and Rio de Janeiro enjoy a distinct advantage over Rio Grande do Sul in the tanning of leather since all the tanning materials are imported. Rio Grande do Sul exports most of its hides in crude form.

São Paulo leads in the chemical field, producing 41 per cent, while Rio de Janeiro city produces 34 per cent. The chemical industries are closely tied to foreign sources of raw materials. Before the beginning of the Second World War most of these industries were carried on by branches of the large European chemical industries, notably those of Germany.

São Paulo produces 46 per cent of the matches manufactured in Brazil. The city of Rio de Janeiro produces 28 per cent, Paraná 13 per cent, Rio Grande do Sul 8 per cent, and Santa Catarina 4 per cent. The match industries in Paraná and Santa Catarina are related to the common use of Paraná pine for the sticks.

In the production of rubber goods the city of Rio de Janeiro led Brazil with 55 per cent of the total until 1939, but new establishments in São Paulo city have now taken the lead away from the national capital. There are also small rubber industries in Belém and in Porto Alegre, the latter specializing in the manufacture of rubber tubing and raincoats.

São Paulo leads Brazil in the manufacture of wood products and paper. Of the wood products 54 per cent come from São Paulo, and 11 per cent from Rio de Janeiro. The greater part of São Paulo's wood products are various items of furniture; São Paulo manufactures 73 per cent of Brazil's furniture. This furniture industry is based in part on the abundant sources of cabinet woods of great variety in western São Paulo State and northwestern Paraná. Along the western frontier in these states there are numerous small saw mills from which boards and logs are sent to São Paulo city by rail. The furniture industry is notable for its new combinations of woods and its new designs. São Paulo also produces 50 per cent of the paper manufactured in Brazil, using chiefly imported wood pulp. With an increase in the utilization of the Paraná pine for pulp, São Paulo and Paraná can be expected to continue as leaders in the manufacture of paper.

In 1939 the city of Rio de Janeiro led Brazil in the production of cigarettes, 38 per cent of the total. Tobacco for this industry was brought by steamer from Rio Grande do Sul, which grows 60 per cent of Brazil's tobacco, and from Bahia and other parts of the Northeast and North. In addition certain brands make use of imported tobaccos. The State of Bahia leads in the production of cigars, which have long been manufactured in Salvador. The Bahia factories produce 74 per cent of the Brazilian cigars.

With a varied industrial structure already in existence, São Paulo offers advantages for new industrial establishments which cannot be offered by other cities in Brazil. The abundance of hydro-electric power, the increasing supply of trained factory workers, and the more intangible but nevertheless real advantage offered by the faster tempo of life: these all contribute to increase the rate of industrial growth. Recently it was reported that a process has at last been discovered for the use of coffee beans in the manufacture of plastics. A new substance made from the coffee bean, cafelite, is to be manufactured in São Paulo city, and will enter largely into the export field. It is said to combine easily with rubber or Carnauba Wax and to possess other desirable qualities which will insure it an important place on the world markets. The Brazilians estimate that the new plant will consume something like 5,000,000 bags of coffee a year.

Difficulties of Industrial Development

Industrial development in Brazil has not gone forward without difficulties. As in all productive enterprises in Brazil, the foremost problem is the labor supply. Brazil also lacks a sufficient domestic production of metals, chemicals, and fuels; and the transportation system, with the few exceptions already noted in previous chapters, is quite inadequate to support a major industrial growth. Since all these deficiencies interact on one another, the first steps taken in the establishment of large-scale manufacturing industries have been attended by very serious problems.

In spite of the chronic shortage of labor in Brazil, the prevailing wage scales are very low. In 1938, more than 22 per cent of the Brazilian workers received less than one hundred cruzeiros (about $5.00) per month. Minimum wage laws are in force for six regions of the country and are based on the cost of living in these six areas. The minimum in Rio de Janeiro in 1938 was two hundred and forty cruzeiros a month (about $12.00).[2] A general rise in the wages of industrial workers would result in a very large increase in the domestic market for manufactured goods, and in a general quickening of the tempo of Brazilian economic life.

Such an increase in the prosperity of urban workers, however, would not only enlarge the market for manufactured

[2] See the description of Brazilian industrial development in José Jobim, *Brazil in the Making*, New York, 1943.

goods and so hasten the construction of new industrial establishments, but would also lead to a demand for more workers. Eventually the rural districts of Brazil will suffer a serious depletion of population as more and more of the able-bodied workers leave for the cities. Far from developing a westward movement, such as pushed the farm frontier across the United States at the same time that North American cities were growing, in Brazil the growth of the cities will result in a stagnation or even a retrogression of the frontier. Only a very great increase in the national rate of population growth, through a vigorous program of health and nutrition, and a considerable increase in the volume of immigration can remedy this situation.

IMMIGRATION PROBLEM

Brazil, therefore, is faced today with no problem of more fundamental significance than the problem of immigration. Since 1822 a little more than 4,600,000 foreigners have come to Brazil, about half of them to remain. This figure places Brazil second only to Argentina in numbers of immigrants in Latin America. The following table shows the national composition of the immigrants:

IMMIGRATION INTO BRAZIL BY PRINCIPAL NATIONALITIES[3] 1822 TO 1937

Nationality	*Number of People*	*Percentage*
Italians	1,502,958	32.6
Portuguese	1,394,156	30.3
Spanish	595,002	12.9
German	222,951	4.9
Japanese	180,359	3.9
Russian	116,398	2.5
Others		12.9

[3] Figures from the Pan American Union.

The figures in this table have been greatly modified in the more recent period. The Italians have dropped far below their previous position, and the Japanese have moved up to first place because of the large numbers coming between 1920 and 1935. The following table presents the immigration statistics for two periods—between 1920 and 1930, and between 1931 and 1937:

AVERAGE ANNUAL IMMIGRATION INTO BRAZIL OF SELECTED NATIONALITIES BY PERIODS [4]

Nationality	*1920–1930*	*1931–1937*
Japanese	6,578	11,387
Portuguese	29,150	7,461
German	7,271	2,236
Italian	10,099	1,856
Polish	2,977	1,684
Spanish	7,741	1,211

Control of Immigration

Of all the various peoples who came to Brazil before 1914, few brought with them such strong feelings of national sentiment that they could not accept loyalty to a new flag. But since the First World War national feeling has run high, and immigrants, especially from Italy and Germany, have been filled with such strong patriotism that assimilation in the Brazilian pattern would seem most difficult. The Brazilians feared the undigested alien groups. In 1934, therefore, a policy of immigration restriction was established; and a new and carefully restated code governing the arrival of foreign immigrants in Brazil was adopted in 1938.

The new code not only limits future immigration in proportion to the nationalities already represented among the Brazilian people, but it also greatly restricts the arrival of people who would elect to stay in the cities. The quotas are assigned in

[4] Ibid.

proportion to the total number of immigrants of any one nationality who entered the country between 1884 and 1933, but no nation is given a quota of less than 3,000 a year. The system is quite flexible, however, for quotas can be shifted from time to time by action of the commission in charge of immigration. The code also states that 80 per cent of each quota must be made up of farmers or rural technicians and that these must remain in their rural occupations for at least four consecutive years after their arrival. As a matter of fact, the recruiting of farm immigrants is a very difficult matter, for most people, other than refugees, who desire to come to the New World, whether to North or South America, hold pecuniary gain as a primary motive. As long as pecuniary gain is attractive in rural pursuits, as when many small proprietors have an opportunity to pocket the increase of land values resulting from the progress of settlement—the unearned increment—immigrants may be willing and anxious to become farmers. But when the unearned increment is taken by the large landowners, or has already been taken by the first generation of owners, pecuniary gain must be sought chiefly from the wages of urban industries. Most of the immigrants desiring to come to Brazil before the beginning of the Second World War wished to remain in the large and growing cities; to get them permanently into rural pursuits was so difficult that labor shortage remained chronic on the coffee fazendas of São Paulo State. Only the Japanese and some of the nationalities of eastern Europe (Lithuanians, Russians, and Poles) furnished immigrants who chose to remain in the rural areas. What the refugees from a war-torn Europe may be willing to do in the future, however, is another matter.

The new immigration code also contains provisions which regulate the establishment of colonies of foreigners in Brazil. In each new pioneer colony to be established from now on, at least 30 per cent must be made up of people born in Brazil, and not more than 25 per cent can be made up of foreign-born people of any one nationality. This part of the code also regulates the teaching of foreign languages in the schools, and prohibits the operation of foreign schools in rural districts. The whole program is aimed at the protection of Brazil from the formation of large alien groups in which the Portuguese language and Brazilian institutions are not predominant. The difficulty is that most Brazilians prefer urban life; they do not wish to become pioneer colonists, or, at best, they are willing to undertake rural pursuits only temporarily and for the sake of rapid profits. Under this code—to say nothing of the effect the Second World War has on the migration of people—no large increase in immigration to Brazil can be expected.

Areas of Potential Settlement

No discussion of the population capacity of Brazil or of the possibilities of pioneer settlement has any validity unless it takes into consideration not only the attitude toward immigration held by the Brazilian government but also the attitudes of the immigrants themselves. Until we know who the settlers are, what their objectives are, what their equipment not only of capital but also of technical knowledge is, what their capacity for rural labor is, and in what kind of economic and social environment they must operate—until we are able to analyze all these factors, we can make no true estimate of the significance of the nature of the land with which the pioneers would have to deal. It may be true that 80 or 90 per cent of Brazilian territory is potentially productive for farming or grazing under present conditions; but if 80 or 90 per cent of the Brazilian territory, or even half that percentage, were actually utilized, present conditions would no longer exist. A westward movement would not perpetuate the way of living now successfully practiced in the sertão. The statement made by Freise that slopes up to an inclination of 35° may be considered arable presupposes cultivation carried on with a hoe—or even with a pointed stick; but if we think of cultivation in terms of the use of a plow, the proportion of arable Brazilian land must be greatly reduced.

If measured strictly in terms of "present conditions," which will not be changed by the process of settlement itself, the parts of Brazil which can be considered immediately available for pioneer settlement are few. Only in the South are Brazilian-born citizens to be found who are not reluctant to engage in the hard labor of frontier colonization without the hope of speculative gain. There are plenty of Brazilians ready to work hard where the chances of spectacular rewards are sufficiently good; but settlement with this objective has produced only the hollow frontier, not the kind of stabilized population which is contemplated when either Brazilians or foreign students of Brazil speak of pioneer settlement. Three requirements must be met before colonies of farmers can be established in close attachment to the land: first, a supply of people who are willing and eager to become permanent rural settlers must be found; second, land physically suited to the kind of agriculture they are capable of practicing must be identified and delimited; and third, this land must be made accessible to a market either by all-weather road or railroad. The latter requirement is essential because even those pioneers who may be willing to forego gamblers' chances for quick profits are nevertheless unwilling to bury themselves in a wilderness where they must produce not only food and clothing for themselves, but also tools and machines. The opportunity to sell a steady surplus of products and the ability to purchase the countless little gadgets that today have become more than luxuries are not to be denied modern colonists if their attempt at pioneer settlement is to be successful.

Our discussion of the various parts of Brazil indicates that pioneer lands which satisfy these requirements are by no means easy to find. The most important area of this sort is in the forests of western Paraná and Santa Catarina, and northwestern Rio Grande do Sul. Possibly certain parts, perhaps a large part, of southern Mato Grosso should be included as potential pioneer land. Close to the suburbs of Rio de Janeiro and São Paulo reclamation activities are making considerable areas of swamp land available for cultivation—a kind of internal frontier zone. Compared with the vast size of Brazil, and considered in terms of the prevailing attitude regarding the inexhaustible possibilities of the land, the total area of potential pioneer settlement is small indeed; yet it is the largest such area in South America, and perhaps one of the largest in the world.

THE BRAZILIAN CITIES

Our study of the different regions of Brazil brings to light the fact that, outside of the expanding colonies of small farmers in the South, the rest of Brazilian settlement is governed by two strongly opposed tendencies: the tendency to excessive dispersal, and the tendency to excessive concentration. One leads to the sertão; the other leads to the city. One causes rural families, even of the chief regions of settlement, to seek places for their homes which are out of sight of all their neighbors; the other causes urban families, even in some of the smaller towns, to have their homes as close together as possible. The complex social and economic factors which produce these tendencies have yet to be investigated; their results on the present arrangement of people, however, may be observed and described.

In a country where so few physical barriers impede the spread of people from the primary centers of settlement, the tendency to dispersal results in a widely scattered population. In most areas today the density of settlement is insufficient either to admit of the enjoyment of anything more than a frontier mode of living, or to provide the human contacts necessary for the evolution of what we may call, for want of a more specific phrase, a civilized society. The only period of Brazilian history when a rural aristocracy was actually attached to the land was the period of the sugar plantations—and the place was the sugar region of the Northeast. Otherwise, only in the cities did the Brazilians concentrate in sufficient numbers and with sufficient density to advance their manner of living beyond the rude conditions of a frontier society. In the larger cities were concentrated the activities and interests derived from a wide extent of sparsely or temporarily occupied land. Whatever there is, therefore, of stability and permanence in each region of settlement is to be found in its urban nucleus. Here the Brazilian way of living reaches its highest or most elaborate expression.

The contrast thus developed between city and sertão has been growing ever more profound. But because there is no geographical separation between political areas which are predominantly feudal and political areas which are predominantly industrial, it would be difficult to conceive of a Brazilian civil war based on really fundamental issues.

For all their imported ideas, however, the Brazilian cities still eloquently express the basic qualities of the people who built them. If it may be said that the Brazilians are more inclined to poetry than to economics the characterization finds illustration in such uses of public funds as the construction of the Manaus opera house, or the rearrangement of the central section of Rio de Janeiro. If over one of the poorest slum districts of the national capital there blazes forth every night a huge electric sign with the words *Fique rico*, this, too, is an expression of an attitude of mind by no means submerged by the incoming tide of industrialization. The modern period, in fact, is marked by the concentration of speculative fever in these very cities where increasing population, rapid new construction, and rapidly rising land values are bringing new wealth. The cities, viewed in this perspective, offer no small part of the answer to the riddle of empty Brazil.

INDEX

(Figures in italics refer to pages on which maps are to be found.)

Acre Terr., *23,* 210, 225
Alagôas state, *6, 23, 56,* 58, 59
Alegrete, *9*
Alfredo Chaves, *9,* 187
Amapá, *23*
Amazon Region, *211. See* North Brazil
Amazon R., 209-216, *211, 212, 213, 214, 215*
Amazonas state, *23, 215*
Anapolis, 169
Aracajú, *6, 23*
Araçatuba, *8*
Araguaia R., *211*
Araguarí, *8,* 146
Araraquara, *8*
Araucaria forest, *21,* 24, 130

Bagé, *9, 173*
Bahia, city, *32;* State, *23,* 34, 45, 48; cacao district of, 62-64; diamonds, 54; land tenure, 64; Negroes, 61; population, *72;* sertão, 115; sugar, 98
Bahia de Sepitiba, 123
Baixada Fluminense, 77; pioneer settlement, 110
Bananal, 7
Bananas, *90, 142,* 155
Bandeirantes, 37, 131-132, 162, 183-184; routes, *32*
Barbacena, 7
Barra do Piraí, 7
Barra Mansa, 7, *90*
Barretos, *8*
Baurú, 8, 146
Bauxite, *214*
Belém, *23, 32, 211, 212;* colonial settlements, 220, 221, 225; rubber, 223, 224
Belo Horizonte, 7, *23, 75;* growth and importance of, 95, 96; railroad, 92, 93; temperature, 78
Belterra, Ford plantation, *211,* 229
Bertholletia excelsa nuts, 228
Billings, A. W. K., 151
Blumenau, *9, 173;* European settlement, 195, 196, 197; temperature, 181
Blumenau, Herman, 195
Bomfim, *6*
Botocudo Indians, 81
Botucatú, *8*
Bragança, *211, 212*
Branco R., *211, 212,* 216
Brazil, agricultural colleges, 106; cities and the sertão, 255-256; domestic trade, 57, 114, 238-239; foreign trade, 234-235; highest elevation, 435; immigration, 40, 134-136, 250-253; mineral resources, 26; origin of name, 51; physical, 1-10; population, 27, 40-44, 188, 196, 202-203, 206; regions: North, 206-231; Northeast, 45-70, São Paulo, 120-170; South, 171-205; Southeast, 71-119; States and capitals, *23;* steel plant, 112. *See also* under regions.
Brazilian Highlands, 3, 5, 7, 9, 10
Brusque, 7; settlement, 195

Caatinga, 50, 81
Cabo Frio, 7
Caboclos, 200
Cacao, 39, 236, 238; Bahia, 62
Cachoeira de Sete Quedas. *See* Guayra Falls
Cachoeiro, *173*
Caeté, 7, 95; steel plants, 112

Cajú rains, 49
Campina Grande, *6;* fairs, 53
Campinas, *8, 75;* coffee plantations, 141
Campo Belo, 7, 116
Campo cerrado, 81, 165
Campo Grande, 165
Campo limpo, 81, 165
Campos, 7, *75*
Cape São Roque, *6*
Caravellas, *63*
Carnauba wax, 51, 59, 236
Casa Branca, *8*
Castilla ulei tree, 222
Castor oil, 59
Castro, *8*, 200, 201
Cattle. *See* Pastoral economy
Caxaça, 66
Caxambú, 7, 95
Ceará state, *6, 23;* climatic calamities, 67; grazing, 53; population, 56
Central do Brasil, 92, *92*, 100, 113
Chapada do Araripe, *6*, 47; agriculture, 66
Christãos novos, 53
Chromium, 25, 114
Coal, 25, 113, 180, 193-194
Coffee: decline of, 152-154; limits of expansion, 144; Northeast, 57; pattern land use near Taquaritinga, *139;* production and trade, 234-235; São Paulo, 39, 121, 133, 134-145, *140*, *142*, 157-158; Southeast coffee cycle, *90*, 99-100, 109; spread since 1835, *140*
Collatina, 109
Copper, 26, 180
Corn. *See* Maize
Corumbá, 168
Cotton, 39; Amazon and Guinea Coast, 214; different types, 58; Northeast, *55*, 58-59; production and export of, 234; São Paulo, *142*, 145, 149, 150; Southeast, 116; southern Bahia, northern Espírito Santo, *63*
Cresciuma, *177*
Cruzeiro, 7
Cubatão, *8*, 151
Cuiabá, *23;* gold, 37, 162
Curitiba, *8*, *9*, *23*, 160, *173*, 174, 196; European colonies, 199; founded, 200; maté, 201-202; population, 203-204

Devonian cuesta, South Brazil, *8*, *9*, 176
Diabase Plateau. *See* Paraná Plateau
Diamantina, 7, *90;* diamonds, 82
Diamonds, 25; discovery, 37; Northeast, 54; Southeast, 82, *90*, 110, 115
Distrito Federal, *23*
Doce R., 5, 7, 74, 75, 76, 114
Dom Pedro I, 186; — II, 67

Eastern Border Upland, 7
Engenho, 52
Entre Rios, 7
Espírito Santo, *23*, *63*, *72;* cacao district, 62; pioneer settlements, 107-108
Expanding economy, 238-239

Fazendas: Minas Gerais, 88; Northeast, 52, 59-60; São Paulo, 136-141
Federal Territories, *23*
Feira de Sant'Anna, *6;* fairs, 53
Florianópolis, *9*, *23*, *173*, 179, 184; industry, 197; settlement, 195
Ford plantations, *211*, 229-231
Fordlândia. *See* Ford plantations
Forests, effect on Portuguese settlement, 130-131, 162, 183-205
Fortaleza, *6*, *23*, 67
Frost, northern limit in Brazil, 14, 129, 180

German colonies, 107-108, 133, 186-190, 194-198, 199-201
Goiânia, *23*
Goiaz state, *8*, *23*, *143;* sertão, 115, 168-170
Gold, 25, 234; Amazon and Guiana Coast, *214;* discovery and rush, 36-38, 132; Northeast, 54; South, 183; Southeast, 82-83, *90*, 110; decline of importance, 86-87
Grande R., 7, *8*, *75*
Grão Mogol, 7
Grazing. *See* Pastoral economy

Great Escarpment, *4*, 5, 7, *8*, *9*, 9, 10, 76, 77, 122-124, 174
Guanabara Bay, 71
Guaporé, *23*
Guarani Indians, 27-28
Guarapuava, *9*
Guayra Falls, 10, 179
Guiana Highlands, 3

Hevea brasiliensis tree, 222
Humidity, effect on human comfort, 11

Iguapé, port, *8*, 183; —, River, 123
Iguassú, *23*
Iguassú Falls, *9*, 180
Iguassú R., *9*, 180
Ilex paraguayensis, 201
Ilheus, cacao, 62, *63*, 81
Inner lowland, *8*, *9*, 124, 175
Inspetoria Federal de Obras contra as Secas, 68
Intertropical front, *16*, *17*
Iron ore, 3, 25; South 180; Southeast, *90*, 111-114
Itabira, 7, *75*, *90*; iron mines, 114
Itajaí, *9*, *173*, 179, 197
Itajaí R., *9*, 195

Jacareí, 7
Jacuí, R., *9*, *173*, 179, 192; —, Valley, 180, 186, 187, 190-191
Januaria, 116
Japanese in Brazil, 40, 135, 156, 228
Jardim de Seridó, *6*, 58
Jataí, *8*
Javary R., 208
João Pessoa, *6*, *23*
Joazeiro, *6*, 61
Joinville, *9*, 173, 196, 197
Juiz de Fora, 7, *75*, 95, 100
Jundiaí, *8*, 146
Juruá R., 208, *211*
Jute, 97

Lages, *9*, *173*
Lagôa dos Patos, *9*, *173*, *176*, *177*, 179, 192
Lagôa Mirím, *9*, *173*, *176*, *177*
Lambarí, 7, 95
Land: factors in habitability, 217
Lavras, 7, 107
Lead, 26
Limeira, *8*, 133
Londrina, *8*, 160

Maceió, *6*, *23*
Madeira R., 10, 209, 210, *211*
Maize: São Paulo, 145; South, *177*, 186, 191, 197
Mameluco, 37
Manaus, *23*, 210, *211*, *212*; colonial settlements, 221, 224; humidity, 217; rubber, 223-224
Manganese, 26, *90*, 115
Manioc, 28, 197
Manufacturing industries, 239-250; clothing, 246-247; difficulties of development, 249-250; foodstuffs, 242-244; iron and steel, 245-246; reasons for development in São Paulo and Rio de Janeiro, 239-240; textiles, 244-245
Marajó Is., *211*, *212*, 213
Maranhão state, *6*, *23*, *56*; babassú nuts, 228; coffee, 57, *215*; colonial settlements, 219-222
Marañón R., 208
Mariana, 7, 82
Marilia, *8*, 157
Mascates, 116
Massapê, 126
Mata, 81
Maté, 39, *177*; Western Parana, 201
Mato Grosso state, *8*, *23*, *143*; sertão, 165, 167-168
Mestiço, 37
Minas Gerais, *8*, *23*, *63*, 72, *143*; coffee, 99; emigration, 86; gold, 37-38, 54, 82-83, 86-87; iron, 112; pastoral industries, 104-105; sertão, 115, 168-169; sugar, 98
Misiones territory, 202
Missions, 220
Mogi-Mirím, *8*, 124
Montes Claros, 7
Morro Velho, *90*, 111

Mule trade in colonial period: between the Banda Oriental and Southeastern Brazil, 132, 185
Mundo Novo, *8*, 201

Natal, *6*, *23*
Negro R., 208, 210, *211*
Negroes, 27-28, *31*, 36, 61, 100
Niteroi, 7, *23*, *75*
NORTH of Brazil, 206-231, *211;* Ford plantations, *211*, 229-231; land use map, *214;* North American colony, 222; physical, 208-219; population map, 215; rainfall seasons, 18-19; rubber period, 222-227; settlement, 224-225; surface configuration map, *212;* vegetation, *213*, 218-219; Wallace's description, 207
NORTHEAST, 45-70; cacao district, 62-64, *63;* climatic calamities, 14, 16, *22*, 48-51, 66; cotton, 58-59; Dutch invasion, 36; emigration, 54-57; fazenda, 59; land use maps, *55*, *63;* physical, 46-48; physiographic history, 47; population map, *56;* railroads, *55;* sugar plantations, 51-53, 54-58; surface configuration, *6;* vegetation, *50*
Nova Friburgo, 7
Nova Lima, 7, 111

Obidos, 209, *211*, *212*, 221
Oiticica oil, 51, 59
Olinda, 35
Oranges: Southeast, *90;* orange cycle, 103-104; São Paulo, *142*, 155, 158; exports, 236
Ouro Preto, 7, *75;* colonial, 83-84; decline, 95-96
Oyapock R., *212*

Pará, city, *32;* —, state, *23*, *215;* agriculture, 228-229; settlement, 219
Paraíba do Sul, 7, 85
Paraíba, R., 5, 7, *75;* as travel route, 76, 77; capture, 124; —, Valley, *8*, 97; land use, 99-103; proposed steel plant, 113-114
Paraíba state, *6*, *23*, *56;* coffee, 57; cotton, 58-59; typical fazenda, 59-60
Paraná pine. *See* Araucaria
Paraná Plateau, *4*, *8*, *9*, 124, 125, 174, 179
Paraná R., *8*, *9*
Paraná state, *8*, *23*, *143;* maté, 201, 202; physical character, 171-182; population and colonies, *175*, 198-203; settlement, 159-161, 171-172, 184
Paranaguá, *8*, *9*, *173*, 184
Parnaíba, *6*
Paranaíba R., *8*, *75*
Paranapanema R., *8*, 159-160
Pastoral economy: North, 221; Northeast Pastoral Sertão, 65-68; São Paulo Sertão, 165-168; South, 189-191; Southeast, 104-105, 115
Paulo Affonso Falls, *6*, 10
Pelotas, *9*, *173*, 193
Pernambuco, city, *32;* —, state, *6*, *23*, 35, 45, 59; cotton, 58; sugar, 52
Petropolis, 7, *75*, 78
Piauí state, *6*, *23*, *56*, 228
Pico da Bandeira, 5, 7, 74, *75*
Pico de Itatiaia, *75*
Piracicaba, *8*, *75*, 155
Piraí, *8*, 201
Pirapora, 7, 116
Poços de Caldas, 7, 95
Pomba, R., 7, *75*, 76; —, Valley, 99
Pongo de Manseriche, 209
Ponta Grossa, *8*, *9*, *173*, 200
Ponta Porã, *23*
Porto Alegre, *9*, *23*, *173;* industrialization, 192; temperature, 181, 184
Porto Velho, *211;* railroad, 225
Portuguese: characteristics, 28; conquest, 29-38, 81-82; recent immigration, 40, 135, 250-253
Potatoes, 191
Prairie, 130
Purús R., 208, *211*

Recife, *23*, *32*, 35; colonial wealth, 219-220; Dutch and Portuguese in, *6*, 36; rain, *48;* sugar, 52
Recôncavo, Bahia: sugar, 52; Negroes and agriculture, 61
Ribeirão Preto, 7, *8;* coffee, 141
Riberalta, *211*, 225

Rice: Brazil, *55*, *63;* São Paulo, 145; South, *177*, 191, 197; Southeast, *90;* Southeast rice cycle, 100-103
Rio Branco, *23*
Rio Branco, city, *23*, *211*
Rio de Janeiro, city, 7, *23*, 71-72, *75;* coffee, 39; colonial transportation, 84-85; development and modern function, 117-119; founded, 35, 81; railroads, 93-95; temperature and humidity, 11, 14; —, state, *23;* pastoral industries, 72, 98, 104
Rio Grande do Norte, *6*, *23*, *56*
Rio Grande do Sul, port city, *9*, *173*, 193; trade, 238; —, state, *23*, *175;* coal, 193-194; physical character, 172-182; settlement, 172
Rio Grande Upland, 7
Rio Negro, city, *9*, 196
Rio Preto, city, *8*
Roraima Mt., 5, *212*
Rubber, 39, 67, 234; Amazon region Ford plantations, 229-231; "Rubber Period," 222-229; wild and plantation product, 226

Sabará, 7, 82, 95, 112
Salvador, city, *6*, *23*, *32*, *63;* agricultural center, 60-61; colonial, 219; founded, 34; sugar, 34, 52; trade, 238
Santa Barbara, 7
Santa Catarina, state, *23*, *175;* coal, 113, 194; physical character, 172-182; settlement, 41, 171-172, 183, 194-198
Santa Cruz, 7, *9*, 191
Santa Maria, *9*, *173*, 181, 193
Sant'Anna do Livramento, *9*, 193
Santarém, 209, *211*, *212;* settlement, 221; temperature, 11, 217
Santos (São Vicente), 7, *8*, 35, *75;* emigration to South, 183; sugar, 35; temperature, 127, 181; trade, 238
São Carlos, *8*, 141
São Francisco, *9*, *173*, 184
São Francisco, R., *6*, 7, *10*, 75, 197; —, Valley, 115
São Jerônimo, *177*, 180; coal, 194
São João del Rey, 7, 82
São Leopoldo, *9*, 186, 188
São Luiz, *6*, *23*, *32*, *211*, 216; climatic data, 48; colonial wealth, 220; shipping center, 228
São Paulo, city, 148-152, 169-170; climate, 127; colonial roads, 84-85; founded, 130; industrial, 149-151; primary settlement center, 37, 161-169, 183-186; railroads, *92*, 92-93, 146, 151
SÃO PAULO, region, 120-170; frontier, 156-161; immigration, 134-136; land use, *142*, 145, 160-161; motor trucks, 164; physical, 122-130; population, 134, *143;* railroads, *92*, *140*, *142*, 145-146; roads, *140;* sertões, 161-165; settlement, 130-133, 141-145; settlement of Minas Gerais, 37; settlement of South Brazil, 182-186; sugar, 57, 98; surface configuration maps, *8*, *75;* trade, 239-240; vegetation map, *129*. *See also* Coffee, Oranges, manufacturing industries
São Sebastião Island, 7
São Vicente. *See* Santos
Savanna, 23, 130
Selva. *See* Tropical rain forest
Sergipe, *6*, *23*, *56*, 60
Serra da Mantiqueira, 7, 74, *75;* pioneer settlements, 107
Serra de Baturité, *6*, 66
Serra do Espinhaço, 7, 75, 76; gold, 82, 111; iron ore, 111; manganese and other minerals, 114
Serra do Mar, 5, 123; climate, 127
Serra dos Orgãos, 7, 74, 75, 107
Serra Geral, 174, 195
Sertão, 42-44; Northeast, 53-54, 65, 69; São Paulo, 161-170; Southeast, 87, 115-116
Settlement, 186, 195-198; pioneer settlement centers, Map, *32*
Soils: in rainy tropics, 19, 216; São Paulo, 126
Solimões R., 208
Sorocaba, *8*, 75, 82, 132-133, 155; fairs, 185
Sorocabana Railroad zone, *92*, 146

South America: air masses, *16*, *17*; population, *30*; racial character, *31*; temperatures: January, *12*; July, *13*
SOUTHEAST, 71-119; coffee cycle, 99-100; colonial roads, 83-85, *140*; colonies, 107-110; fazenda, 88-89; gold period, 82-83; land use map, *90*; minerals, 110-115; orange cycle, 103-104; pastoral base, 104-105; physical, 74-81; population map, *72*; railroads, *90*, 91-93, *140*; rice cycle, 100-103; Rio de Janeiro, 71-72, 117-119; sertões, 115-116; settlement pattern, 88-96, 105-106; sugar cycle, 98-99; surface configuration maps, 7, *75*; tree lines, 74; vegetation map, *80*
Steel plants, 112
Sugar (including sugar cane), 234; Amazon and Guiana coast, *214*; colonies, 35; in the north, 220; Northeast, *55*, 66; plantations of Northeast, 51-52; decline of, 54-58; São Paulo, *142*, 155; Southeast sugar cycle, *90*, 98-99; southern Bahia, northern Espírito Santo, *63*
Sugar-Loaf Mt., 77
Surface configuration: Map of South America, *4*. *See also* under countries and regions

Tapajóz R., 10, 210, *211*, 229
Taquarí R., *9*, 187, 190-191
Taquaritinga, detail of land use near, *139*
Taubaté, 7, *75*, 82
Teresina, Piauí, *6*, *23*
Terezina, Paraná, *8*, 201
Terezopolis, 7
Terra roxa, 126, 144, 159, 165, 179
Theophilo Ottoni, 7
Tieté R., *8*, *75*, 150; capture, 124
Tijuco. *See* Diamantina
Tobacco, 51, *63*; Bahia, 60-61; Northeast, *55*; São Paulo region, 168-169; South, *177*, 191, 197
Tocantins R., 10, 210, *211*, 228
Tordesillas, Treaty, 219
Transhumance, 105
Travessão, 65
Tres Corações, 7, 116
Tres Lagôas, *8*
Triangulo mineiro, *8*, 73, 162; sertão of, 168
Tropical rain forest, 19, 81, 129, 219
Tropical scrub forest, 23, 50, 81, 129
Tropical semideciduous forest, 23, 129
Tubarão, *9*, *173*, *177*; coal, 194
Tumuc-Humuc Mts., *212*

Uberaba, *8*, *75*, 162
Uberabinha, *8*
Uberlandia, 168
União da Vitória, *9*, 200
Uruguaiana, *147*, 193
Uruguay R., *173*
Usinas, 58

Valorization of coffee, 152-153
Vargas, Getulio, 153
Viçosa, 107
Villa Rica. *See* Ouro Preto
Vineyards, *142*, *177*
Vitória, 7, *23*, *63*, *75*, 114
Volta Redonda, 113-114, 245-246

Wickham, 226

Xarque, 190
Xingú R., 10, 209, 210, *211*

Zinc, 26